GALILEO'S INTELLECTUAL REVOLUTION

GALILEO'S INTELLECTUAL REVOLUTION

WILLIAM R. SHEA

Associate Professor, Faculty of Philosophy, University of Ottawa

MACMILLAN

© William R. Shea

First published 1972

Published by
THE MACMILLAN PRESS
London and Basingstoke
*Associated companies in New York Toronto Dublin Melbourne
Johannesburg and Madras*

SBN 333 14105 9

Printed in Great Britain by
A. WHEATON & CO.
Exeter

To Evelyn

CONTENTS

PREFACE

Until fairly recently, historians of science focused their attention on some important law of contemporary science and then proceeded to trace its origin in the philosophical tangle of the scientific revolution in the seventeenth century. This method conveniently by-passed the breakdown of once pervasive and useful theories, and neglected the long intellectual journeys along devious routes. Historians knew what they were looking for and they were careful to limit their search to areas where their quarry was sure to be found. History of science read like a success story, and the fame of Galileo and other great men was undisturbed by any reference to their less successful ventures.

This approach, which may be dubbed the linear view of the history of science, stands in contrast to the contextual method, which aims at a better understanding of the actual thought-processes of early scientists. On this second view, history of science must not only account for present theories in the light of past developments, it must also assess old theories in terms of the conceptual framework of the scientists who held them, and judge them against the background of the world picture of their age. This may lead historians down the blind alley of the past, but it can also clear the ground for a less anachronistic interpretation of the emergence of modern science and the actual process of scientific discovery.

The difference of approach is particularly clear in the case of Galileo. The linear historian of science asks, 'What *is* Galileo's claim to fame?', the contextual historian, 'What *was* Galileo's claim to fame?' or, to frame the question somewhat more precisely, 'What did Galileo think his claim was? On what was he prepared to stake his reputation? What did he believe constituted his greatest and most enduring achievement?' The answer to the first type of question is well known : it is Galileo's discovery of the law that governs the speed of bodies falling freely to the earth. The answer to the second kind of question is less familiar, and when disclosed it is often a cause of embarrassment, for Galileo took pride in the most ill-fated of his arguments for the heliocentric theory, his explanation of the tides as a result of the motion of the earth. It is a skeleton in the cupboard of the scientific revolution, but it can teach us much that is essential to the anatomy of Galilean science, as I hope will become abundantly clear in the last chapter of this book.

Three periods can be distinguished in Galileo's career : an early period (1564–1610), a middle period (1610–1632) and a later one (1632–1642).

The early period of Galileo's life as a student, and later as a lecturer in Pisa and Padua is well documented in Antonio Favaro's *Galileo Galilei e lo Studio di Padova*. The later period which centres on the *Discourses on Two New Sciences* has been the object of several important studies, and recently of an excellent annotated edition of the *Discourses* by L. Geymonat and A. Carugo. The middle period which extends from 1610, when Galileo returned to Florence, to 1632, the date of publication of his epoch-making *Dialogue on the Two Principal World Systems*, has received relatively little attention, largely because of the lack of interest of linear historians for ideas, discoveries and modes of apprehension that did not point to obvious modern developments. It is during this period that Galileo worked out the methodology of his intellectual revolution, and it is for this reason that I have chosen to investigate it. The questions Galileo was mainly concerned with at this time were problems in hydrostatics, recent astronomical discoveries and the definitive validation of the heliocentric theory. The conflict with the Church and the celebrated trial are only incidental.

A detailed analysis of the influence exerted on Galileo by his medieval and Renaissance precursors on the one hand, and of the development of Galileo's ideas on mechanics and dynamics during the Paduan period and their fruition in the *Discourses* of 1638 on the other, would have taken us too far afield, and I have had to content myself with passing references to these questions which would call for a book in themselves.

The first chapter is introductory and outlines the development of Galileo's method from his student-days in Pisa to the end of his sojourn in Padua. The orthodoxy against which Galileo revolted was the natural philosophy inherited from classical, medieval and Renaissance thought. To speak very broadly, it considered nature as a process, and this turned speculation away from questions of structure and mechanism towards questions of function and development. Its chief concern was man, and nature in relation to man, rather than nature as an objective and independent existence in which man is but a part. Physical laws were used as incidental illustrations of general metaphysical concepts. It was more important to understand how form inhered in matter and how the soul was related to the body than to have accurate theories of the flight of projectiles or the action of simple machines. Because metaphysical explanations are comprehensive rather than specialised and detailed, anthropomorphic and organic analogies flourished. This teleological concern was allied to a crude empiricism, which rested on the assumption that natural philosophy could be built directly on perception. The possibility of mathematical physics was denied on the grounds that the colourful and qualitatively determined facts of common experience could not be replaced by mathematical abstractions, and that movement could not be deduced from mere geometrical considerations.

As a lecturer in mathematics, Galileo was relatively free from the academic pressure and the weight of institutional tradition that had determined the direction in which philosophical speculation had proceeded for centuries. He had been introduced to the Archimedean view of the universe, and latent in this novel perspective—but still implicit at this stage—were the principles that would challenge and overthrow the basic tenets of the official philosophy.

Chapter two traces the history of the debate on floating bodies in which Galileo became involved upon his return to Florence in 1610. He tried to expand Archimedes' principles deductively, but he soon discovered that he had inferred correct conclusions from erroneous premises. This heightened his consciousness of the regulative use of experiments, but he did not abandon his model of science as a deductive process. Along with the rediscovery of Archimedes went a revival of interest in Democritus and atomism, and the gradual emergence of the conviction that inanimate matter had, in essence, none but the simple geometrical and mechanical qualities. This understanding of nature in terms of simple mathematical variables was to rule out of court the organic analogies because they were more complex than the inorganic situations with which they were compared.

Chapters three and four survey the protracted controversies over the sunspots of 1612 and the comets of 1618 respectively. Galileo was convinced that change occurred throughout the entire realm of nature, and he was eager to find support for his belief. His opponents, on the other hand, were sceptical about the possibility of change in celestial bodies, and reluctant to interpret evidence in a way that would favour such a contention. Consequently, when black spots appeared on the surface of the sun, Galileo hailed them as clouds, while his adversaries suggested that they were merely hitherto undetected stars. The debate on the comets illustrates equally well how the basic assumptions of a scientist determine the general limits within which he is prepared to theorise and the kind of questions he is willing to entertain. Galileo feared that the unwieldy path of the comets would present a serious threat to the heliocentric system if they were real physical bodies. It was tempting, therefore, to assume that they were not. This is precisely what Galileo did when he postulated that they were refractions of sunlight in the atmosphere. When his explanation broke down, he remained undaunted in his conviction that the earth moved, and that events would not fail to bear him out in the end.

Chapter five gives an account of the state of cosmological speculation prior to Galileo, and discusses his account of the Aristotelian double-tiered cosmos in the First Day of the *Dialogue on the Two Principal World*

Systems. The obstacles Galileo had to overcome were not only philosophical, but sociological and psychological as well. The main intellectual difficulty concerned the concept of motion and its division into natural and constrained, rectilinear and circular. The sociological difficulty was due partly to the Church's ban on Copernicanism, and partly to the adherence of brash young *letterati* to the heliocentric theory simply because it went against the established doctrine of the schools. Finally, there was a psychological block created by the visual representation of the geocentric universe which men had been brought up to use as the imaginative setting of their cosmological speculation. Galileo found that astronomers tended unconsciously to retain the mental image of the system with which they were familiar even when they wished to consider a radical reappraisal of its spatial and temporal features.

Chapter six examines the arguments advanced for the diurnal and the annual motions of the earth in the Second and the Third Days of the *Dialogue*. Galileo's proof rests on an appeal to mathematical elegance or simplicity. This aesthetic approach conveniently by-passed the practical problems of dynamics, and enabled Galileo to avoid discussing the nature of forces acting on bodies. He never, in fact, troubled himself over the detailed intricacies of planetary theory, nor did he seriously tackle the question why heavenly bodies move in the orbits they do. Yet he demanded reality. He wanted astronomy to be a science of representation rather than one of calculation, a science dealing with real physical bodies rather than with mere mathematical magnitudes. It was not merely because of a pragmatic use of the principle of economy that simpler hypotheses had to be chosen : it was nature herself that did not do by many things what could be done by few.

In this light, chapter seven analyses Galileo's physical proof of the motion of the earth from the phenomenon of the tides. It is here, perhaps, that we find the best illustration of his scientific method. Galileo felt assured that he had explained the tides when he had deduced their period from geometrised physical postulates.

The same themes will be found to recur throughout the different chapters. These are mainly the interplay of mathematics and experiment, and the pervasive influence exercised by conceptual schemes in the interpretation of nature. At one time, taking Galileo literally, it was assumed that he led a life of constant experimentation. It is now generally recognised, especially after the work of Alexandre Koyré, that Galileo conducted most of his experiments in his head and on paper. Lately, it has been shown by Prof. Thomas B. Settle that some of Galileo's descriptions of experiments are accurate, and Prof. Stillman Drake, in a series of persuasive essays, has argued that Galileo was something of an empiricist, perhaps even something of a positivist. I owe much to the learning of these two scholars, but I believe that my own conclusions bear out the correctness of Koyré's analysis. Few if any experiments in the seventeenth century were utterly incapable of being interpreted in more than one way when the making of them was significant. They took on various meanings against differing theoretical backgrounds. I have tried to let Galileo speak for himself by quoting him extensively and the translations are either my own or revised versions of existing ones. References to translations in the footnotes are for the convenience of the reader who may wish to look up the context of a particular quotation; they do not indicate that these translations are actually cited in the main body of the text.

In the course of my research I have incurred many obligations. I should like first of all to thank Mr. Gerd Buchdahl, Dr. M. B. Hesse and Dr. M. A. Hoskins, who kindly read the manuscript, and who by their diverse knowledge, encouraging remarks and limited criticism permitted me to feel that I was not entirely wrong. I also wish to acknowledge my deep and general indebtedness to Prof. Allen G. Debus for his friendly guidance and the stimulating effect of his probing comments on various aspects of my work. I am aware of particular help, derived mainly through conversations, from the Master and the Fellows of Darwin College, Cambridge, where this book was written, from Prof. I. B. Cohen, Dr. A. C. Crombie, Prof. Stillman Drake, Prof. Carlo Maccagni, Prof. L. M. Righini-Bonelli, Prof. Paolo Rossi, Dr. C. B. Schmitt, Dr. T. B. Settle, and Dr. D. T. Whiteside. In some cases they have expostulated with me in vain, and I alone am answerable for the results, but they deserve the credit for any good ideas which I have appropriated and used here.

I owe special thanks to Mr. John Oates, the librarian of Darwin College, Mrs. Rita van der Straeten, the librarian of the Whipple Science Museum, Mr. Maurice Alarie, the librarian of the Vanier Library, Ottawa, and the officials of the Archivio di Stato, Venice, the Biblioteca Nazionale in Florence, the Biblioteca Nazionale in Rome, the British Museum, the Cambridge University Library, the Domus Galilaeana in Pisa, the Istituto e Museo di Storio della Scienza in Florence and the Widener Library of Harvard University.

I am grateful to the Canada Council for grants which enabled me to spend three summers working in libraries in Europe, and to Dean Gilles Cazabon and Mrs. Jeanne Laviolette of the Faculty of Philosophy of the University of Ottawa for their invaluable assistance. My thanks also to Mrs. Verna Cole and Mrs. Estelle Diagle for their skill in deciphering and typing.

Finally, I wish to express my heartfelt gratitude to Evelyn, my wife, for her constant encouragement, her scholarly advice and her unparalleled patience.

Some of the material in this book has been published already in other forms in *Ambix, British Journal for the History of Science, Isis, Physis, Revue de l'Université d'Ottawa, Saggi su Galileo Galilei* and *Studi Secenteschi.*

Faculty of Philosophy   WILLIAM R. SHEA
University of Ottawa
June 1971

1. THE DISCIPLE OF ARCHIMEDES

The Pre-Paduan Period

Galileo was born in Pisa on 15 February 1564, and in 1581 he entered the University of his native city where he was enrolled as a student in the faculty of arts. During the summer vacation of 1584, he met Ostilio Ricci, a former pupil of Niccolò Tartaglia, and an exponent of the 'new' mathematics in the Florentine *Accademia del Disegno*. Galileo was immediately drawn to the subject and he gave himself to the study of geometry. He developed several theorems on the centre of gravity of solids, and it is largely on the strength of this work that he was appointed to the chair of mathematics in Pisa in 1589. As is evidenced by his early writings, Galileo's interest in mathematics was sustained, and he devoted himself to mastering the works of Archimedes. His first extant work in Italian, *The Little Balance*, dates from 1586, and was inspired by the hope of finding the method Archimedes used to solve the problem of a crown fashioned for King Hiero by a smith of rare skill but doubtful honesty, whom the King suspected of having used an alloy instead of pure gold. Galileo prided himself that the hydrostatic balance he had invented was actually the one Archimedes had devised. Along with contemporary mathematicians, he believed that there could be no greater achievement than to walk in the footsteps of the great Syracusan. 'Those who read his works', he wrote with youthful admiration, 'realise only too clearly how inferior are all other minds compared with Archimedes', and what small hope is left of ever discovering things similar to the ones he discovered'.[1]

Steeped in the Florentine tradition, Galileo also produced literary works. These include *Two Lectures to the Florentine Academy on the Shape, Place, and Size of Dante's Inferno, Considerations on Tasso, Postils to Ariosto* and a satirical poem entitled *Against Wearing the Gown*. In the first of these Galileo attempted to determine certain physical characteristics of Dante's *Inferno*, but his approach was mathematical rather than experiential or observational.

It is an admirable and difficult thing . . . that men should have been able by long observations, continuous vigils, and perilous navigations, to measure and determine the intervals of the heavens, the ratios of their fast and slow motions, the size of the neighbouring and the distant stars, and the place of earth and sea, things that completely, or for the greater part, *fall under the senses*. How more wonderful should we consider the study and the description of the place and size of hell which lies in the bowels of the earth, *hidden from all the senses, and by experience known to no-one*.[2]

Here again, it is to Archimedes that he turned for guidance and inspiration: 'We shall reckon according to the things demonstrated by Archimedes in his books *On the Sphere* and *On the Cylinder*'.[3] In an illuminating essay, Charles B. Schmitt comments: 'Whereas we might expect the analysis to contain some elements of the technology and craftsmanship so vividly and graphically portrayed by Dante himself in the description of the *Inferno*, they are wholly absent. The whole approach to this problem is mathematical and one might observe that, not only is "the book of nature" written in mathematical terms, but, in this case at least, the "book of the supernatural" is as well'.[4]

Although Archimedes was not completely unknown in the Middle Ages, it was not until the sixteenth century that his works received serious and scholarly attention.[5] Their rediscovery opened a new and fresh vista on the world, and they exerted the fascination of novelty on a young man who had been subjected to the tedium of the spent force of Aristotelianism. All of Galileo's extant letters which do not concern personal matters are addressed to the mathematicians Christopher Clavius, Guidobaldo del Monte and Michel Coignet. To these we may add an anonymous letter praising one of his geometrical theorems, and attestations of the originality of his *Theoremata circa centrum gravitatis solidorum* by Guiseppe Moletti, the professor of mathematics at Padua, and other notabilities.

During this period, Galileo does not seem to have been interested in problems of technology. The first documentary evidence of any direct concern with applied science occurs in his description of the hydrostatic balance where he notes possible difficulties:

> Since the wires are very fine, as is needed for precision, it is not possible to count them visually, because the eye is dazzled by such small spaces. To count them easily, therefore, take a very sharp stiletto and pass it very slowly over the wires. Thus, partly through our hearing, partly through our hand feeling an obstacle at each turn of wire, we shall easily count the number of turns.[6]

One does not find such practical indications in the two versions of Archimedes' method that have been handed down to us.[7] An incipient experimentalism is also manifested in the table of specific gravities which Galileo derived from the hydrostatic balance. This represents his closest approximation during this period to what was later to become known as 'experimental science'.

Professor Stillman Drake has recently drawn attention to another possible source of Galileo's subsequent interest in experimental verification of mathematical laws. Between 1585, when he left the University of Pisa without a degree, and 1589, when he obtained the chair of mathematics in Pisa, Galileo lived mainly in Florence, giving private instruction in mathematics. It was precisely during these years that his father, Vincenzio Galilei, carried out a number of experiments to refute the belief common among musical theorists that the small number fractions, 2:1, 3:2 and 4 :3, were always associated with agreeable tones. Vincenzio Galilei agreed that these numbers will give octaves, fifths and fourths for equally tense strings of the same material when their lengths are in these ratios, but he found by experiment that if the lengths are equal and the tensions are varied, then the weights required to produce the tensions giving the same intervals are as the square of the numbers. In addition, he experimented with strings of different materials and different weights and discovered that unison cannot be consistently obtained between two strings if they differ in any respect whatever. It is not unlikely that his son Galileo, who was also an accomplished musician, was fully informed of his research. The evidence is circumstantial but it is heightened by the fact that music was still considered at the time a special branch of mathematics, and that Galileo was interested by the problem of ratios. We have no indication, however, that he conducted any of the experiments mentioned by his father.[8]

The popular notion of Galileo as the first hard-headed and thorough-going experimentalist owes much to his first biographer, Vincenzio Viviani. Following the fashionable hagiographical style of his day, Viviani seriously misrepresented Galileo's early interests by claiming that he had discovered the isochronism of the pendulum and the law of uniform acceleration of falling bodies by performing experiments while still a student at Pisa. According to Viviani, Galileo's attention was arrested one day by the regular swinging of a lamp in the cathedral : '. . . making very precise experiments, he realised that the oscillations were equal. On the spot, he decided to adapt this discovery to the problem of measuring the pulse-rate, as is required in medicine'.[9] There is no evidence, however, that Galileo ever invented a pulsilogy, or instrument to count the pulse-rate. Furthermore, he never mentioned the isochronism of the pendulum prior to 1602 when he discussed it in a letter to Guidobaldo del Monte, who would have been apprised of the discovery much earlier if it had dated from Galileo's student days.

The second legend we owe to Viviani is the vivid description of Galileo ascending the Leaning Tower of Pisa before the assembled University, and proving 'with repeated experiments' that bodies fall at the same speed regardless of their weight.[10] It is true that in his *De motu*, written about

1590, Galileo mentioned towers eight times in relation to four different sets of problems, but we must consider after what fashion and with what kind of results.

In the first case, he seeks to refute Aristotle's theory that the speeds of freely falling bodies are proportional to their weight. 'We can see experientially [*videmus enim experientia*] that if two spheres of equal size, one of which is double the other in weight, are dropped from a tower, the heavier one does not reach the ground twice as fast'.[11] Galileo's contention, however, is not that all bodies fall at the same speed regardless of their weight, but that the speed of a falling body is proportional to the difference between its specific gravity and the density of the medium in which it falls. In other words, he reaches the erroneous conclusion that bodies of the same material but of different sizes fall at the same rate while bodies of the same size but of different materials do not.

Secondly, he mentions that objects dropped from high towers are always accelerated and never descend at a constant velocity. He accounts for this by assuming that existing towers are not high enough for falling bodies to reach their 'natural' uniform speed.[12]

Thirdly, in rehearsing an old argument against Aristotle's opinion that there occurs an interval of rest at the turning point of motion, Galileo argues that a pebble thrown up 'against a large stone dropped from a tower' does not stop before beginning its downward motion.[13]

Finally, and with greater 'experimental' emphasis, bodies dropped from towers are said to illustrate that light objects fall faster than heavier ones at the beginning of their natural motion.

> It is true that wood moves more swiftly than lead at the beginning of its motion; but a little later the motion of the lead is so accelerated that it leaves the wood behind it. And if they are both dropped from a high tower, the lead moves far out in front. This is something I have often tested.[14]

Of these four cases, the second and the third are clearly thought-experiments. The same can be said of the fourth whose conclusion is easily falsified : a ball of wood does not fall faster than a ball of lead for any perceptible amount of time in spite of what Galileo alleges. This leaves the first case in which he claims that Aristotle's law of free fall is disproved. Galileo may have attempted to refute Aristotle on experimental grounds but the wrong theory he arrives at through the unsatisfactory application of general principles of hydrostatics makes this appear unlikely.

It would seem, therefore, that Galileo's basic methodological principles were not derived from detailed observation of natural phenomena. This is not to say that he spurned the craft tradition, but merely to affirm that his early orientation was mathematical; all that he wrote between 1584, the date of his first acquaintance with mathematics, and 1592, when he went to Padua to embark upon a new venture, confirms this.

The originality of Galileo's position is best understood against the background of the structure of the university in the latter part of the sixteenth century. His appointment as professor of mathematics may have been less lucrative than that of his colleagues who taught philosophy but it suffered from less intellectual constraints. A lecturer in philosophy was expected to explicate the thought of Aristotle, and the chief end of his scholarly endeavours was to master his writings. The assumption present in this, of course, was that if Aristotle were correctly understood and properly taught, the students would be equipped with the conceptual tools and the basic categories with which to interpret the physical world. Galileo's own situation was different. As a teacher of mathematics he had a much less clearly defined assignment than a philosopher who had to contend with the totality of earlier Aristotelian commentaries. His task was to understand and explain the works of Euclid and Ptolemy, the two authors whom he discussed in his formal lectures, but he was not fettered by several centuries of institutional philosophical tradition.

The distinctive mental perspectives of the philosophers and the mathematicians implied a different way of looking at the world. On the one hand, philosophers, following Aristotle, saw the universe on the model of a living, biological entity, teleologically oriented and best understood through experience and syllogistic reasoning. Their system was close-knit, and to live in this world, where every aspect of every question was dealt with in meticulous order and detail, was in itself a fascination. On the other hand, mathematicians, under the guidance of Euclid and Archimedes, viewed the world in terms of geometrical shapes which obeyed mathematically expressible laws. Although many Aristotelians saw the importance of experiments, they failed to appreciate the significance of mathematics, and, to their lasting misfortune, the proper method in physics turned out to be quantitative and not qualitative.

In his *De Motu*, which is not a textbook for students but a scholarly essay on motion, Galileo enjoyed the relative freedom of an independent thinker from whom no rigid doctrinal commitment was expected. 'As a teacher of mathematics he leaned heavily toward the methodology of Euclid and Archimedes, it is true, but, as an investigator of questions concerning the motion of heavy and light bodies, he was essentially searching for a new approach to a problem—i.e., motion—which had for centuries fallen within the province of the Aristotelian–Scholastic philosophers. He thus shows a more "open" attitude toward introducing non-traditional elements into his investigation.'[15]

He could also be completely fearless in his attack on Aristotle, and the *De Motu* is a work of protest as well as an attempt to introduce a new solution. Six chapters begin with the somewhat pugnacious phrase *'in quo contra Aristotelem concluditur'*, and Galileo declares that 'Aristotle, in practically everything that he wrote about local motion, wrote the opposite of the truth'.[16] In another passage, he states that he is 'weary and ashamed of having to use so many words to refute such childish arguments and such inept attempts at subtleties as those which Aristotle crams in the whole book of *De Coelo*'.[17] He takes Aristotle to task for failing to grasp the significance of mathematics and relying on mere experience. 'Aristotle was ignorant not only of the profound and more abstruse discoveries of geometry, but even of the most elementary principles of this science'. Those who try to defend him are 'even more inept in geometry'.[18] The real master to turn to is the 'divine', the super-human Archimedes, whose name I never mention without a feeling of awe'.[19] In fact, explanation in the *De Motu* is conceived almost exclusively along the lines of an Archimedean solution to a geometrical problem. For instance, Galileo assumes that a volume can be considered as a summation of an infinite number of plane segments, and he uses the lever as an interpretative model to explain the behaviour of rising and falling bodies.

> Since it is most useful to compare bodies in natural motion with weights on a balance, this correspondence will be shown throughout the entire discussion on natural motion.[20]

In providing Galileo with the lever (of which the balance is merely a special case) as a means of reducing motion to quantitative treatment, Archimedes became the father of the modern science of dynamics. By means of the principle of virtual velocities, Galileo extended the principle of the lever to problems of hydrostatics and later to all the simple machines. In all instances, the governing principle is the equality of the product mv at one end of the lever to that at the other. The *momento* (moment) of the lever thus easily transforms itself into the *momento* (momentum) of the moving body. A possibility of serious ambiguity is built into this model and Galileo was to slip into it unawares. Since both ends of the lever move in identical times without acceleration, it is immaterial whether one uses the virtual velocities of the two weights or their virtual displacements. Velocities must be in the same proportion as displacements, and whenever Galileo states the general principle of the lever, he expresses it in terms of velocity. He does not seem to have realised that the equivalence holds only for the lever and the analogous instances in which a mechanical connection ensures that each body moves for the same time, and in which, because of equilibrium, the motion involved is virtual motion, not accelerated motion. The case of free fall does not fulfil the conditions of equilibrium on the plane because the times involved are not identical, and because two separate, accelerated motions take place. If there is an equality of the products of weight × distance, there cannot be an equality of moments (mv) but rather of kinetic energies ($mv^2/2$).[21]

Aristotle's second weakness, according to Galileo, was his uncritical reliance on sensory experience. He attacks him for affirming that a body moves faster in a rarer than in a denser medium 'for no other reason than experience [*et hoc non alia ratione confirmavit nisi ab experientia*], namely, because we see a body move faster in air than in water'. To this he opposes his own method :

> But to employ reasoning at all times rather than examples (for we seek the causes of effects, and these are not revealed by experience), we shall set forth our own view, and its confirmation will mean the collapse of Aristotle's opinion.[22]

In Galileo's eyes, unaided and untutored experience can become only too easily a source of misguided generalisations : 'It sometimes happens that certain opinions, however false they may be, attain long-standing currency among men, because they offer at first sight some appearance of truth, and no one bothers to investigate attentively whether they are worthy of belief'.[23] The real master, Archimedes, did not allow himself to be fettered by empirical considerations. For instance, he assumed that weights suspended from a balance are at right angles, whereas they are directed toward the centre of the earth and therefore converge. 'He did this perhaps to show that he was so far ahead of others that he could draw true conclusions from false premises.' But lest the reader should infer that the master was wrong, Galileo adds : 'We must not suspect that his conclusion was false, for he had demonstrated the same conclusion earlier with the aid of another geometrical proof'.[24]

It seems clear, therefore, that the role of experience and experiment as a regulative factor was practically absent from Galileo's early writings. He considered a mathematically orientated approach to be more fruitful, and it is only gradually during the Paduan period that he began to realise the importance of devising systematic experiments.

The Paduan Period

In 1592, with the aid of his friend the Marquis Guidobaldo del Monte, Galileo exchanged his Pisan chair for the corresponding one in Padua, vacant since the death of Giuseppe Moletti in 1588.

One could not be a professor of mathematics in the University of Italy's greatest seafaring nation without coming in contact with the docks and the shipyard. The rulers of the Republic believed in using their scientific manpower—something about which Galileo was later to complain—and he had not been in Padua long when his professional advice was sought by Venetian noblemen. Giacomo Contarini, who later became one of the overseers of the shipyard, asked him whether it was preferable to place the rowlock on the side of a ship or on a projecting strut. Galileo explained that the oar functioned as a lever with the fulcrum at the blade, and that the position of the rowlock was immaterial as long as the ratios of the distances between the fulcrum, the force and the weight remained the same. He also made it clear that it was important to avoid expending force in moving the water which should be kept at rest as much as possible. A few months later another leading Venetian patrician, Alvise Mocenigo, asked him to explain the construction of an oil lantern mentioned by Hero. Galileo replied by forwarding a paraphrase of Hero's text, and admitting that he was not too clear about its meaning.[25]

Although these are the only semi-official requests we know for certain Galileo received from members of the Venetian ruling class, it is probable that he was also consulted on irrigation, which had become a pressing problem with the development at the end of the sixteenth century of rice and corn growing in the Venetian territories of the Po valley. In any case, Galileo soon became interested in the problem and by the end of 1593 he applied for a patent for a horse-driven pump to hoist water and irrigate land. On 18 February 1594, the patent officers reported that they had not seen Galileo's machine or a model of it, and recommended that he be given a patent for twenty years instead of the forty he had requested. This was granted by the Senate on 15 September of the same year. Galileo, however, does not seem to have built a working model of his machine until 1602.[26] This would seem to indicate that he was not very keen on applying the fruits of his invention or that there was only slight incentive to do so. If Galileo was not pressed by demands for practical applications of his mathematical science, he had friends, especially Gianfrancesco Sagredo and Paolo Sarpi, who were interested in various aspects of technology. From 1602 when they first heard of Gilbert's *De magnete*, they discussed and repeated his experiments with a loadstone. Sagredo himself had a bent for instrument-making. He devised a machine to make screws, and he relied on Galileo's help to secure tools and skilled craftsmen. Paolo Sarpi was more concerned with theoretical problems, and it is in reply to one of his queries that Galileo first formulated the correct law of free fall, which he deduced, however, from the wrong assumption that the speed is directly proportional to the distance.[27]

A large number of students to whom Galileo gave private tuition were young noblemen who were mainly interested in the relevance of geometry and mathematics to practical problems of military warfare. Galileo supplied them with an elementary handbook on castrametation, fortifications and sieges. For their use, he also improved and incorporated several features of earlier sectors in a military and geometrical compass which he began selling, for a handsome sum, as early as 1597. Two years later Marcantonio Mazzoleni, a skilled craftsman, entered his service, and from that time seems to have been mainly responsible for the compasses, surveying instruments and later the lenses that came out of Galileo's workshop.

In addition to lecturing on Euclid and Ptolemy as he had done at Pisa, Galileo also taught Sacrobosco's *Sphere* and Aristotle's *Mechanics*. This latter series of lectures gave rise to a small but important work *On Mechanics* in which Galileo extended the principle of the lever by means of the principle of virtual velocities to simple machines : the windlass, the capstan, the pulley, the screw and the Archimedean screw. Galileo mentioned the useful applications that can be derived from the science of mechanics and from its instruments, but he mainly intended to dispel the illusion of some engineers who believed that they could cheat nature by overcoming a greater force with a smaller one.[28]

During this period, Galileo also carried out experiments on the measurement of temperature. Reminiscing in a letter to Ferdinando Cesarini on 29 September 1638, Benedetto Castelli writes

I remember an experiment which Galileo showed me more than thirty-five years ago. He took a small glass bottle about the size of a hen's egg, the neck of which was two palms long and as narrow as a straw. He warmed the bottle in his hands, and then inserted its mouth in a vessel containing a little water. When he withdrew the heat of his hand from the bottle, instantly the water rose in the neck more than a palm above its level in the vessel. Galileo later used this effect to construct an instrument for studying the degrees of heat and cold.[29]

The instrument, therefore, consisted of a glass tube ending in a bulb. The air in the tube was partially expelled by heat and replaced by water from a glass vessel into which the open end was plunged. The different degrees of temperature would then be indicated by the expansion or contraction of the air which remained in the bulb. Since the water would stand at the highest level in the coldest weather, the scale was the reverse of the one in the thermometers now in use. Galileo did not suspect the phenomenon of barometric pressure and he left the opening of the tube unsealed. This made it impossible to distinguish the expansive and contractive effects of heat and cold from the effects of varying atmospheric pressure, and the instrument was rather unreliable.

By 1609, Galileo had spent seventeen years away from his beloved Florence and he longed to return to his homeland. For some time now he had been assiduously cultivating friends at the Tuscan court, and in this year he requested an appointment as philosopher and mathematician to the Grand Duke. From his letter to the Florentine Secretary of State, we know that he considered writing on sound and speech, on light and colours, and on the movements of animals. There is no evidence that he actually undertook any work on these topics while in Padua, and when he removed to Florence he did not pursue this project. We have indications, however, that he was interested in hydrostatics and that he made experiments with bodies of varying densities. This question was to occupy him during the first years after his return to Florence.

Galileo might have experienced considerable difficulty in securing the post he coveted at the Tuscan Court had it not been for his happy invention of the telescope and his still more felicitous idea of pointing it to the stars. In the early summer of 1609, Galileo was in Venice when he heard that a Fleming had constructed an eyeglass by means of which distant objects were seen as nearby. Upon his return to Padua, he set himself to the task of fitting lenses together and he readily hit upon a successful combination of a convex glass and a concave one. His first telescope had a magnification of three diameters but he soon constructed one of eight diameters which he presented to the Venetian government in August. As a reward for his invention, he was granted a substantial increase in salary and tenure at the University of Padua. By the end of 1609, Galileo had improved his telescope (perhaps with the assistance of his instrument-maker) to a magnification of thirty diameters. He then turned it to the sky, and by March 1610 his new instrument had disclosed the existence of unknown stars, revealed the nature of the Milky Way, shown that the moon was covered with mountains and depressions, and taught that Jupiter had four satellites. Galileo published this truly earth-shattering news in a twenty-nine-page booklet entitled *Sidereus Nuncius*. His fame was established overnight and the Grand Duke became only too anxious to welcome home such a distinguished subject.[30]

The seventeenth century was above all an age in which the idea of experimenting came into its own, and the young Galileo is often credited with having seen that experiment is the main route to the advancement of learning. We can conclude that this view is an over-simplification. Galileo became interested, but by no means absorbed, in some aspects of the craft tradition during his twenty years in Padua. He answered questions on the most suitable position of rowlocks and on the construction of lanterns, he built compasses, he discussed problems of military engineering, he experimented with loadstones, he designed a model for a water-pump and he invented a primitive thermometer. He remained, however, a mathematician in his method and in his outlook. His instinctive reaction was to work out the properties of the behaviour of bodies in good Archimedean fashion from geometric considerations of motion or of equilibrium on the model of a lever. When he did perform an experiment it was usually to illustrate a conclusion arrived at through mathematical reasoning. What was novel in Galileo's approach, when contrasted with that of his Aristotelian opponents, was not so much his attitude to experimentation as his faith in the relevance of mathematics.

NOTES

1. Galileo, *La Bilancetta* (*The Little Balance*), in *Le Opere di Galileo Galilei*, ed. A. Favaro, 20 vols. (Florence: G. Barbèra, 1890–1909), 1, 215–216. In the translation by Gilberto Bernardini and Laura Fermi *Galileo and the Scientific Revolution* (New York: Fawcet Premier, 1965), 114

2. *Opere di Galileo*, 9, 31, italics mine

3. *Ibid.*, 34

4. C. B. Schmitt, 'Experience and Experiment: A Comparison of Zabarella's View with Galileo's in *De Motu*', *Studies in the Renaissance*, 16 (1969), 130–131, n. 119. I have inverted the order of the sentences

5. Luca Gaurico, a Neapolitan mathematician, published the Latin texts of the *Measurement of the Circle* and the *Quadrature of the Parabola* in Venice in 1503, using Moerbeke's thirteenth-century translation. In 1543, Tartaglia published a literal copy of the 1503 edition, and added *On the Equilibrium of Planes* and Book I of *On Floating Bodies*. In the following year, Thomas Gechauff Venatorius published the *editio princeps* at Bâle. In 1558, Federigo Commandino published in Venice Latin translations of *Measurement of the Circle*, *On Spirals*, *Quadrature of the Parabola*, *On Conoids and Spheroids* and *The Sand-Reckoner*. His translation of *On Floating Bodies* (*Archimedis de iis quae vehuntur in aqua*) appeared seven years later in 1565. The same year, from the legacy of Tartaglia, the entire *On Floating Bodies* (*Archimedis de insidentibus*) was published by the Venetian printer Curtius Troianus. A complete translation of Archimedes was also published in Sicily in 1570 by Francesco Maurolico but it was almost completely lost in a shipwreck. See E. J. Dijksterhuis, *Archimedes* (Copenhagen: Ejnar Munksgaard, 1956), 40–41; Marshall Clagett, *Archimedes in the Middle-Ages*, 1 *The Arabo-Latin Tradition* (Madison: University of Wisconsin Press, 1964), 13–14

6. Galileo, *The Little Balance*, *Opere di Galileo*, 1, 220; G. Bernardini and L. Fermi, *Galileo*, 118

7. They are explained in T. L. Heath, *The Works of Archimedes* (New York: Dover, 1953) 259–261. Sources of the story are Vitruvius, *De Architectura*, bk. 9, preface (in the edition and translation of F. Granger (London: Heinemann, 1962), 202–207), and the *Carmen de ponderibus et mensuris*, written about 500 A.D. and printed in 1475. For a discussion of the method described by Vitruvius and the author of the *Carmen de ponderibus*, see Marshall Clagett, *The Science of Mechanics in the Middle Ages* (Madison: University of Wisconsin Press, 1961), 85–90.

8. Stillman Drake, *Galileo Studies* (Ann Arbor: University of Michigan Press, 1970), 43–61

9. Vincenzio Viviani, *Racconto istorico della vita di Galileo Galilei*, *Opere di Galileo*, 19, 603

10. *Ibid.*, 606. In 1612, two decades after Galileo left Pisa, Giorgio Coresio dropped different weights of the same material from the Leaning Tower and found that the lighter weight was always left behind, proving that Aristotle was right (Giorgio Coresio, *Operetta intorno al galleggiare de' corpi solidi*,

[Florence, 1612], *ibid.*, **3**, 242). Vincenzo Renieri did the same experiment in 1641 with balls of lead and wood and reached analogous results (letter to Galileo, 13 March 1641, *ibid.*, **18**, 305)

11. Galileo, *De Motu, ibid.*, **1**, 267, critical apparatus to line 10. See also *ibid.*, 263, 317. A special case is Galileo's remark that a body which should fall twice as fast as another body, according to the 'correct' law of free fall, is not found to do so, *ibid.*, 273. The *De Motu* is partly translated in Galileo Galilei, *On Motion and On Mechanics*, ed. and trans. J. E. Drabkin and Stillman Drake (Madison: University of Wisconsin Press, 1960)
12. *Ibid.*, 329
13. *Ibid.*, 326
14. *Ibid.*, 334. See also 269, critical apparatus to line 10, and 406–407. C. B. Schmitt reports a suggestion made by Donald A. Miklich to explain Galileo's baffling statement that wood moves more swiftly than lead at the beginning of its motion. 'If one attempted the experiment of dropping a lead and a wooden ball simultaneously—especially if he had been holding the two for some time to line them up accurately, for example—then the muscular fatigue would be greater in the hand holding the heavier object. This would result in his being unable to release the lead ball as quickly as the wooden one and, consequently, he would see the wooden ball move ahead of the lead one' (Schmitt, Experience and Experiment', 118–119, n. 95)
15. Schmitt, 'Experience and Experiment', 126
16. Galileo, *De Motu, Opere di Galileo*, **1**, 307. Another chapter begins with the words *'in quo error Aristotelis manifestatur'*. Aristotle is mentioned by name no less than 109 times in the brief span of the 89-page treatise
17. *Ibid.*, 292
18. *Ibid.*, 302–303
19. *Ibid.*, 303, 300
20. *Ibid.*, 259–260. See also 274–275
21. See Richard S. Westfall, 'Force in Galileo's Physics', in *Galileo Reappraised*, ed. Carlo L. Golino (Berkeley and Los Angeles: University of California Press, 1966), 84, n. 22
22. Galileo, *De Motu, Opere di Galileo*, **1**, 260, 263. He then suggests using a mental experiment as a starting point: 'If we imagine [*si mente conciperemus*] that the water on which a beam of wood and a small piece of the same wood are afloat is gradually made lighter' (*ibid.*, 264). Galileo uses the expression 'to test' [*periculum facere*] four times in the *De Motu*. Once in reference to Aristotle who did not test whether fire falls when air is removed (*ibid.*, 377), once to observe that testing may well show that a sphere is not set in motion by a minimal force (*ibid.*, 310), and twice in relation to his own experiments. These are, first, the test which reveals that bodies do not fall according to the ratios inferred from hydrostatic principles, and, secondly, the experiment which is purported to show that a ball of wood precedes a ball of lead for a brief period when they are dropped together (*ibid.*, 273, 334)
23. *Ibid.*, 314
24. *Ibid.*, 300
25. Letter to Giacomo Contarini, 22 March 1593, *Opere di Galileo*, **10**, 55–57; letter to Alvise Mocenigo, 11 January 1594, *ibid.*, 64–65
26. Niccolò Fabri di Peiresc wrote to Galileo on 26 January 1634: 'It is already more than 30 years that . . . I witnessed the successful testing of your small model of a large machine to be erected, if I recollect correctly, in the gardens of the illustrious Contarini family (*ibid.*, **16**, 27). The date 1602 is suggested by Galileo's letter to Baccio Valori, 26 April 1602, in which he promised to show him a model of his invention in the coming summer (*ibid.*, **10**, 87–88)
27. Letter to Paolo Sarpi, 16 October 1604, *ibid.*, **10**, 115–116
28. Galileo, *On Mechanics, ibid.*, **2**, 155–157. Translation by S. Drake in Galileo, *On Motion and On Mechanics*, 147–150

29. Letter to Ferdinando Cesarini, 29 September 1638, *ibid.*, **17**, 377. See also Galileo's letter to Cesare Marsili, 25 April 1626, *ibid.*, **13**, 320
30. For an excellent account of these incidents, see Stillman Drake, *Galileo Studies*, 140–158

2. HYDROSTATICS AND THE REGULATIVE USE OF EXPERIMENTS

I THE HISTORY OF THE DEBATE

When Galileo applied for a position at the Tuscan Court in 1609, he insisted on the title of philosopher as well as mathematician to the Grand Duke, 'as I assure you that I have studied a greater number of years in philosophy than months in pure mathematics'. He promised Belisario Vinta, the Secretary of State, that he would make good his boast 'whenever it pleases their Highnesses to provide me with an opportunity of discussing with the most distinguished men in the profession'.[1]

Such an opportunity arose during the summer of 1611, when professors on leave from the University of Pisa and young Florentine gentlemen met at the villa of Filippo Salviati near Florence for informal discussions. Galileo was a regular participant and it is here that the debate on floating bodies originated. The matter of hydrostatic principles did not come up directly. The point at issue was philosophical and concerned the qualities of hot and cold. Someone introduced ice as an illustration of the peripatetic position that the action of cold was to condense. Galileo suggested that since ice was lighter than water the real nature of cold was to rarefy. This was denied by the philosopher who then proceeded to explain the floating of ice by its shape rather than its density. Galileo retorted that ice floats whatever its shape but he failed to convince his opponent who departed, and returned three days later to say that he had found someone who 'by means of reasons and experiments' would prove Galileo wrong. This was Lodovico delle Colombe, or Colombo, an amateur philosopher who had written a pamphlet against the motion of the earth which Galileo had declined to answer.

Colombo's apparatus consisted of pieces of ebony, some in the form of thin plates and some in spherical or cylindrical shapes. Since the former floated while the latter invariably sank, he concluded that the shape affected the floating of bodies, and he proceeded to perform his experiment in various public places. He exchanged letters with Galileo, and they finally agreed on the conditions of a contest to be judged by Francesco Nori and Filippo Arrighetti. For reasons that remain obscure, Colombo failed to appear at Nori's house at the appointed date, and

Galileo did not present himself at the villa of Salviati on another occasion. By this time, however, the controversy had become notorious and Galileo's foes were using it to discredit him at court. Cosimo II gently rebuked Galileo and praised the pen as the only way of settling this kind of dispute. In compliance with the Grand Duke's request, Galileo produced a fifteen-page essay in which he outlined the main arguments for his position.

In a subsequent phase of the debate, at which Colombo was not present, Galileo engaged in further discussions when the philosopher Papazzone visited the court sometime between 11 September and 11 October 1611. As Cardinals Maffeo Barberini and Ferdinando Gonzaga happened to be in Florence at the time, the Grand Duke invited Galileo and Papazzone to repeat their arguments before the distinguished visitors. It was on this occasion that Cardinal Barberini sided with Galileo while Cardinal Gonzaga upheld the Peripatetic position.

Galileo fell ill immediately afterward. As a result, it was a few months before he could expand his initial essay and write the *Discourse on Floating Bodies*, which emerged from the press at the end of May 1612 and was so speedily exhausted that he prepared a second edition before the year was out.[2] By August, a rejoinder was published by a Pisan professor who signed himself the 'Unknown Academician', and has been identified by Antonio Favaro as Arturo Pannochieschi de' Conti d'Elci, the Overseer of the University. His mild and often light-hearted criticism was followed by scathing attacks from Giorgio Coresio, the lecturer in Greek at Pisa, from Lodovico delle Colombe, and from Vincenzio di Grazia, a professor of philosophy at Pisa. Benedetto Castelli prepared a refutation of Coresio, but it was decided not to print it when Coresio, who was a Greek Orthodox, became involved in serious difficulties with the ecclesiastical authorities. Colombo and di Grazia, however, were jointly taken to task in a work published in 1615.

The debate on hydrostatics began as a friendly discussion but ended in a bitter feud. With the exception of the Unknown Academician, Galileo's opponents were often personal in their attacks, and Galileo repaid them in the same currency. This was a tactical error for he made good his claim to the title of philosopher at the cost of the general esteem he enjoyed when he first arrived from Padua. For a man who could laugh at the discomfiture of an adversary, Galileo singularly lacked the grace and the humour to take a joke against himself. Yet he knew that he could not answer an opponent without losing his temper, and he waited two years before committing his rebuttal to print. But by allowing Castelli to sign it, he conveyed the impression that it was below his dignity to answer the objections of his fellow professors. It was not a slight they were likely to forget.

II THE DISCOURSE ON FLOATING BODIES

At the very outset of the *Discourse on Floating Bodies*, Galileo stresses the importance of recalling 'the real, intrinsic, and total cause' why some bodies float while others sink because what Aristotle wrote on the subject is unsatisfactory.[3] 'The cause why some solids sink', he writes, 'is the excess of their weight over the weight of water'.[4] Although this was demonstrated by Archimedes in his work *On Floating Bodies*, Galileo intends to 'reach the same conclusion with a different method and by other means, reducing the causes of such effects to more intrinsic and immediate principles'. This does not imply, however, that he wishes to depart from the ideal of rigorous mathematical deduction : 'As required by the demonstrative order, I define certain terms, and explain certain propositions which I use as true and obvious principles'.[5]

First, the two basic terms :

I call equally heavy *in specie* those materials of which equal bulks weigh equally . . . But I call equally heavy in absolute gravity two solids of the same weight, even if they are unequal in size.[6]

Next, the two basic principles :

I borrow two principles from the science of mechanics. The first one is that absolutely equal weights moving with equal speeds are of equal force and moment in their operation. . . . The second principle is that speed increases the moment and the force of the weight.

Galileo interprets these principles with the aid of the lever. For the first principle, he uses a balance of equal arms from which two identical weights are suspended :

If the balance moved, the weights would go through equal spaces in the same time, i.e., they would move with equal speeds, so that there is no reason whatever why one weight should descend more than the other. Therefore, equilibrium is established, and their moments of force remain identical.

The second principle is illustrated with a balance or steelyard of unequal arms. In this case, two equal weights do not exert the same force, but the one which is a greater distance from the centre descends and lifts the other in such a way that

the motion of the one that ascends is slow, while the motion of the other is swift. The force and the virtue that is conferred by the speed to the moving body is such that it can perfectly compensate the additional weight of the body that moves more slowly.[7]

These principles were familiar to Galileo's contemporaries from the pseudo-Aristotelian *De Mechanica* where it is argued that a given weight on a lever arm has a greater effectiveness on a longer arm because it has greater velocity there, namely it sweeps out a greater arc in the same time. If the free weights are inversely proportional to the velocities, the total effectiveness of each weight will be the same and equilibrium will obtain. It follows that since the arm lengths are directly proportional to the potential simultaneous displacements of area, equilibrium will result when the free weights are inversely proportional to the arm lengths of the lever. What struck Galileo's readers was his use of the word moment for the combined force of weight and speed. As the Unknown Academician remarked : 'This word *momento* is Latin and Ptolemaic and it is not used, in the suggested sense, in our modern vernacular, and still less in the ancient, for there is no example of it in the copious and exquisite Vocabulary della Crusca'.[8] In a postil, Galileo commented, 'In your vernacular not only this word *momento*, but none of the commonest words in the whole field of mathematics is to be found', and in the second edition of his *Discourse on Floating Bodies*, he inserted the following definition of moment :

> Moment, among mechanics, signifies that virtue, that force, that efficacy, with which the mover moves and the moving body resists. This virtue does not depend simply on the weight, but also on the speed and on the various inclinations of the spaces over which the motion occurs. A descending body has more impetus in a steep slope than in a less steep one, and, whatever the cause of such a virtue, it still retains the name of moment. It did not seem to me that this sense would appear new in our little story, for, if I am not mistaken, we very often say, 'This is a weighty matter, but the other is of little moment', and, 'We consider the light things and we skip those of moment', metaphors that are, I believe, taken from mechanics.[9]

Galileo had already defined moment in terms of weight and speed in his work *On Mechanics* and this had enabled him to make an effective use of the principle of virtual velocities. It is the same concept that he now applies to the problem of floating bodies. This method, however, is the one adumbrated in the pseudo-Aristotelian *De Mechanica*, as Galileo himself recognises : 'This correspondence between the weight and the speed is found in all mechanical instruments, and was considered by Aristotle as a principle in his *De Mechanica*'. This statement is unexpected since Galileo introduced his observations on method by declaring that he was dissatisfied with Aristotle's account. Why should he have departed from a strictly Archimedean approach? Despite his commitment to the mathematical deductive method of proof in hydrostatics, he does not use

Archimedes' axioms or theorems as the basis for his deduction. To my knowledge, this has not been satisfactorily accounted for. It is true, of course, that Archimedes' doctrine, albeit clear and rigorous, lacks generality. The laws of the lever as he formulated them rest on hypotheses restricted to the case he initially considered of two weights suspended from the arms of a balance. When he tackled the problem of floating bodies he had to appeal to principles that were unrelated to the postulates he had stated at the beginning of his treatise *On the Equilibrium of Planes.* But this is being wise after the event for it is only the historical unproductivity of the Archimedean principles that informs us of their barrenness. Galileo could not have known this without noticing the failure of others or learning from his own abortive efforts that hydrostatics could not be expanded deductively from Archimedes' postulates. It would indeed be surprising if he had not tried to use Archimedes' premises as a basis for deduction. In point of fact, we have conclusive evidence that he made such an attempt, and that it is only when it failed that he turned to the Aristotelian *De Mechanica.* A comparison of the first draft of the *Discourse on Floating Bodies* with the printed version reveals more than textual amendments; it discloses a complete change in Galileo's main proof.

The first draft did not borrow two principles from mechanics; it proposed two axioms from Archimedes :

> In order to proceed with our demonstration, I take one of the two following axioms : I suppose, all other circumstances being identical, that a greater weight cannot be lifted and raised by a smaller one; or, that natural order requires that heavier bodies be under less heavy ones.[10]

The first axiom may be considered as an intuitively self-evident principle, or preferably, since the reference is obviously to the lever, a simplified version of Archimedes' Postulate II, Book I of *On the Equilibrium of Planes.* The second axiom is a physical interpretation of Proposition VII, Book I of Archimedes' treatise *On Floating Bodies.* With the help of these axioms, Galileo tried to demonstrate that a solid lighter than water necessarily floated in that medium. He offered two proofs, in which he successively used the first and the second axiom.

In the first proof, a solid, lighter than an equivalent volume of water, is placed in a tank partly filled with water. If the solid sank, it would raise a volume of water equal to its own. But this is impossible since an equal volume of water is heavier than the solid, and the first axiom precludes a greater weight being raised by a smaller one. The solid, therefore, cannot be entirely submerged.

The proof is an elegant *reductio ad absurdum* worthy of Archimedes himself, but it is rooted in the false assumption that the volume of water that is displaced when a solid is immersed is equal to the total volume of the solid immersed whereas it is only equal to the volume of that part of the solid under the initial level of the water. In his *De Motu*, Galileo had presented this argument twice in practically the same form.[11] The fact that the 'Father of Experimental Science' could make such a mistake after some twenty years of University teaching is perhaps indicative of his real approach to physical problems.

The second proof, which was left incomplete, embodies the same error. The lighter solid would float, he asserted, because 'the water raised is always equal in volume to that of the solid that is submerged'.[12]

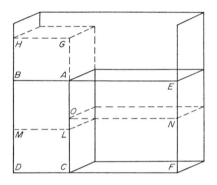

FIG. 1

Sometime between October 1611 and March 1612, Galileo recognised the fallacy in his argument. In a passage of the *Discourse on Floating Bodies* which we could be misled into considering as an attack on his opponents, it is really against his former self that he is arguing.

> It is necessary to compare the weights of the water and the solids. This comparison might at first sight seem sufficient to conclude and deter-mine what solids float, and what solids sink, asserting that those less *grave in specie* float in water, while those that are more *grave in specie* sink. For it seems that when a solid sinks it raises as much water as that part of the solid which is submerged. It is impossible, therefore, that a solid less *grave in specie* than water should sink completely since it is unable to raise a weight greater than its own. . . . The matter, however, proceeds otherwise, and although the conclusions are true, the causes that are alleged are wrong. It is not true that when a solid sinks it raises and displaces a volume of water equal to its submerged parts. On the contrary, the water raised is always less than the volume of the

submerged parts of the solid, and so much the less by how much the vessel in which the water is contained is narrower.[13]

Since Galileo does not breathe a word about his initial error, we are left to conjecture how he detected it. There are strong indications that he did so, not by making experiments, but by working out the various geometrical ratios that a trained mathematician would normally look for. In the first edition of the *Discourse on Floating Bodies*, Galileo starts off by proving that when a rectangular solid is partly raised out of water, the ratio of the fall of the water to the ascent of the solid is equal to the ratio of the base of the solid to the surface of the surrounding water. A rectangular body *BDCA* is placed in a container which is filled with water up to the level *AE* (figure 1). The body *BDCA* is then raised until it occupies the position HMLG, while the level of the water drops to *ON*. *HBAG*, the volume of the part of the solid raised above the water is equal to *AONE* the volume of the water that has fallen. Since the bases of equal volumes are inversely proportional to their heights, then

$$\frac{OA}{AG} = \frac{GH}{NO}$$

namely

$$\frac{\text{fall of the water}}{\text{ascent of the solid}} = \frac{\text{base of the solid}}{\text{surface of the water}}$$

Galileo illustrates the conclusion of his theorem with the aid of the following example : if a round column, placed in a pond 25 times its size, is raised by 1 yard above the surface, the water in the pond will drop by 1/24th of a yard, whereas if it is placed in a well only 1/8th larger than itself, and then raised by the same height as before, the water in the well will fall by 7 yards. This suggests that the concept of moment might find a useful application, but the concept itself does not appear in the formal proof of the theorem.

From this theorem, it is an easy step to the next one Galileo takes in the second edition of the *Discourse on Floating Bodies* when he investigates the ratio of the volume of the water raised to the volume of the solid immersed (figure 2).

Let the water in the container be at the level *EFG* before the rectangular body *HIK* is submerged. When *HIK* is submerged the level of the water rises to *LM*. Now the volume of the water raised is the volume of the area *LG*. But the volume *LG* is not equal to the volume *HIK*, but to the volume *EIK* contained under the first level *EFG*. Since

$$\text{volume } LG = \text{volume } EIK,$$

adding volume *EN* to both,

$$\text{volume } EM \text{ (i.e., volume } EN + \text{volume } NF) = \text{volume } HIK$$

Therefore

$$\frac{\text{volume } LG}{\text{volume } EM} = \frac{\text{surface } LM}{\text{surface } MH}$$

and

$$\frac{\text{volume } LG}{\text{volume } HIK} = \frac{\text{surface } LM}{\text{surface } LM + \text{base of body } HN}$$

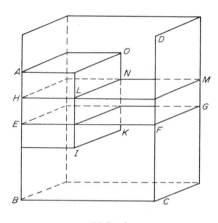

FIG. 2

Hence the ratio of the volume of the water raised to the volume of the solid immersed is the same as the ratio of the surface of the surrounding water to the same surface plus the base of the solid. Here again, the demonstration is Euclidean in its simplicity and involves no direct reference to the principle of virtual velocities. But it is crucial since it establishes that Galileo's early assumption was false : the volume of the water that is raised when a solid is immersed is not equal to the total volume of the solid immersed, but only to the volume of the part under the initial level of the water.[14]

If the second theorem proves that a strictly Archimedean approach is unrewarding, the first theorem suggests the usefulness of the concept of moment. Galileo realised that it was not sufficient to consider the relative weights, but that the virtual displacements had to be taken into account. This discovery sent him back to the *De Mechanica*. Whereas in the draft of the *Discourse on Floating Bodies*, he merely speaks of giving a clearer proof than the one found in Archimedes, in the printed version he states that he intends to proceed 'with a different method and with other means' than those used by Archimedes. He is confident that this new approach will enable him to 'discover the causes of some admirable and almost incredible effects, such as a very small quantity of water lifting and sustaining with its light weight a solid weighing one hundred and even one thousand times more than itself'. This he hopes to achieve

> by comparing the moments of the resistance of the water to be raised with the moments of the weight of the solid pressing down. If the moments of the resistance of the water are equal to the moments of the solid before its total immersion, then equilibrium will undoubtedly be established and the solid will sink no further.[15]

With the aid of the concept of moment, Galileo deduces two new theorems : firstly, that a solid less dense than water rises when submerged, and secondly, that the same solid placed on the bottom of a vessel does not float until its total height bears to the height of the water the same ratio as the density of the water does to the density of the solid.

The fact that these are the only two theorems to be demonstrated with the aid of the concept of moment corroborates the view that Galileo arrived at the correct method not by making experiments but by using mathematical reasoning. This is further confirmed by the surprise caused by the corollary that a solid can float in a very small amount of water if the water rises to such a height that a volume of water equivalent to the volume of the solid immersed weighs as much as the whole solid.

> At first sight, this may seem to many a great paradox, and raise doubts whether the demonstration of such an effect does not rest on a fallacy. But experiment is there [c'è l'esperienza di mezzo] to assure those who entertain this suspicion.[16]

Geometrical demonstrations can lead to startling conclusions that have to be tested and verified, but it is mathematical analysis that draws attention to the extraordinary phenomena, rather than the extraordinary phenomena that cry out for mathematical interpretation. The curious and striking facts are always there, of course, but they remain unnoticed, or are deemed irrelevant, until they are recognised as part of an explanatory scheme. The errors that Galileo made in the first draft of *The Discourse on Floating Bodies* taught him that a mathematician can arrive at the right conclusion for the wrong reasons, and this heightened his consciousness of the regulative use of experiments. The printed version of the *Discourse on Floating Bodies* does not abandon the mathematical approach however : Galileo still moves from geometrised physical postulates by formal deductive steps to various theorems, but he avoids the exclusively abstract mathematical reasoning of Archimedes for the more inferential technique of introducing appeals to experience. *The Discourse on Floating Bodies* is in fact a defence and an illustration of Archimedes' conclusions with the aid of Aristotle's principle of virtual velocities.

Galileo's great achievement lies in this successful combination of two great traditions : the static approach of Archimedes and the dynamic approach of the pseudo-Aristotelian *De Mechanica.*

It is worth noting that in all the passages which mark a significant scientific advance, Galileo is not scoring a victory against his adversaries, who do not even understand the basic issues, but against positions that he himself had uncritically assumed. The hydrostatic debate is the occasion rather than the instrument of progress : it provides Galileo with the

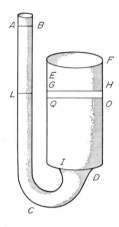

FIG. 3

challenge he needs to reason himself out of inconsistencies that his opponents do not even perceive.[17]

In the second edition of the *Discourse on Floating Bodies,* Galileo seeks to apply the principle of virtual velocities to the hydrostatic paradox. He uses a diagram (figure 3) to illustrate that the level of the water in two connecting vessels is the same regardless of their size. He explains this by commenting on the fact that when the water in the large tube is depressed to *QO*, the water in the small one is thrust upward to the height of *AB* :

> The rise *LB* is greater than the fall *GQ* by as much as the breadth of the vessel *CD* exceeds the width of the tube *LC*, which, in sum, is the excess of the water *GO* over the water *LC*. But since the moment of the speed of the motion in one body compensates that of the weight in the other, what wonder is it, if the swift rising of the small quantity of water *CL* resists the very slow rising of the large quantity *GO*.

The interpretative model is again the lever :

> What happens in this case is exactly what happens in the steelyard

when a weight of two pounds counterpoises another weight of two hundred pounds as long as it moves in the same period of time through a space one hundred times as great.[18]

Galileo is confident that his proof will dispel the error of engineers who, following in the footsteps of Aristotle, believe that a ship floats with greater ease in deep waters. Galileo never misses the opportunity of teaching the Aristotelians how to use their own principles, but in this case we may ask whether his application of the principle of virtual velocities to the hydrostatic paradox is warranted. His terminology is at least imprecise. The displacements of the columns of water are inversely proportional to the areas of their transverse sections rather than to the width of the tube. More basically, it can be argued that the hydrostatic paradox and the equilibrium of simple machines are not identical cases. With liquids in communicating tubes, every disturbance of the common level of the liquids produces an elevation of the centre of gravity; in the case represented in our diagram, the centre of gravity of the liquid displaced from *GH* to *QO* is elevated to halfway between *AB* and the initial level at *L*, and the rest of the liquid can be considered as not having been moved.[19]

The Role of the Shape

Archimedes' doctrine vindicated, Galileo turns to the problem that gave rise to the debate on hydrostatics : the role played by the shape in the floating and sinking of bodies.

Colombo had used a ball and a thin board of ebony to prove that the shape is the main cause of the floating of bodies heavier than water. Galileo improves the experiment by using wax, a material that can be moulded into different shapes. A ball of wax can be made just heavy enough to sink by adding a few lead filings to it, and if it is moulded into different shapes, it sinks equally well. When the lead filings are removed, the wax, whatever its shape, bobs to the surface. Hence the shape is immaterial to either sinking or floating.

By modern standards, this experiment seems cogent enough, but we must remember that Galileo is arguing against the exponents of late scholasticism who had reason to feel differently. Aristotelians considered reality as bipolar, and sought to explain physical objects as compounds of act and potency, of matter and form, and of substance and accident. In this framework, form is the actuality of the physical body, informing matter and forming with it the substance or corporeal entity. Form determines the matter to which it imparts existence, but it is in turn determined by matter without which it cannot subsist. This is usually expressed by saying that matter and form are co-principles of one being. Whatever the philosophical merits of this approach, its relevance to experimental science in terms of suggestiveness is nil, for neither form nor matter are physically (i.e., experimentally) discernible. They are part of the ontological structure that science presupposes but does not investigate. Until the seventeenth century no such distinction had been drawn and all questions were framed within this context. When the answers failed to reach the ontological level, they hovered about its fringe in a no-man's land where science, as we know it, was beginning to stake its claim.

The natural question arising within this philosophical perspective was whether the shape (or the accidental form) could operate without its corresponding matter. Each synthesis of matter and form was considered a distinct and autonomous entity, and it was assumed that the shape could produce its natural effects only when joined to a suitable material. To say, for instance, that a sharp edge has more cutting power than a dull one is true if, only if, the sharp edge is found in a suitable material, such as steel. If the material is wax, a sharp edge is not more incisive than a dull one because the 'form' is in the wrong 'matter'. As Galileo did not discuss the problem within these terms of reference, his adversaries believed that he was indulging in abstract mathematical reasoning and speaking of disembodied 'Platonic' forms. They considered unsuitable for experimental purposes any material that could not be given a shape capable of overcoming the resistance of the water. They argued that a material lighter than water could never reveal the natural effect of the shape, and was therefore as unsuitable in this case as wax would be to prove that a sharp edge cuts more than a dull one. On the other hand, they accepted ebony, which is heavier than water, and it can be clearly shown that a thin lamina of ebony floats while a ball sinks. Galileo invites his opponents to go back and take a good second look at the lamina : it does not merely touch the surface of the water but depresses it. This, he suggests, indicates the correct solution : the plate or lamina sinks to a depth such that a volume of water equivalent to the combined volumes of the plate and the depression weighs as much as the plate itself. For instance, on this theory, the plate *ABCD* in the diagram (figure 4) floats because a volume of water equivalent to the combined volumes *NADM* and *ABCD* weighs as much as the plate *ABCD*. This follows as a simple application of the theorem Galileo previously deduced with the aid of the concept of moment. A further consequence is that any solid, whatever its specific gravity, can float as long as the height of the depression it causes bears to the thickness of the solid the same ratio as its weight bears to an equivalent volume of volume. Galileo gives the following examples : gold, which is 20 times heavier than water, will depress the surface of the water to a depth 19 times its thickness, and tin, which weighs 8 times as much as water, will depress it to a depth 7 times its thickness. He even argues that any solid substance can be shaped into a pyramid or a cone that will float without wetting more than its base. His proof can be summarised as follows :

Let the height of the rampart be *BD*, and the diameter of the pyramid be *BC*, at right angle to *DB* (figure 5).

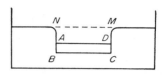

FIG. 4

Let

$$\frac{\text{s.g. of pyramid } ABC}{\text{s.g. of water}} = \frac{\text{height of rampart}}{1/3 \text{ height of } BE}$$

Proof that pyramid *ABC* will float:

$$\text{cylinder } EC = 3 \text{ pyramids } ABC$$

and

$$\frac{\text{cylinder } DC}{\text{cylinder } CE} = \frac{DB}{BE}$$

but

$$\frac{\text{cylinder } CE}{\text{pyr. } ABC} = \frac{BE}{1/3 \, BE}$$

Therefore

$$\frac{\text{cylinder } DC}{\text{pyr. } ABC} = \frac{DB}{1/3 \, BE}$$

but

$$\frac{DB}{1/3 \, BE} = \frac{\text{s.g. of pyr. } ABC}{\text{s.g. of water}}$$

Therefore

$$\frac{\text{vol. } DC}{\text{vol } ABC} = \frac{\text{s.g. of } ABC}{\text{s.g. of water}}$$

and from the known lemma : solids whose volumes are inversely proportional to their s.g. are equal in weight, we have that pyramid *ABC* weighs as much as a volume of water equal to volume *DC*. But the water that is driven out of its place by the pyramid *BAC* is precisely as much as would lie in *DC*, and is thus equal to the weight of the pyramid that displaces it. Therefore, equilibrium is established and *ABC* will not sink.

It is manifest that Galileo is allowing himself a mathematical holiday. Having laid down a principle, he draws all the possible logical conclusions, untrammelled by any reference to the practical problems of physical application. This is not because experiments are difficult, tiresome or simply liable to erroneous interpretations. The real reason is that Galileo is convinced that once the true cause of a particular phenomenon has been ascertained, the outcome of experiments can be predicted before they are performed.

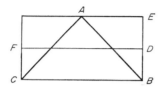

FIG. 5

Now that we have found the true cause of the floating of those bodies, which being heavier than water, should otherwise sink to the bottom, it seems to me that for the sake of completeness and clarity, we should proceed to discover their particular properties by means of demonstrations.[20]

All this is excellent geometry, but is it good physics? Galileo's explanation presupposes that water offers no resistance to bodies of various shapes, and he categorically rejects what to modern ears sounds like a non-technical description of surface tension : 'Those who attributed the cause of floating to the resistance of the water to be divided as a passive principle, and to the breadth of the shape as an efficient principle, were far from the truth'.[21] It is in the process of working out the consequences of this refusal to admit the resistance of water that he saw the necessity of postulating the existence of atoms, and it is to this problem that we now turn.

III THE ATOMIC HYPOTHESIS

It is well known that in *The Assayer* Galileo explains the phenomenon of heat by the motion of fire-atoms. The origin of his theory has received little attention largely because of the general neglect of the *Discourse on Floating Bodies* where the question of the atomic constitution of matter is raised for the first time in relation to the elements of water and fire.

As we have seen, Galileo prides himself on solving all the problems in hydrostatics by appealing only to the greater or lesser specific gravity of the solid relative to the medium. He resolutely discards any other subsidiary explanations such as the shape of the body or the resistance of the medium. He dismisses Colombo's reference to the continuity, the tenacity, and the viscosity of water as a useless multiplication of accidents, and he suggests that water is a discontinuous body composed of atoms. Moving through water is to be understood on the analogy of elbowing one's way through a crowd or thrusting a stick into a heap of sand. In neither case is anything broken up; what is already divided is merely separated.

Fire also provides evidence for the atomic constitution of matter. The basis of the discussion is the passage in Aristotle's *De Coelo* where Democritus is criticised for asserting that heavy but broad plates are kept afloat by heat-particles rising from the water while narrow plates sink because they are opposed by only a few of these particles. Aristotle argues that if this was true, heavy objects would float more easily in air than in water. Galileo objects that this criticism is misguided : bodies weigh more in air than in water, and there is no reason to believe that fire-atoms move more swiftly in air. Galileo uses this as an opportunity of exposing what he considers to be mere Aristotelian nominalism, for Democritus 'not happy with mere names tried to determine more particularly what weight and lightness were'.[22] The Aristotelians are content to restate the effects in terms of unknown powers producing them. They ignore the importance of precise prediction which makes experimental verification meaningful.

Galileo suggests that Democritus' theory be subjected to the following empirical test. A thin, broad plate slightly denser than water is placed on the bottom of a vessel filled with water. If the fire-atoms are capable of upholding it at the surface, they will undoubtedly be able to raise it from the bottom. Since this is not the case, the implication is either that fire-atoms do not exist or that they are too weak to push up a thin plate of a solid denser than water. Galileo believes that the second alterative is true of cold water. When water is heated however, fire-atoms rise from the incandescent coal, pass through the glass and push the plate to the top. But this obtains only in the case of light plates, and he concludes that the atoms of fire are not sufficient by themselves to explain the floating of bodies.

A few months after the publication of the *Discourse on Floating Bodies*, Galileo read and annotated the Unknown Academician's *Considerations*. A lengthy postil reveals that he was still devoting considerable thought to his atomic theory although it had not been directly challenged by the Unknown Academician. He was puzzling over the process of evaporation and boiling when he was struck by the fact that grains of sand in a liquid medium eventually coalesce to form a clod of earth heavy enough to sink to the bottom. Fire-atoms, he suggests, congregate in a similar fashion in order to break away from the water and escape into the air. The atoms that do not unite also rise to the surface, but in trying to reach the air 'they are held back in large quantity by the adherent water, just as in falling through the air many corpuscles stop when they reach the surface of the water because of the adherence of the air'.[23] The corpuscles that float on the surface, therefore, are not stopped by the water but held back by the air; water can hinder the escape of bodies rising through it, but is unable to offer resistance to the penetration of objects coming from the outside. One cannot help smiling at the mental acrobatics Galileo is willing to indulge in to avoid admitting the existence of surface tension.

The Unknown Academician failed to attack Galileo's fiery atoms, but Giorgio Coresio did not miss the opportunity of setting up a barrage of Peripatetic arguments. He hurled no less than twenty-five objections against Galileo's atomism, and Benedetto Castelli, who took up the gauntlet for his master, fired a volley of eighteen rebuttals. Galileo retrieved the scientific discussion from the smoke of rhetoric, and restricted his criticism to two points. First, he argues that Coresio is wrong in supposing that atoms are indivisible for 'atoms are not called thus because they are not extended [quanti], but because, being the smallest corpuscles, there are no smaller ones that can divide them'. Secondly, he attacks Coresio for assuming that water can extinguish fire-atoms. 'How could water be warmed', he asks, 'if the fire in it is extinguished'.[24] Galileo will have no truck with the idea that water acquires heat as an accidental property, a theory that is part and parcel of the qualitative interpretation of nature against which he persistently campaigns. To his mind, hot water can only result from the presence of fire-particles.

Two years later, Galileo returns to the subject of atomism in his reply to Colombo, whom he provides with a 'sample of his method of philosophising'. The method consisted in filling a bottle with a long narrow neck with water up to the half-way mark, and placing it on a coal fire. Galileo stresses that the water rises in the neck long before it reaches the boiling point.

If you wish to see sensibly [veder sensatamente] from what this increase derives, observe diligently and you will see that as the atoms of fire increase, several congregate together in the water, and form small globules which rise in great number and escape at the surface. The greater their number, the more the water rises in the neck of the bottle, and if you keep the bottle on the coals for a long time, you will see thousands of globules rise and escape. These, Colombo, are not, as you *think, vapours generated from some parts of water that is changed and transformed into vapour by the heat of the fire.* This is obvious, for if you remove the coals after many thousand globules have gone out, and wait until the other globules that are more dispersed and thus invisible leave also, you will see the water descend slowly and finally settle, without the loss of even one drop, at the same level that you noted on the neck of the bottle. If you repeat the operation a thousand times, you will see millions of such small spheres of fire pass through the water without the water dropping by as much as a hair-breadth. In order to be more certain of the results, after putting water in the bottle, you can seal it with glass. You can then leave the bottle on the coals for months on end, and you will always see the globules rising, passing through to the other side and going into the air, and never in a thousand years will a sole dram of the enclosed water be consumed.

The point is urged with the aid of an analogy : just as the wind picks up specks of dust and whiffs them away, so fire-atoms pass through the glass, capture atoms of water and lift them into the air. The particles of dust are not converted into air or vapour; likewise the atoms of water do not lose their identity and can be recovered through condensation. The speed and momentum with which the fire-atoms pass through the glass is attributed to their compression in the coal. When they strike a light plate, they gather under it and form small globules, 'easily discernible in the form of something like dew', and thrust the plate upward.

This, Colombo, is but a sample of Galileo's method of philosophising. I think it is much safer than introducing mere names of generations, transmutations, alterations and other operations, brought in and often used when someone does not know how to cope with problems that he does not understand.[25]

Galileo is being somewhat unfair to his opponents who did not have his lynx-eyes to actually *see* the fire-atoms bubbling to the surface. All Colombo was able to perceive in the dew-like globules was water-vapour. This illustrates how natural philosophers pick out those elements which their theory leads them to expect and seldom look for anything else. Galileo observed that the water was warmer at the surface than at the bottom of the container in which it was being heated. He did not notice however, that a circulation was set up in the vessel, while Colombo did. The reason is clear : Galileo was led to suppose that the water would be warmer at the surface because he believed that a great number of fire-atoms were held back there, whereas nothing in his hypothesis suggested that they might move around in a circle. Colombo, on the contrary, looked for such a circulation : his account of boiling implied that water, which is naturally cold, set itself in motion and circulated to cool off and avoid corruption by heat.

IV THE PROBLEM OF METHOD

The Principle of Authority

What strikes (and usually annoys) the modern reader of sixteenth- and seventeenth-century scientific literature is the constant appeal to the writings of great men of the past. Where a modern scientist introduces experimental evidence to prove a point, a medieval or a Renaissance scholar will quote a relevant passage from one of the Greek philosophers. If we are to make sense of much that is said and argued in the debate on floating bodies, we must remember that this is the intellectual climate in which Galileo lived. Before the sixteenth century, man never expected the progressive nature of human knowledge. He was, of course, aware of certain historical developments of science, but he believed that it was a development to a certain fixed maximum. There was a ceiling to human attainment, and that ceiling had been reached in Greek science; here, as Giorgio Coresio declared, men could turn for guidance :

> It is one of the wonders of nature that she has produced the supreme master in every science and in every art. Nature has applied separately the utmost of her teaching to some persons in which she demonstrated the beauty of her ideas, and to which she now points so that others may know what norm to follow.[26]

The prevailing conviction of the age was that problems either could not be solved because they were beyond human comprehension, or that they had already been solved, and that the answers, at least in their broad outline, were available in the great works of the past. This explains why the deductive aspect of science played such an important part in medieval thought. It also explains why Aristotle could become such an authority in the Middle Ages and why the Renaissance could be a return to the golden age of Greek culture in general. Men might argue as to what authority constituted the highest court of appeal, but they did not question the existence of such an authority. Both scholasticism and humanism, notwithstanding their fundamental differences, looked back to Greek antiquity. They agreed that the first aim of scholarly research was to draw conclusions from the principles laid down by their predecessors. Knowledge could be extended, or it could be disregarded. It could not be drastically revised.

In Italy, at the turn of the seventeenth century, two groups of scholars agreed on this principle of authority but brought their allegiance to different masters. On one hand, we find the Aristotelians who occupied the principal chairs and constituted the Academic Establishment; on the other, a small band of dissident Platonists of sundry shades and tendencies.[27] Mathematicians, who followed Euclid and Archimedes, and physicians, who read Galen, formed independent groups. If they cared to intervene in philosophical disputes it was assumed that they had joined one of the two camps: a Non-Platonist was regarded as a disciple of Aristotle, and an Anti-Aristotelian was expected to uphold the tenets of Plato. Galileo soon found himself in trouble with this automatic labelling. The professors of philosophy might respect him as an expert in geometry (for what the subject was worth), but it would never have occurred to them that he could be a creative genius or a brilliant innovator in philosophy. Quite on the contrary, they felt that he was reviving old stuff, that he was championing obsolete ideas long refuted by Aristotle, as anyone who had read Buonamico's standard textbook on motion would know. When they wanted to be kind, they said that he was only trying to spark a debate. 'I believe', says Coresio, 'that Galileo published his *Discourse* to stir up a discussion among the *letterati*, rather than to propose a different opinion'. Colombo adds that Galileo revives many opinions of the Ancients merely as an intellectual exercise.[28] Arousing interest in worn-out concepts might conceivably be useful if it led to a better appreciation of the truth contained in the Peripatetic position; it would be detrimental if the half-formed and half-informed students were to take them seriously. Older scholars considered it their duty to protect the young from ideas that might seem modern but were really far from being new. Arturo Pannochieschi de' Conti d'Elci, the Overseer of the University of Pisa, calls upon the Grand Duchess to lend her support to the philosopher to whom Alexander the Great himself granted his enlightened protection. If Aristotle, in spite of his greatness 'were not at times supported and reinforced by the favour of new Alexanders, he would fall or greatly decrease in popularity. The majority of men, filled with the restlessness of youth, or envy, or boredom with the continuation of the same doctrine, would turn to new things, albeit less certain, if they were professed at the court'.[29]

A good scholar did not only seek political protection for Aristotle's doctrine, he also took it upon himself to defend his reputation at all times. This may seem strange to us, but it is the logical outcome of a monolithic conception of truth. If truth is one and unique, it cannot be found in mutually incompatible systems of philosophy nor can it be fragmented and picked up in bits and pieces. If Aristotle was right on the basic issues, there was every reason to believe that he had dealt effectively with minor ones. The task of the philosopher was to discover the real unity beneath the apparent inconsistencies. The debate on floating bodies affords two striking instances of this procedure. One was prompted by Galileo's indictment of Aristotle for saying that a needle cannot float on water. The Schoolmen immediately replied that Aristotle intended the needle to be placed erect in the water or that he had in mind a large, heavy needle. To claim, as Galileo had the impudence to do, that Aristotle never made the experiment, was ludicrous. He *must* have performed it since 'it is easy for anyone to make' and 'it could not have been more difficult for Aristotle who wanted to see an infinite number of difficult experiments.'[30]

Giorgio Coresio's reaction to criticism of Aristotle's failure to understand mathematical ratios provides us with a second illustration of this attitude : 'Who will believe', he writes, 'that a man of such eminent doctrine did not study geometry, which at that time was studied by children, just as now they learn the letters of the alphabet'. To try to teach Aristotle the principles of philosophy is attempting to bring light to the sun.[31] Colombo pities Galileo :

> It seems to me that Galileo has wrongly become an Antiperipatetician. In this particular issue, I wish to become an Antigalilean, in gratitude to Aristotle that great prince of so many academies, head of so many schools, object of so many poems, labour of so many historians. He read more books than he had days, wrote more works than he counted years, new and divine Briareus, who, it would seem, with one hundred hands and pens always dictated one hundred works, and, finally, of whom famous writers have said that *natura locuta est ex ore illius*.[32]

The Language of Nature and the Language of Science

'Nature has spoken through his mouth'. For the academic officialdom, the approach to science posed no problem. The trails had been blazed by Aristotle and were there for all to follow. 'Let us conclude, therefore', says Coresio, 'that he who does not want to walk in darkness must consult Aristotle, the excellent interpreter of nature'.[33]

This attitude of mind irritated Galileo for whom the interpreter of nature was neither Aristotle, nor Plato, nor Democritus, nor any of the Ancients but nature speaking for itself. While the Aristotelians sought to solve a problem, as though it were a legal question, by appealing to authority, Galileo went directly to the tribunal of nature—albeit with Archimedes as his barrister. His opponents did not grasp the nature of his enterprise. If he rejected the Peripatetic arguments, they assumed that it was because he did not understand them or because he was a Platonist, or both perhaps. When Galileo protested that he was supporting Plato on one point only, i.e., the absence of positive levity, they saw in this yet another instance of his lack of philosophical sophistication.[34] They urged him to study the arguments of Aristotle 'instead of dismissing them haughtily as though it were sufficient to say, "Pythagoras said it" '. Benedetto Castelli, Galileo's favourite disciple, cleverly retorted :

> Galileo does not intend to go against Aristotle in his philosophy or to revive old ideas, but to say the truth. If it so happens that in order to discover it he goes against Aristotle or revives old ideas, he does not do this out of mischief or caprice but because of his desire to know the truth. This he fittingly places above everything else, just as, in natural questions, he puts nature above the authority of any famous author, as any one who wishes to philosophise properly ought to do.[35]

But granted that nature speaks for itself and not necessarily through Aristotle, how can one know what nature is saying? Galileo would have his readers make the discovery that an increasing number of young noblemen were making in Florence : geometry gives wings, without its aid no one can raise himself above the ground. Castelli marvelled that a man who did not know geometry should have the audacity to criticise Galileo's logic. Galileo himself declared that he wrote for those who understood mathematics, and that he was fully aware that more than eighty per cent of those who scanned his book would be unable to follow his arguments.[36] He lamented the fact that while geometry gave man the possibility of seeing nature, the Schoolmen blindfolded themselves and went after Aristotle.

How, in fact, did the Aristotelians feel about this new mathematical vision? Briefly, they were persuaded that it was completely inadequate for any serious inquiry into nature. The Unknown Academician put it bluntly : 'the propositions and the proofs of mathematics do not succeed in demonstrating the strength and the true causes of the operations of nature'. Mathematics abstracted from the concrete properties of physical bodies. It might be an interesting game, a superior form of mental gymnastics, but it disclosed nothing about the real world. Vincenzo di Grazia shared the same conviction :

> Before we consider Galileo's demonstrations, it seems necessary to prove how far from the truth are those who wish to prove natural facts by means of mathematical reasoning, among whom, if I am not mistaken, is Galileo. All the sciences and all the arts have their own principles and their own causes by means of which they demonstrate the special properties of their own object. It follows that we are not allowed to use the principles of one science to prove the properties of another. Therefore anyone who thinks he can prove natural properties with mathematical arguments is simply demented, for the two sciences are

very different. The natural scientist studies natural bodies that have motion as their natural and proper state, but the mathematician abstracts from all motion.[37]

Galileo had anticipated this kind of underrating of mathematics in his draft of the *Discourse on Floating Bodies* :

I expect a terrible rebuke from one of my adversaries, and I can almost hear him shouting in my ears that it is one thing to deal with matters physically and quite another to do so mathematically, and that geometers should stick to their fantasies, and not get involved in philosophical matters where the conclusions are different from those in mathematics. As if truth could ever be more than one; as if geometry in our day was an obstacle to the acquisition of true philosophy; as if it were impossible to be a geometer as well as a philosopher, so that we must infer as a necessary consequence that anyone who knows geometry cannot know physics, and cannot reason about and deal with physical matters physically ! Consequences no less foolish than that of a certain physician who, moved by a fit of spleen, said that the great doctor Acquapendente, being a famous anatomist and surgeon, should content himself to remain among his scalpels and ointments without trying to effect cures by medicine, as if knowledge of surgery was opposed to medicine and destroyed it.[38]

These quotations illustrate one of the striking features of Aristotelian science in the seventeenth century : its strict division of knowledge into watertight compartments. It is important to see exactly what this implied, and how it was rooted in a static understanding of human knowledge divorced from technical activity. The world of Colombo, di Grazia, Coresio and the Unknown Academician was a stable whole of fixed forms which could not be transformed. Man could only introduce accidental modifications, he could not produce any significant change. Whereas the word *science* in the twentieth century suggests power to transform the world, in Galileo's day it denoted an awareness of the permanent features of this passing show. The limitations set upon human possibilities to modify nature account for the fact that philosophers sharply distinguished between science and technology. The former was 'deep' knowledge, the latter mere handiwork. Mathematics was an idealised way of looking at the three dimensions of a body, but it gave one no real insight into the nature of extension, and it had no practical relevance. Who had ever seen a perfect circle, a line without width, or a point without magnitude? It was not until mathematics enabled man to change nature that it could become a problem for philosophers. We know that the advance of technology was largely dependent on the development of geometry and mathematics, and technology has revealed that nature is not a stable whole of fixed forms but an infinite realm of possibilities for transformation. This has thrown a new light on the role of mathematics in our knowledge of the world, but the Aristotelians can hardly be blamed for failing to foresee this.

When the Unknown Academician said that Galileo, after establishing a kingdom in the sky, was trying to conquer an empire under the moon, he was speaking more accurately than he realised. Galileo not only believed in the possibility of expanding existing knowledge with the aid of mathematics, he was convinced that radically new things could be discovered and that the riches of nature were unbounded : 'all men together, those who came and those who will come into the world, did not know and perhaps will never know but a small part of natural philosophy'. This implied that the study of nature was a long and arduous process, and that scientists were often beset by uncertainty.

> Galileo willingly admits that he can spend months and years undecided about a problem of nature, and that he has no hope whatsoever of acquiring answers to an infinite number of problems. I know that he looks without envy at those who run and think they can penetrate nature's innermost secrets in a flash.[39]

But there was no doubt in Galileo's mind about the possibility of knowing some of the intrinsic causes of natural phenomena. He repeatedly insisted that he had found the true, unique and absolute cause of the floating of bodies, and Benedetto Castelli, writing under the watchful eye of his master, asserted that 'the propositions demonstrated by Archimedes are eternally valid for wet mediums'.[40] Galileo ridiculed his opponents for introducing subsidiary hypotheses that were so general that they lacked empirical relevance.

> Aristotle would not have argued so childishly as to say, 'The cause of this effect is such and such along with the other causes that accompany it', forgetting to specify what they are. If it were sufficient not to exclude a cause in order to philosophise correctly about a natural property, philosophy could be learned in a few words. If you were content with so much, I could satisfy any of your queries. For instance, if you asked me what causes the saltness of the sea, I could answer the spots on the moon with the other accidents that produce salinity; for the inundation of the Nile, I could say that it depends on the movement of Mercury and on the other accidents that contribute to produce this effect.[41]

The Function of Experiments

We have seen how Galileo defined his terms, explained his principles, and proceeded deductively to establish a series of theorems with the aid of the principle of virtual velocities and the lever as a model. But how is the truth of a theory ascertained? An erroneous theory can produce correct results, and Galileo himself in an early draft of the *Discourse on Floating Bodies* derived a true conclusion from a false premise. He learned from his own mistake that the right answer does not necessarily warrant the validity of the theory that generates it, and that experiments speak with an authoritative voice of their own.

The ideal situation for Galileo would seem to arise when a model with well-known properties, such as the lever, is readily available. The principles that hold for the model are then applied to a particular problem, the consequences are worked out and confronted with experience or subjected to experiment. If there is no model available, analogies with familiar occurrences are sought. For instance, Galileo suggests that moving through water is similar to jostling one's way through a crowded room. But analogies can be misleading, as when Galileo compares the action of air on a floating lamina to the attractive force of a magnet.

> Perhaps some of the gentlemen who disagree with me will marvel that I affirm that the contiguous air above the lamina of brass or silver on the water is capable of sustaining it, as if I would, in a certain sense, give the air a kind of magnetic virtue.[42]

Galileo introduces this analogy to meet a difficulty that arises from the fact that a lamina which floats when dry sinks if it is wetted evenly with a thin coating of water. The implication would seem to be that Galileo's theory of floating bodies is wrong, and he seeks to avoid this by ascribing to air the property of attracting dry but not wet plates. An experiment is said to confirm this view. A ball of wax is weighted with just enough lead filings to make it sink to the bottom of a vessel of water. A glass is plunged mouth downward and placed above the ball so that the air in the glass touches it. When the glass is slowly raised the ball follows it to the surface and remains afloat after the glass is removed. Galileo's contention that this establishes the existence of an attractive force in the air met with unanimous disapproval. The Unknown Academician objected that he could not see why the air lost its magnetic virtue when the plate was covered with a thin film of water, and Giorgio Coresio asked why the virtue did not act at a distance as in a loadstone. But the most interesting comments were formulated by Tolomeo Nozzolini, who approved of Galileo's Archimedean approach, but criticised him on experimental grounds for asserting that the ramparts of water did not cover the lamina but folded back, as is illustrated in figure 6. 'I believe I can see in the actual experiment', he wrote, 'that the ramparts project over the plate in the form of semi-circles',[43] as in figure 6. If this was the case, then Galileo's demonstration that a pyramid of any material could float while only wetting its base lost all relevance to the actual physical situation.

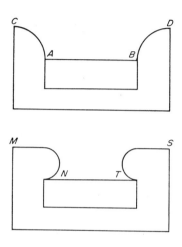

FIG. 6

In his reply, Galileo contested Nozzolini's account of the experiment, but he also welcomed the opportunity of disclaiming the expression 'magnetic virtue'. It was introduced, he said, by an important gentleman who, failing to comprehend exactly what he was explaining to the Grand Duke, exclaimed, 'Then you wish to give the air a magnetic attraction!' In the *Discourse on Floating Bodies*, this idea was mentioned 'to inform those who introduced it that I did not consider it to be true'.[44] Galileo's explanation, therefore, is that a courtier interjected a comparison that he did not ridicule for tactical reasons, but adapted for his purposes in the manner set forth in the *Discourse*. But the truth of the matter is that he was wrangling himself out of an incautious analogy that he had accepted, not only to avoid offending an important member of the court, but because he thought that it could be used to explain how the ramparts of water were held together. Galileo was always fascinated by the loadstone and spent several years making experiments with magnets. He became increasingly annoyed, however, with the difficulties involved in quantifying and measuring their strength. At the time he wrote to Nozzolini, he was still toying with the idea of using the magnet as a model as is evidenced by a passage in the draft of his letter in which he compares water particles to small spherical magnets that cannot be detached but can be made to revolve around each other. Galileo hoped by means of this model to avoid the outcry that he was surreptitiously reintroducing the resistance to division he had so strongly opposed. He soon realised, however, that his distinction between resistance to division and resistance to motion around a contiguous magnetic body would offer no real solution. For how could a solid body sink in a medium where the particles could not be separated from their immediate neighbours. It would be like trying to shove a stick into a box tightly packed with perfectly spherical marbles! Consequently, Galileo abandoned the magnetic analogy, and in his letter to Nozzolini he conveyed the impression that he had never entertained it.

Galileo never wavers, however, in his belief that he has the basic solution to the problem of floating bodies :

> The proximate and immediate cause of floating is the one and only cause already mentioned, namely the excess of the gravity and the moments of the water over the gravity and the moments of the plate.

How the ramparts held together, he considers a secondary question :

> I do not care whether the fact that the ramparts do not break . . . be ascribed to a desire of the parts to stay united, or to the dryness of the plate that resists the humidity of the water, or to the air adhering to the lamina. This is irrelevant to our main tenet, for which it is enough that this much be verified, namely that the plate makes a hole in the water that could contain an amount of water equal in weight to that of the plate.[45]

Galileo has experimental evidence that the ramparts existed, and he thinks he has found the proximate cause that enables him to predict their height. What causes the water particles to cohere is another question, equally interesting perhaps, but one he does not feel he has to answer. His aim is to work out a coherent theory and he does not allow himself to be distracted at every turn by the question whether it is susceptible of actual physical realisation.

It would seem, therefore, that experiments are not essential for Galileo in the sense that their mere mechanical repetition can produce a theory. Rather they are important inasmuch as they play a discriminatory role in the selection of the set of principles that will be used as the basis of a physical interpretation of nature. This means that framing exact hypotheses is only the first step in science. The second one is deriving practical conclusions from them and devising well-chosen experiments to test them. It is one of Galileo's great contributions to the development of the scientific method that he clearly recognised the necessity of isolating the true cause by creating artificial conditions where one element is varied at a time. For instance, in order to find out whether the shape was the cause of floating, he stressed that it was essential to 'remove all the other causes that could produce the same result, leaving only the difference in shape in the bodies'. Since different materials would make it difficult to discriminate between the effects produced by the weight and those resulting from the shape, he specified that a material almost as dense as water

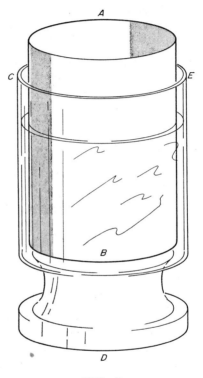

FIG. 7

should be chosen in order to allow a slight difference in shape to cause an appreciable change in the speed of rise and fall. Galileo's experimental flair is revealed in his choice of wax which is malleable and can be made almost as dense as water by adding a few lead filings to it.

The Unknown Academician tried to follow these methodological canons and suggested an experiment whereby the air could be removed from the depression produced by the floating solid without altering the solid or the water. He covered the surface of the floating plate with a plate of the same size, but without touching either the plate or the sides of the ramparts.

The air is pushed out and taking flight seeks refuge in its own element, and abandons the plate, which, nevertheless, remains safe and afloat. The floating shape delighted cries out : 'Victory! Victory!'[46]

Galileo had left himself open to such an attack by comparing air to a magnet. The objection compelled him to work out his solution on strictly hydrostatical principles, and to propose two new experiments which he described with increasing accuracy in postils to the Unknown Academician's *Considerations*, and, a few months later, in his letter to Nozzolini.

The first experiment consists in lowering a solid metal cylinder into an empty glass until it is four finger-breadths from the bottom, fixing it to some solid support, and then pouring water into the space left in the glass. In spite of the small quantity of water, it is as difficult to raise the glass as when it is filled with water to the brim. In a subsequent note, Galileo describes the experiment at greater length. This time the glass *CDE* is filled with water and slowly raised so that the weight *AB* expels the water. The weight of the glass is found to remain unchanged throughout the entire operation.[47] Galileo outlines the same experiment to Nozzolini, and adds that if a weight were lowered into a floating wooden vessel until the water was almost completely expelled, the vessel would still float, 'as experiment will make this clear to anyone, but apart from the experiment the reason is not lacking'.[48] The reason, of course, is Archimedes' principle interpreted with the aid of the principle of virtual displacements. 'Sig. Accademico, the piece of lead you place in the hole of the ramparts expels the air that is there, but it confers to the vessel moments equal to those of the expelled air'.[49]

In the second experiment, a glass container filled with enough lead shots to make it gently sink to the bottom of a vessel of water is heated over a charcoal fire. The opening is then sealed and the container allowed to cool before being replaced on the water where it floats because the air has been removed and nothing has been introduced to take its place, 'as you will see by experience if you open the cylinder and feel the air rushing with great impetus into the cylinder'.[50] In his letter to Nozzolini, Galileo suggests an improved version of this experiment which involves fitting the glass container with a long narrow tube and noting the depth to which it sinks. He shows his awareness of experimental difficulties when he writes that 'the piece of wax or of other material used to seal the opening should be placed on the glass container (without closing it) before the air is removed, otherwise it could easily add more weight than that of the air expelled'.[51] The glass must also be given time to cool before it is replaced on the water in order to allow the 'igneous exhalations' to escape. Their weight would presumably tip the balance against Galileo!

Two rival theories claimed to interpret the hydrostatic phenomena. In Galileo's words, these are 'the rule of the predominance of the four elements', and 'the rule of Archimedes'.[52] The first rule is scientifically irrelevant because it does not enable one to predict whether a body will float until it is actually seen lying on the surface of the water.

The elements do not operate except insofar as they are heavy or light. To say therefore that the wood of the fir-tree does not sink because air predominates in it, is to say no more than it does not sink because it is less heavy than water. Moreover, the immediate reason is being less heavy than water, and the cause of the lesser weight is the predominance of air. Therefore, anyone who produces the predominance of an element as the cause, gives the cause of the cause and not the proximate and immediate cause. Now who does not know that the true cause is the immediate and not the mediate? Furthermore, he who alleges weight gives a cause well known to the senses, for it is easy to find out whether ebony or fir, for instance, are more or less heavy than water. But how will we know whether earth or air predominates in them? Surely, there is no better experiment than to observe whether they sink or float. It follows that if someone does not know whether a solid floats unless he knows that air predominates in it, he does not know that it floats until he actually sees it floating.[53]

This passage embodies three major tenets of what was to become the scientific method. First, it declares that we must look for proximate rather than remote causes; secondly, it removes from the field of science non-falsifiable hypotheses, and thirdly, it stresses the importance of prediction. The predominance of an element adduced by the Aristotelians tells us nothing about the behaviour of bodies before we actually carry out experiments. It even fails to determine what compounds are predominantly air, water, earth or fire. For instance, iron floats in mercury, but since Aristotle affirms that air predominates in mercury and earth in iron, the predominance of air becomes an ambiguous quality.

The Peripatetics claimed to have experimental evidence that water decreases in volume upon freezing, and they pointed to the empty space left between the surface of the water and frozen ice in a bottle.[54] Galileo comments that ice also comes out of the neck of bottles in winter, and that bottles are often broken because their necks are blocked by ice. Since this cannot be verified in the summer, he proposes an experiment that can be performed at any time of the year. This consists in placing a few chunks of ice in a bottle half-filled with water and observing whether the level of the water rises when the ice melts, as the Peripatetic theory entails, or whether it drops as he predicts. The test is easy to perform, and the outcome confirms Galileo's position.

Another interesting Aristotelian theory assumes that a ship floats better at sea than in port. It is difficult to verify this hypothesis because of the pitching and rolling on the sea, but Galileo removes the question from the realm of inconclusive theoretical debate by suggesting a practical experiment. A small vessel is placed in a tank of water and filled with lead shots to the point where one more shot would make it sink. The vessel is then placed in a tank one hundred times larger, and the number of additional shots of lead required to make it sink are counted. 'Let Grazia make the experiment . . . I have already performed it and I know that he is wrong'.[55]

Galileo worked out the practical consequences of other theories of his opponents and confronted them equally devastatingly with experience. If so-called 'light' bodies had a natural tendency to move upward, they would move faster in a medium that offers less resistance, for example, in air than in water. But this is wrong since bodies that ascend rapidly through water stop when they reach the surface or are considerably slowed down upon entering the air. Likewise if shape made a difference in the sinking of solids, two wooden cylinders of different sizes would not float equally well. Yet, the ratio of the submerged part to the part above the water is identical regardless of the shape.

The importance Galileo attaches to experiments does not entail a relentless accumulation of confirming instances. His faith in the uniformity of nature[56] and his certitude that there is one basic cause implies a belief in the sufficiency of one or at the most of a few well-chosen experiments. Science for Galileo is an explanatory pattern of logically connected geometrical concepts derived from a few (and preferably from one) principles. The 'true cause' of the floating of bodies is determined by applying the principle of virtual velocities to hydrostatics. The only experiment that is discussed at any length in the first part of the *Discourse on Floating Bodies* is the moulding of a ball of wax into various forms to prove that the shape does not influence the motion of the body. Galileo considers this sufficient to establish the relevance of geometrical reasoning and to allow him to proceed deductively. The outcome of further experiments can be safely predicted from his armchair : this explains why he insists on experimental verification and yet is content with so few actual experiments.

Galileo recognises the regulative use of experimentation but his main concern is the internal consistency of his theory. He is prepared to compromise on the shape and the nature of the ramparts, but he is adamant on the depth of the depressions caused by thin foils of metals on the surface of the water. The reason is clear : different explanations of the force holding the ramparts are compatible with his main theory, but the depth to which the thin plates sink is a direct outcome of his 'proximate and immediate cause', namely 'the excess of the gravity and the moments of the water over the gravity and the moments of the plate'.

Another instance of Galileo's response to the requirement of coherence is his solution to the problem posed by an apparent clash of principles in his account of the formation of water. On the one hand, he affirms that ice is rarefied water because it is lighter than water; on the other, he maintains that the property of cold is to condense. But if ice is formed by condensation how can it be rarefied water? Galileo's solution is a tribute to the art of logic rather than the art of experimentation : ice is formed, he asserts, not mainly from water, but from the air above the water. It is, therefore, condensed air or rarefied water vapour![57]

Students usually start with the conclusions handed down to them by their master, and Galileo was no exception. He was a disciple of Archimedes and it is as such that he set out to investigate the problem of floating bodies. It is only when this attempt proved inadequate that he broadened his approach to include the more dynamic method suggested in the pseudo-Aristotelian *De Mechanica*. The turning point was the crucial discovery that he had wrongly assumed that a solid always displaced a volume of water equal to its own. He detected this error not through experimentation but in the process of working out the theorems he needed to explain the floating of bodies in water.

Galileo campaigned vigorously against the authoritarianism of the Schoolmen who allowed nature to state only what Aristotle had heard it say. Yet he himself did not escape the accusation of reintroducing another authority in the person of Archimedes. Because he was convinced that Archimedes' Principle was the true expression of nature's Law, he felt he could declare surface tension impossible, and determine *a priori* the depth to which a thin plate of metal must sink if it floats. His initial error led him to a greater awareness of the regulative use of experiments, but he restricted it to cases which were not rigorously deduced from certain principles. Experiments never had to be numerous, but it was important that they should be well chosen. One such experiment, where one element could be varied at a time, was sufficient to confirm a theory, provided the theory was mathematically articulated and yielded forecasts about the behaviour of physical objects. Technology and the craft tradition did not enter the debate on hydrostatics directly. What is significantly different in Galileo's approach, when we compare it with that of his Aristotelian opponents, is not so much his attitude towards experimentation as his twofold belief in the relevance of mathematics and in the progressive nature of science. Galileo was convinced that human knowledge had not reached its ceiling in Greek science and that new vistas could be opened by the application of geometry to physical problems.

NOTES

1. Letter to Belisario Vinta, 7 May 1610, *Opere di Galileo*, **10**, 353
2. This is the only one of his books to have received such a treatment at his hands, in spite of his promises to reissue his treatise on the compass and his *Sidereus Nuncius*. For the story of the successive drafts of this work, see Stillman Drake, *Galileo Studies* (Ann Arbor: University of Michigan Press, 1970), 159–176
3. *Discorso intorno alle cose che stanno in sù l'acqua o che in quella si muovono, Opere di Galileo*, **4**, 67. Literally, *Discourse on the Things that Stay on the Surface of the Water or that Move in It*. It was translated by Thomas Salusbury in the seventeenth century as *A Discourse Concerning the Natation of Bodies upon, and Submersion in, the Water*. This has given way to the shorter *Discourse on Floating Bodies* which I retain. The passage in Aristotle which Galileo has in mind is the last Chapter of book IV of *De Coelo*
4. The word used by Galileo is 'cagione' which means 'cause' but also the more vague 'reason for'. It is difficult to translate Galileo without making him appear more advanced in conceptual distinctions than he actually was. The classical example of this mishap is the Crew–de Salvio translation of the *Discourses Concerning Two New Sciences* where *gravità in specie* is rendered by *specific gravity* to the greatest peril of the unwary reader. Maria Luisa Altieri Biagi makes a major contribution toward establishing the various nuances of Galileo's floating terminology in *Galileo e la terminologia tecnico-scientifica* (Florence: Olschki, 1965), but she occasionally exaggerates Galileo's awareness of finer conceptual points. Lest I should indulge in the desire to achieve clarity at the price of accuracy, I list a few words that frequently occur in Galileo's writings but lack the clear-cut meaning of their modern equivalents:

    (*a*) *mole* is translated by *mass* in the Salusbury version and by *volume* in modern translations. This is sharpening the concept; the words *size* and *bulk* are closer approximations to the original undifferentiated meaning of *mole*.

    (*b*) *gravità* is usually employed by Galileo instead of *peso* to denote weight, and it has none of the connotations of the Newtonian concept of gravity. *Gravità in specie* is a technical term, but it is not limited to a comparison of the densities of a substance and a liquid medium.

    (*c*) *velocità* simply means *speed*. There is no difference between velocity, speed and acceleration. This is often overlooked to the detriment of a proper understanding of the difficulties that faced seventeenth-century scientists.

    (*d*) *virtù* and *forza* present a special problem. They can be translated by *power*, *strength*, or *force* according to the context. I have maintained the word *virtue* in my translation of passages from Galileo. For *forza*, see Richard S. Westfall, 'The Problems of Force in Galileo's Physics', in *Galileo Re-Appraised*, ed. Carlo L. Golino (Berkeley and Los Angeles: University of California Press, 1966), 67–95; also M. Jammer, *Concepts of Force* (Cambridge, Mass.: Harvard University Press, 1957), 94–103.

    (*e*) *momento* is already a technical term but it has no single modern equivalent. It can be rendered at times by *static moment* and at others by *momentum*. But it is never the case of one rather than the other; it is always both with a greater emphasis on one according to context.

    (*f*) *impeto* is frequently interchangeable with *momento*, but *momento* is more general and covers statical and dynamical situations, while *impeto* implies the idea of motion and has a more restricted usage. See Galileo,

Discorsi intorno a due nuove scienze, eds. L. Geymonat and A. Carugo (Turin: Boringhieri, 1958), 783, note 215

5. Galileo, *Discourse on Floating Bodies, Opere di Galileo*, **6**, 67. Galileo shared the ambition of the mathematicians of his day to prove by other (and preferably easier) means what Archimedes had discovered. Michel Coignet congratulated Galileo on such an achievement: 'I have received your proof of the centre of gravity of the parabola and I admire it greatly, since (be it said in all modesty) I find it much easier and more practical than Archimedes' own proofs' (letter to Galileo, 31 March 1588, *ibid.*, **10**, 31–32)

6. *Ibid.*, *Gravià in specie* probably derives from the medieval treatise *De insidentibus in humidum* (see E. Moody and M. Clagett, *Medieval Science of Weights* [Madison: University of Wisconsin Press, 1961], 91–93, 113–145 and for the methodological implications, 673–676)

7. *Ibid.*, 68–69

8. *Considerazioni . . . da Accademico Incognito* (Pisa, 1612), *Opere di Galileo*, **4**, 158. In the second edition of the *Vocabulary of the Crusca* (Venice, 1623), the technical sense of *momento* was added: 'quella forza, peso, o violenza, che acquistano i corpi gravi nel muoversi naturalmente verso il loro centro, termine di meccanica. Onde per metaf. cosa li momento, cosa d'importanza'

9. Galileo, *Discourse on Floating Bodies, Opere di Galileo*, **4**, 68

10. *Ibid.*, **4**, 36

11. *De Motu, ibid.*, **1**, 256, 351–352

12. *Ibid.*, **4**, 37–38

13. Galileo, *Discourse on Floating Bodies, ibid.*, 70

14. *Ibid.*, 71–73

15. *Ibid.*, 67, 70

16. *Ibid.*, 77

17. Vincenzo di Grazia dismisses Galileo's mathematical demonstration offhand: 'I should now go on to consider each proof and each proposition; but since all his demonstrations rest on false principles, I have decided to forego the drudgery' (*Considerazioni sopra il discorso di Galileo Galilei* [Florence, 1613], *ibid.*, 388)

18. Galileo, *Discourse on Floating Bodies, ibid.*, 78

19. See Ernst Mach, *The Science of Mechanics*, trans. Thomas J. McCormack, 6th edition (La Salle, Illinois: Open Court Classics, 1960), 111. Stevin discussed the hydrostatic paradox in strictly Archimedean terms in his *Elements of Hydrostatics* (*The Principal Works of Simon Stevin*, ed. E. J. Dijksterhuis, 2 vols. in 3 [Amsterdam: Swets and Zeitliner], 1955, **1**, 417–418). Pascal was the first one to employ the principal of virtual displacements in a genuinely satisfactory manner. See his *Traités de l'équilibre des liqueurs et de la pesanteur de l'air*, in *Oeuvres Complètes* (Paris: Bibliothèque de la Pléiade, 1962), 412–420

20. Galileo, *Discourse on Floating Bodies, Opere di Galileo*, **4**, 108–109

21. *Ibid.*, 117

22. *Ibid.*, 133

23. Postil to the *Considerazioni . . . da Accademico Incognito, ibid.*, 195

24. Benedetto Castelli, *Errori di Giorgio Coresio, ibid.*, 281–282, postils 23, 26

25. Benedetto Castelli [and Galileo], *Risposta alle opposizioni* (Florence, 1615), *ibid.*, 654–656, italics mine

26. Giorgio Coresio, *Operetta intorno al galleggiare de' corpi solidi* (Florence, 1612), *ibid.*, **4**, 218. Ancient stories had acquired by long prescription a status in the common imagination indistinguishable from fact. An example is Seneca's tale of a lake in which bricks floated. It was introduced by Buonamico, Galileo's professor at Pisa, to show that Archimedes was wrong on experimental grounds, and it is repeated by Coresio, Colombo and di Grazia. Galileo recognised it for what it was and explained it as the natural outcome of a process of embellishment: 'There was perhaps a body of water

slightly heavier than the ordinary, where bodies somewhat heavier than those that float in our water did not sink. Fame, according to its style, exaggerated the fact in such a way that it became fabulous. We have a sign that this could have happened in the modern poet who talks about the lake and says that not only stones but iron floats in it, trying to make the tale still more wonderful' (*ibid.*, 787). Another instance is Colombo's proof that diamonds are porous although they appear otherwise: 'If diamonds were not porous, they would be odourless. Naturalists, however, write that a dog or a similar animal finds them by their scent' (*ibid.*, 346)

27. By the end of the sixteenth century the crest of the Platonic wave had long been broken, and we find a Venetian patrician writing to a Florentine friend in 1589 about the desirability of *introducing* the study of Plato in Padua (letter of Benedetto Zorzi to Baccio Valori, 2 December 1589), *ibid.*, **10**, 42
28. Coresio, *Operetta, ibid.*, **4**, 204; Colombo, *Discorso Apologetico, ibid.*, 317
29. *Considerazioni . . . da Accademico Incognito, ibid.*, 147
30. Coresio, *Operetta, ibid.*, 235
31. *Ibid.*, 240
32. Colombo, *Discorso Apologetico, ibid.*, 317–318
33. Coresio, *Operetta, ibid.*, 238
34. Galileo's Platonism in the debate on floating bodies is explicitly qualified and limited to a defence of Plato's denial of positive levity. Castelli wished to inform Coresio that 'Galileo did not promise to defend Plato, nor Anaximander, nor Democritus, in their belief (if they had such a belief) of the infinity of the universe, but only in this particular point in which they deny that levity is a real quality in natural bodies' (*ibid.*, 264). Galileo himself usually does not refer to Plato individually but rather as the member of a group: 'Plato and the Ancients' (*ibid.*, 85, 194), 'Plato and the others' (*ibid.*, 670). He emphatically denies ever having adhered to the Platonic philosophy of forms: 'dico che le figure, come semplici figure, non solamente non operano nelle cose naturali, ma nè anche si ritrovanno dalla sustanza corporea separate, nè io le ho mai proposte denudate della materia sensibile' (*ibid.*, 90). The debate over Galileo's Platonism stems largely from the multiplicity of 'Platonisms' that are not always distinguished by historians of science. Even Alexandre Koyré's remarkable 'Galileo and Plato', *The Journal of the History of Ideas*, **4** (1943), 400–428, suffers from this ambiguity. Ernst Cassirer's distinction between a *sceptical*, a *mystical*, a *Christian* and a *romantic* Platonism is valuable but incomplete ('Galileo's Platonism in *Studies and Essays . . . in Homage to George Sarton*, ed. M. F. Ashley Montagu (1947; reprinted, New York: Kraus Reprint, 1969), 279–297. There is also a *mathematical* Platonism that can be either *arithmological* or *geometrical*, a *literary* Platonism and a Platonism that is merely a *cloak* worn by those who are against the establishment. No one will doubt the literary influence of Plato's *Dialogues* on Galileo's style, but the extent of his philosophical influence is a moot question to which we shall return in chapters five and six
35. Castelli, *Risposta alle opposizioni, Opere di Galileo*, **4**, 466–467
36. *Ibid.*, 443. The popular view that Galileo was appealing to the ordinary layman above the heads of scholars will not bear examination
37. *Considerazioni . . . da Accademico Incognito, ibid.*, 165; di Grazia, *Considerazioni, ibid.*, 385
38. *Fragmenti, ibid.*, 49–50
39. Castelli, *Risposta alle opposizioni, ibid.*, 567, 653
40. Castelli, *Errori di Giorgio Coresio, ibid.*, 261
41. Castelli, *Risposta alle opposizioni, ibid.*, 501. 'Thus if someone said that the poison in the head or the tail of the dragon causes the moon to become dark and livid when it comes close to it, he would be reasoning exceedingly well, as long as he did not specifically exclude the interposition of the earth which is the real cause of lunar eclipses' (*ibid.*, 579)

42. Galileo, *Discourse on Floating Bodies, ibid.*, 101–102
43. Letter to Mons. Marzimedici, 22 September 1612, *ibid.*, 292
44. Letter to Tolomeo Nozzolini, January 1613, *ibid.*, 299
45. *Ibid.*, 304
46. *Considerazioni . . . da Accademico Incognito, ibid.*, 102
47. *Ibid.*, 182–183, postil. It is worth noting that Galileo gives no precise measurement. The container is merely held in the hand, 'if you hold the container . . . You will feel its weight increase'
48. Letter to Tolomio Nozzolini, *ibid.*, 307
49. Postil to the *Considerazioni . . . da Accademico Incognito, ibid.*, 183
50. *Ibid.*, 184
51. Letter to Tolomeo Nozzolini, *ibid.*, 309
52. Castelli, *Risposta alle opposizioni, ibid.*, 665, note 2. This passage was not included in the printed version
53. Galileo, *Discourse on Floating Bodies, ibid.*, 87
54. The assumption that water decreased in volume upon freezing was widely held by Aristotelians and Anti-Aristotelians alike in the sixteenth century (see Charles B. Schmitt, 'Experimental Evidence for and against a Void: the Sixteenth-Century Arguments', *Isis*, **58** [1967], 357–359). The Unknown Academician mentioned this belief (*Opere di Galileo*, **4**, 153–154), and Colombo introduced the problem of the empty space between the ice and the water (*ibid.*, 346). Colombo was unperturbed by the fact that ice decreased upon melting, and he maintained that since water had *decreased* upon freezing there was 'no reason why it should not decrease again upon melting' (*ibid.*, 349)
55. Castelli, *Risposta alle opposizioni, ibid.*, 756. This is one of the rare instances where Galileo explicitly says that he performed the experiment
56. Colombo accused Galileo of adhering too rigidly to this principle: 'The cause of your erroneous reasoning is your refusal to allow that the same cause can produce different effects in the same body' (*Discorso Apologetico, ibid.*, 327)
57. Postil to the *Considerazioni . . . da Accademico Incognito, ibid.*, 192–193

3. SUNSPOTS AND INCONSTANT HEAVENS

In the autumn of 1611, Christopher Scheiner, a Jesuit lecturer at the University of Ingoldstadt, wrote three letters to his friend Mark Welser in Augsburg, informing him that he had discovered spots on the sun. Welser had these letters printed and sent copies abroad, notably to Galileo and the members of the Lincean Academy.[1] As Scheiner was forbidden by his superiors to use his own name, lest he be mistaken and bring discredit on the Society of Jesus, he concealed his identity under the pseudonym of *Apelles latens post tabulam*. Galileo, however, identified him as a Jesuit and took him to task in two letters which he sent to Welser in 1612. When Scheiner published an expanded version of his views in the *Accuratior Disquisitio*, Galileo retorted with a third letter to Welser, and the following year Prince Federico Cesi published Galileo's own letters in Rome.

Scheiner's *Tres Epistolae*

In his first letter, dated 12 November 1611, Scheiner affirmed that he had detected spots on the sun seven months earlier but that they had not arrested his attention until he noticed them again in October. His reaction, on seeing them this time, was to suspect that they were caused by some defect in the eye, some fault in the lenses, or possibly some disturbance in the atmosphere. He carefully examined these three hypotheses and rejected them as unsatisfactory. The spots could not be attributed to some defect in the eye because they had been witnessed by several independent observers. Neither could the lenses be blamed, for eight different telescopes had yielded the same results. Finally, atmospheric disturbance was ruled out for several reasons: firstly, given the small visual diameter of the sun, no cloud or vapour could follow the diurnal motion of the sun from sunrise to sunset; secondly, the spots showed no parallactic displacements; thirdly, their motion across the sun was constant, and, fourthly, they could be seen through thin clouds. Scheiner concluded that the spots were 'either on the sun, or outside the sun in some celestial region'. But he made no bones about the hypothesis he preferred:

> I have always considered it inconvenient to place spots darker than any ever seen on the moon (with the exception of one small spot) on the bright body of the sun. It is not plausible to do so, for if they were on

the sun their motion would imply that the sun rotates, and we should see the spots return in the same order and in the same position they had among themselves and with respect to the sun. So far, they have failed to reappear although other spots have followed the first ones across the solar disc. This is a clear argument that they are not on the sun. I do not think, therefore, that they are real spots, but rather bodies partly eclipsing the sun, namely stars located either between the sun and ourselves or revolving around the sun.[2]

He added—without further specification—that this discovery would enable astronomers to settle two major problems in astronomy : the position of Venus and Mercury, and the relative size of the sun. He cautioned Welser that his diagrams were rough approximations, and he explained how he observed the sunspots. His methods included placing a blue or green neutral lens on the objective, looking directly at the sun at sunrise and sunset, observing the spots through clouds, and taking peeps at the midday sun, closing in on the centre from the circumference.

In the second letter, Scheiner reminded his readers that Magini's *Ephemerides* (a standard reference book for practising astronomers) had forecasted a forty-hour conjunction of the sun and Venus for 11 December at 11.00 p.m. Acting on this information, he observed Venus on 12 December, expecting to see it appear as a spot of exceptional size on the surface of the sun if it were situated between the sun and the earth. When no spot appeared Scheiner acknowledged several possible explanations : his observations might have been inaccurate, Magini's calculations could have been wrong, Venus could shine by some intrinsic light, or, simpler still, Venus did not revolve around the earth but around the sun. He rejected the first two interpretations on the grounds that his observations were made with great care and that Magini was noted for his precision. As for the hypothesis of a self-luminous Venus, it clashed with 'the experiments, the arguments, and the common doctrine of all the mathematicians'. He concluded, therefore, that Venus revolved around the sun.[3]

The third letter, dated a week later, announced that it was now possible to 'free the sun completely from the injury of spots'. If the spots were on the sun, they should return in the same position and order every fifteen days. Having observed the spots for two months, Scheiner was reasonably certain that this was not the case and, therefore, that the spots were not on the sun. He failed to take into account that the shape and size of the spots changed considerably, even to the point of being unrecognisable during the period they were visible, something that was obvious from his own diagrams of the sunspots. The implication that they could have altered beyond recognition during the next fifteen days was equally clear, but only to the mind that was prepared to accept the necessary premise, namely that real change, and not mere rearrangement of parts, was possible in the heavens. Scheiner cannot be accused of ignoring this possibility, but it must be said that he never entertained it seriously. Trained to think within the traditional cosmological framework, he was reluctant to place any blemish on the sun. From the very outset, he had been thinking of saving the immutability of the heavens, of fitting the new data into the old theory. The argument he put forward merely betrayed his tacit methodological bias.

The absence of parallax compelled Scheiner to locate the spots near the sun, but his refusal to allow change in heavenly bodies precluded the possibility of countenancing the idea that they might be clouds, 'for who would place clouds here? If they were clouds, what would be their number? Why should they all move in the same direction? How could they produce such large shadows?'[4]

To place spots on the sun would have been to admit radical change in the Aristotelian cosmos; to see new stars was only to affirm what had been there all along, albeit undetected. The spots *had to be* stars, and Scheiner, intent upon finding evidence, saw a sure indication that the spots had phases like the moon in the occasional darkening of the side of the spots nearest the rim of the sun. Convinced that he had found the right answer, he extended his conclusions to the satellites of Jupiter and suggested that they were more numerous than the four discovered by Galileo. This was a hasty generalisation, and not one that was likely to recommend him to Galileo, as he was only too soon to find out.

Galileo's Letters

Galileo replied to Welser on 14 May 1612. He pleaded ill-health as an excuse for his delay, and regretted that the difficulty of the matter combined with his inability to make continuous observations still kept his judgment in suspense. But this did not prevent him from voicing his criticism of other interpretations, and after informing Welser that he had already observed the sunspots some eighteen months earlier, he proceeded to administer a sound rebuff to the author of the *Tres Epistolae*.

Galileo admitted that the spots were real but he quibbled on the appropriateness of describing their motion as eastward or westward, and he chided Scheiner for ignoring the telescopic discovery of the phases of Venus which alone left 'no room for doubt about the orbit of Venus'. He criticised him for begging the question by supposing that if the spots were on the sun they would return every fifteen days as though they were not subject to genuine alteration. He then drew an analogy between sunspots and clouds, allowed for the eventual discovery of other satellites and planets, and ended by stating that he considered it unlikely that Saturn's companion-stars (Saturn's rings) would undergo any change.

Shortly after despatching this letter, Galileo was incensed by rumours from Bologna that his work was the object of ridicule in academic circles, and he decided to publicise what he justifiably thought was his prior discovery of the sunspots.[5] He wrote to several influential friends, and he sent a second letter to Welser in which he propounded his own theory on the sunspots. Briefly, he affirmed that the spots were contiguous to the surface of the sun, that their properties were analogous to those of clouds, and that they were carried around by the rotation of the solar body. He argued that his interpretation, based on the mathematical relationships between the spots, agreed with the observational data while Scheiner's account led to inconsistencies and contradictions. Scheiner was not apprised of this second letter until some time later, and in the meantime he wrote a short treatise on the sunspots. It took the form of three letters to Welser, dated 16 January, 14 April and 25 July 1612, and was published in the summer of the same year under the title of *De maculis solaribus et stellis circa Jovem errantibus accuratior disquisitio*. It did for the *Tres Epistolae* what Galileo's *Second Letter* did for his *First* : it gave mathematical form to his original insight. Scheiner realised that his reasoning crumbled unless he could show that a conjunction of Venus and the sun should have resulted in a large spot appearing on the face of the sun. He appealed to Kepler's mistaken observation of an eclipse of Mercury, but it is mainly on 'the general agreement of philosophers and mathematicians, both ancient and modern', that he relied : Plato and his disciples, Ptolemy and his followers, Clavius and his school were cited as witnesses to the fact that Venus can eclipse the sun. The phases of Venus—the only convincing evidence—were mentioned, but they were not given any prominence.

Scheiner included thirty diagrams quite inferior to those of Galileo, and announced the discovery of a fifth satellite around Jupiter.[6] He sought to give the sunspots status, as it were, by recording not only the names of the astronomers who actually observed them, but a long list of 'luminaries of this age who immediately admitted the fact' although they did not see it.[7]

Scheiner's approach is a reminder that scientific inquiry is always prompted and guided by a motive, in this case by the desire to save the unalterability of the heavens. It comes as no surprise, therefore, that he should have described an eclipse of the sun in the following terms : 'we saw *what we were looking for* : the part of the moon that covered the sun was as translucent as crystal or some other kind of glass, but unevenly'.[8] A translucid moon would have enabled Scheiner to account for the moon's secondary light without introducing terrestrial reflection, which contradicted Aristotelian doctrine. What happened here—let us call it the bewitchment of theory—was to befall Galileo a few years later in the controversy on the comets when he twisted and turned to maintain that the comets were exhalations rising from the earth, and not heavenly bodies.

But all this was makeshift and Scheiner himself realised that the foundations had been shaken :

It is still doubtful whether the spots are on the sun or away from it, whether they are generated or not, whether they should be called clouds or not. But this much seems certain : the common teaching of astronomers about the hardness and the constitution of the heavens can no longer be maintained, especially in the regions of the sun and Jupiter. It is fitting, therefore, that we should listen to the leading mathematician of our time, Christopher Clavius, who, in the last edition of his works, moved by these phenomena recently discovered (though ancient in themselves), advised astronomers to start thinking of some other cosmic system.[9]

In this context the first name that came to Scheiner's mind was not Copernicus but Tycho Brahe, who was to become the mentor of the revised version of the old world system, the leader of those who thought of themselves as 'progressive conservatives'.

Galileo would have liked to reply with scalding irony, but he kept his wit in check so that Mark Welser, who had become a member of the Lincean Academy, would not be offended. It is amusing to listen to the lion admit how difficult it is for him not to growl : 'I intend to show in what a silly way the matter has been dealt with by the J[esuit], and to reprimand him as he deserves. But to do this without offending the Signor Welser is no small undertaking'.[10] Galileo eventually succeeded in maintaining a civil tone, and the third letter, a point by point rebuttal of the *Accuratior Disquisitio*, was despatched to Welser on 1 December 1612.

The Problem of Verification

The interest of the debate on sunspots lies not so much in its subject matter as in the method of falsification and confirmation developed by Galileo on this occasion. Initially, he was wary of committing himself to any definite position. 'It is more difficult for me to discover the truth than to refute what is false, and it seems to me that I know what the sunspots are not, rather than what they really are'.[11] The *First Letter* cleared the way for subsequent theorising by refuting the interpretation proposed by Scheiner. Galileo showed that Scheiner's arguments rested on the unwarranted assumption that the sun was unalterable, and that the spots could only be on the sun if they did not change shape. He criticised him for inconsistency, in particular for affirming that Mercury revolved around the sun in a smaller orbit than Venus, and then reversing the order by claiming that Venus had a smaller parallax. He attributed this wavering to the restraint exerted by a whole habit of thought about the problems of planetary astronomy : 'He [Scheiner] has begun to lend his ear and assent to true and sound philosophy . . . but still he cannot wrench himself from those previously impressed fancies to which he returns from long use and habit'.[12]

The difference between the methodological postulates of Scheiner and those of Galileo is apparent from the kind of problems they were prepared to entertain : questions that appeared ridiculous to Scheiner seemed quite natural to Galileo :

> To his query, 'Who would ever place clouds around the sun?' I answer, 'Anyone who sees the spots and wants to say something plausible about their nature, for nothing known to us resembles them more'. To his question about their size, I say, 'As large as we see them to be with respect to the sun; as large as those clouds that sometimes cover a large province on earth', and if that is not large enough I say two, three, four or ten times that. And finally, to the third 'impossibility' he adduces—how sunspots could possibly be so dark—I reply that they are not as dark as very thick clouds when these are interposed between the sun and our eyes.[13]

Galileo's own conjecture could be surmised from his criticism of Scheiner's hypothesis, but he refused to commit himself publicly to the view that the spots were contiguous to the sun. This caution was dictated by the fear of having his name associated with a theory that might eventually be disproved. But within three weeks of writing the *First Letter* he found 'rigorous demonstrations' for his theory, and on 2 June 1612 he wrote to Cardinal Maffeo Barberini that it had now been confirmed. In his *Second Letter* to Welser he stated that 'continued daily observations show me, with every conceivable confirmation and no contradiction whatsoever. that my opinion squares with the facts'.[14]

After summarising the available data, Galileo distinguished between what was immediately obvious to sense perception and what had to be arrived at discursively from the evidence supplied by observation.

> The different densities and degrees of darkness, their changes of shape, their collecting and separating are directly evident to our sight without any need of reasoning, as a glance at the diagrams I am enclosing will show. But that the spots are contiguous to the surface of the sun and are carried around by its rotation has to be deduced and concluded by

reasoning from certain specific properties [*certi particolari accidenti*] which our observations yield.[15]

Galileo's intention was twofold; first, to show that 'all the appearances agree with the hypothesis that the spots are contiguous to the surface of the sun, and that they are carried around by it, without any inconvenience or difficulty', and, secondly, to prove that rival hypotheses were false because of 'obvious inconsistencies and contradictions'.[16]

The two theoretical problems—the distance of the spots from the sun and the rotation of the sun—were considered separately. In the first part, Galileo proved that the spots were contiguous to the surface. His argument rested on three characteristics of the sunspots that could not be explained otherwise. First, the spots appeared thinner when they were near the edge than when they were close to the centre of the sun. Secondly, the distance they travelled increased as they approached the centre and decreased as they receded towards the circumference. Finally, they separated more and more as they moved towards the centre.

> For those who understand what is meant by foreshortening on a spherical surface, this is a clear argument that the sun is a globe, that the spots are close to the surface, and that as they are carried on the surface toward the centre they always grow in breadth while preserving the same length.[17]

Galileo argued that if the motion took place on circles at even short distances from the sun, the spaces passed in equal times would appear to differ very little, the spots would not become narrower, and the distances between them would not change noticeably. He considered this last argument, 'so cogent that alone it would be enough to prove what is contended'.[18] His demonstration, based on the foreshortening of spots on a spherical surface, can be summarised as follows with the aid of the diagram he introduced (figure 8).

Let CE = diameter of the sun, and CDE = a parallel of latitude on the circumference of the sun where two spots, A and B, were observed by Galileo from July 1st to July 8th, 1612.

Let G = centre of the sun

$\quad Z$ = position of terrestrial observer, and

$\quad GZ$ = distance of the sun from the earth

Because of the sun's great distance the rays coming from the sun are assumed to be parallel.

From the observations made on 1 July, let

$\quad CF$ = distance observed between spot A and the circumference of the sun, and

$\quad FI$ = distance observed between spot A and spot B

Draw *FH* and *IL* at right angles to *CE*, cutting *CDE* at *H* and *L* respectively. Because *H* and *L* = actual positions of the spots, and

   F and *I* = apparent positions, therefore

   FI = apparent distance

As the spots move toward the centre, the apparent distance between them increases since they are seen less and less obliquely, until their real distance

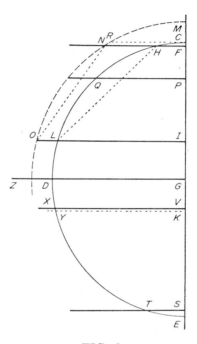

FIG. 8

HL is revealed when they are near the centre. On July 5th, spots *A* and *B* were equally distant from the centre and their separation from each other was equal to the line *HL*.

   On July 8th, spot *B* was removed from point *E* by the same distance as spot *A* was from *C* on July 1st.

Let *SE* = distance observed between spot *B* and the circumference

   SV = distance observed between spot *B* and spot *A*

Draw *ST*, *VX*, at right angles to *CE* as in the previous instance.

Measure *TX*, which yields :

$$TX = HL$$

   Galileo argued that if the spots were removed to an orbit the observed ratios would be contradicted.

   Let arc *MNO* = orbit of the sunspots removed from the sun's surface by 1/20th of *CE*, and prolong *FH* to meet *MNO* at *N*, and *IL* to meet *MNO* at *O*. Therefore, the real distance between the spots *A* and *B* = *NO*, which is considerably less than *HL*.

When the spots *A* and *B* have moved until they are equally distant from the centre, the distance observed between them should be equal to *NO*, whereas, from observations made on July 5th, their distance is equal to *HL*. In other words, the ratios implied by the hypothesis that the spots are not on the sun contradict the ratios that were in fact observed.

Even if the arc *MNO* were removed from the surface by a mere one-hundredth of the sun's radius, the inferred ratios would still contradict observational reports :

> For instance, let the arc *CH* be 4°. Then *CF* will be equal to 24 parts when the radius *CG* is equal to 10,000 parts, and the chord *CH* will be 419 parts, i.e. seventeen times greater than *CF*. Now if the radius *GM* were greater by only one-hundredth of the radius *GC*, so that *GC* being equal to 10,000, *GM* were equal to 10,100, then the arc *MR* would be 8°.4', the arc *NRM* 8°.58', the arc *RN* 0°.54', and its chord 94 when *CF* is 24, i.e. hardly four times greater. This goes against experience which agrees with the other interpretation.[19]

Galileo's argument calls for some comment :
If angle *GHC* = 4°, and
　　CF = 24, then
　　GF = 9976
But if this is the case, then
　　HF = 698, and
　　RC = 698.4, and not, as Galileo affirmed, 419
Likewise, if angle *NGR* = 0°.54', then
　　RN = 158, and not, as Galileo claims, 94
However, the ratio of the correct values 698/158 and that of the values given by Galileo, 419/94, yield approximately the same value, namely 4.4. It is possible that an error in one computation was carried over (as a 'scaling' factor) into the other. On closer inspection, however, this does not appear to be the case, and perhaps the approximation (4.418 to 4.468) is sheerly accidental, for Galileo's argument is not affected by the numerical error. His calculations of the implied angles are quite accurate, depending in no way on the value 419, but only on the versines 24 and 100 and on the use of good tables. It appears that he took the value 419, corresponding to 2°.24' instead of the assumed 4°, by inadvertance, and did not consult the tables again for the chord *RN* of 54' or 0.9°. Since he was dealing with small angles, to which the sines are roughly proportional, he probably derived the latter by a ratio equivalent to *RN*/419 = 0.9/4; *RN* = 3771/4 = 94[0.3].

In the second part of the letter, Galileo concluded that the sun rotated and carried the spots along with it, but he did not contend that all his hypotheses were equally well confirmed. He claimed genuine proof for the contiguity of the spots to the surface of the sun, but only probability for the rotation of the solar body, and even less certainty for the hypothesis that vanishing spots returned after fifteen days. At the end of his *Second Letter*, he had originally ventured a further and more daring speculation.

> Natural philosophers [*i fisici*] will have in the future ample opportunity to speculate about the substance and the mode of production and rapid dissolution of bulks so large, that some of them greatly surpass in size the whole of Africa and Asia, and both Americas. I would not dare say anything definite about this problem, but I should like to draw the attention of inquiring minds to the fact that the occurrence of all the sunspots in that strip of the solar globe that is under that part of the heavens where the planets move and wander, and not elsewhere, indicates that the planets might play some role in producing such an effect. And if, in agreement with the opinion of a famous writer in antiquity, some compensation were made to so great a lamp for the diffusion of so much light to the planets that revolve around it, then, since it would have to take the shortest route, it could not reach any other part of the solar surface.[20]

This passage did not appear in the printed edition of the *Letters*, but it was circulated in the first manuscript copy sent to Rome, and was praised by G. B. Agucchi in his letter to Galileo of 1 December 1612.

The Role of Mathematics

Data only speak the language of the theory in which they are imbedded. This is not to deny the importance of careful observation in falsifying and confirming theories but to recall that experiment—in contradistinction to mere experience—is a question we put to nature. As A. Koyré pointed out, the Galilean revolution can be boiled down to the discovery of the language of nature, to the discovery that mathematics is the grammar of science. While the Aristotelians believed that qualitative properties disclosed the essence of things, Galileo maintained that quantitative relationships were the real clues to an understanding of reality. Without a geometrical model, the structure of things remained confused; it was to the mathematician, and to him only, that certain relationships were pregnant with meaning.[21] It is what Galileo termed 'perspettiva' that enabled him to grasp the significance of the fact that the spots were thinner near the edge, that their speed increased as they approached the centre, and that the interval between them widened as they moved away from the limb. Galileo repeatedly urged that mathematical proportions be studied with care. In a characteristic passage, he wrote :

> We must observe diligently the ratio of increase and decrease in the speed of the spots from their first to their last appearance, for this ratio will enable us to demonstrate whether the motion is on the surface of the solar body or on a detached circle.[22]

New observational facts become evidence when they have been interpreted mathematically. Galileo was convinced that Aristotle himself would have modified his views had he witnessed what could now be seen, namely 'sensati accidenti che a più certe conclusioni c'invitano'. What are these 'sensati accidenti' that invite to more certain conclusions than those of the traditional textbook? They include the comets, the new stars and the sunspots; but it is geometry that spells out their meaning :

> Here to remove all doubt from our minds, some are inspired from on high with rigorous methods of demonstrations [metodi necessari], by which we understand that comets are generated in the celestial region.[23]

The 'rigorous method' is the determination of parallax and its interpretation in mathematical terms. But before arguing from the vantage-point of geometry, Galileo wished to show with the aid of common-sense propositions that the spots were not in the atmosphere but on the surface of the sun. Granted, for the sake of argument, that they were close to the sun, they could not be larger than the smallest clouds since they occupied so little of the sun's surface. But this already raised a host of difficulties : how could so small a bulk be dense enough to resist evaporation? Why should all the spots fall between the earth and the moon? Or, again, how could the spots follow the rapid course of the sun when other atmospheric phenomena were known to travel over much greater distances in a few moments? Galileo felt that these objections could not be answered 'without introducing great improbabilities'. But what was to stop his opponents from adding a few epicycles to their thought in order to make their position logically unassailable? 'Fortunately', commented Galileo, 'we have necessary demonstrations that admit of no reply whatever'. Of these, the main one was the mathematical interpretation of the identical arrangement of the spots from whatever point they were observed on the earth.[24]

In the hands of Galileo, geometry became a tool to prove that Scheiner's theory contradicted his own observational data :

> But even if we were unable to compare the diagrams already made with those that will be drawn in the future, it seems to me that we can show that the things advanced and admitted by Apelles imply a contradic-

tion. It is reasonable, therefore, to doubt the truth of his alleged observation and, consequently, of the conclusion deduced from it.

Scheiner had to assume that the spots were all on one orbit, but he also had to accept the fact that they did not extend beyond 30° north or south of the sun's equator. 'Granted this, I believe I can show that what he adduces here as an argument to remove the spots from the surface of the sun is ineffectual'.[25] First, Galileo showed that when two spots, one at the equator and the other above or below it, crossed the solar disc, the ratio of their times was smaller than the ratio of the distances travelled. He then examined Scheiner's assertion that one spot crossed the sun's surface at the equator in sixteen days while another spot crossed it at some other latitude in fourteen days, and he pointed out that if the difference in time were increased by three and a half hours only (so that the ratio became sixteen days to thirteen days, twenty hours and a half) the result would be impossible, because the ratio of the times could not be greater than the ratio of the diameter to the length of the circle at 30° latitude. Scheiner avoided an absurdity, but this did not make his argument convincing; if a spot, located at 30° from the sun's equator, crossed the surface of the sun in six-sevenths of the time taken by a spot moving at the equator, it would have to move in an orbit whose radius would be twice that of the sun. If this were the case however, the spots would appear to move at the same speed and the distance between the spots would not vary. Even a slight discrepancy in the speed of the spots crossing the solar disc would require that the fastest one be 50° or 60° north or south of the sun's equator, 'which disagrees not only with my observations but with those of Apelles as well'.[26]

Galileo regarded the occurrence of planets between the sun and Mercury as a genuine possibility, but he argued that they would not look like sunspots as Scheiner assumed because their motion would be both too rapid and too uniform. Too rapid, because they would move in a smaller orbit than Mercury which passed beneath the solar disc in approximately six hours; too uniform, because they would be too close to the sun not to give the impression of foreshortening as on a spherical surface.

Galileo was convinced that geometry put an end to what would be otherwise an endless and futile debate. This is why he considered mathematicians forerunners in the physical sciences. In fact, Galileo distinguished two categories of men : the expert astronomers for whom 'it was enough to understand what Copernicus wrote in his *De Revolutionibus* to be convinced that Venus revolves around the sun as well as of the truth of the rest of Copernicus' system', and men of average intelligence 'who cannot be persuaded by the necessity of geometrical demonstrations', but need the additional proof of the comets, the novae and the sunspots.[27]

The Importance of Observations

Galileo was fully aware that the architectonic role of mathematics presupposed careful measurement of the available data. In the *First Letter*, he pleaded that the impossibility of making continued observations kept his judgment in suspense, and it was only after 'daily observations' had confirmed his conjecture that he was willing to make it public. He sent Scheiner 'observations and diagrams of the sunspots, most accurate both as to their shape and their change of position, and drawn without a hairsbreadth of error in a very elegant manner discovered by a pupil of mine', in the hope that 'they may serve him in further speculating about their nature' [*le quali potranno essergli per avventura di giovamento nel filosofare circa la loro essenza*].[28] Galileo stressed that the phases of Venus (the conclusive evidence for its heliocentric motion),[29] and the correspondence between the bright and the dark spots on the sun could only be confirmed or disproved by observation. He criticised Scheiner for failing to notice the difference between the spots that appeared and disappeared at the circumference and those that were generated in the middle, and for considering a curtain of moving dots as though it were one large spot. More seriously, he took him to task for mistaking a star for a fifth satellite around Jupiter :

I would like Apelles to observe their number with renewed diligence. He will find that they are no more than four, and that the fifth one he mentions is unquestionably a fixed star. The conjectures that led him to believe it was a planet were founded on various fallacies. It is clear to begin with that his observations were often wrong as can be gathered from his diagrams where a star which was then conspicuous is omitted. In the second place, the distances of the satellites from each other and from Jupiter are almost all wrong, I suppose from lack of a suitable method and instrument to measure them. In the third place, he makes gross errors in their displacements and then mistakes one for another, confusing the more distant with the closer, and failing to recognise them on consecutive nights.[30]

Aristotelians reacted to the discovery of the sunspots by suggesting that they were congeries of essentially unchangeable stars. When the Jesuits actually proposed such a revised version of the doctrine of the inalterability of the heavens in a public debate at the Collegio Romano in the summer of 1612, a Dominican pointed out that stars were round and regular in shape whereas sunspots were not. The Jesuits replied that a cluster of stars would not be expected to appear round and regular. Galileo considered this reasoning flimsy :

It is true in general that when objects that are too small or too distant to be visible on their own congregate, they may form an aggregate which becomes perceptible to our sight. However, we cannot stop at this vague generalisation, we must come down to the particular properties observed in stars and in spots, and carefully examine what measure of agreement they can be said to have.[31]

Since small stars hardly one-fiftieth the size of large ones had been observed, it was tempting to conjecture that fifty such starlets could come together to create the impression of a sunspot with a visual diameter the size of a large star. Galileo remarked, however, that just as it was unlikely that fifty boats moving at various speeds should happen to join and stay united for any length of time, it was equally improbable that fifty stars should chance to congregate to form a sunspot lasting several days. Galileo also pointed out that the hypothesis of a translucent moon suggested by Scheiner entailed a number of consequences that were contradicted by observation. If the moon were translucent it would not reflect light, the border between the part directly illuminated by the sun and the rest would either vanish or become blurred, the mountains on the moon would remain invisible—the rays would simply pass through them—and, finally, the brightness of the lunar hemisphere facing the sun would remain invariant or, if it changed, it would appear darker at the time of new moon when the rays would have to penetrate a thicker layer of the moon's substance. 'These considerations', wrote Galileo, 'and many others which I omit for the sake of brevity, establish that this hypothesis is in disagreement with the appearances, whereas if we assume such manifest and true hypotheses as that the moon is opaque and uneven and reflects the light of the sun on the earth, we can answer any problem with wondrous ease and thoroughness'.[32]

Equally important is the role played by observations in discovering familiar analogies to interpret the nature of things that cannot be experienced directly. This presupposes the ability to place the evidence in a suggestive order, an art at which Galileo was a master. For instance, in the *First Letter*, he wrote :

Sunspots are generated and decay in longer or shorter periods; some condense and others greatly expand from day to day. They change their shape, most of which are irregular, and more or less dark in various places. Their bulk must be enormous since they are either on the sun or very close to it, and they impede the sunlight in varying degrees because of their uneven opacity. Sometimes many spots are produced, sometimes few, and sometimes none at all.

These observations suggested an analogy to the astronomer whose cosmic framework allowed him to think of the sun as another planet endowed with properties similar to the ones he experienced on earth. 'Now of all the things we are familiar with, only clouds are enormous bulks that are produced and dissolved in brief times, that last for longer or shorter periods, that easily change shape, and that are more dense and opaque in some places than in others'.[33] On the contending model, in which heavenly bodies were essentially different from sublunary ones, the only forthcoming analogy was stars. But stars and sunspots, as Galileo observed, differ in important respects while the properties they share are too general to be helpful :

> The spots should not be called stars because they are opaque and denser than the material of the sky, and consequently stand out against the sun, and are brightly lighted on one side and produce a deep shade on the other, and so on. These properties are common to rocks, to wood, to denser clouds and, in a word, to all opaque bodies. Why a ball of marble reflects light where it is struck by the sun and produces shade on the opposite side, just as the moon and Venus do, so that for this reason it might be called a star! But since these bodies lack other and more essential properties it seems inappropriate to assign to them the name of stars.[34]

The observational data therefore played a doubly suggestive role for Galileo : they drew attention to possible analogies among familiar objects, and they suggested geometrical models which had the same spatial relationships. When rival models contended for the explanation of the observed proportions and ratios, their consequences had to be worked out, and the best one was selected on the grounds of its ability to fit the facts with greater accuracy.

Observation also proved that appeal to 'authorities' had shot its bolt; quoting famous authors on a variety of topics was ruled out as irrelevant by Galileo because of the new evidence available on the intrinsic brightness of Venus and the size of its visual diameter, the immutability of the sun and the constitution of the heavens. He deemed the new observations the 'funeral' and 'the last judgment' of the pseudo-philosophy. The printed word was finally superseded by the textbook of nature.[35]

Mental Experiments

We have already seen in our discussion of the *Discourse on Floating Bodies* that Galileo relied heavily on geometry, and that he appealed to thought-experiments rather than factual ones. We shall consider two instances of this method in the debate on the sunspots.

At the end of the *Second Letter*, Galileo declared that he was uncertain whether the spots moved around the sun because the sun itself rotated or because the surrounding medium revolved. He chose the first alternative and stated two reasons, or rather indicated two lines of argument, to support his view. First, he pointed out that continuous changes in the shape of the spots suggested that the surrounding medium was fluid and yielding, and that such a material would be unable to explain the orderly and constant motion of the spots. This made it likely, therefore, that the motion originated in the solid body of the sun. Secondly, he argued that even if the medium revolved, it would communicate its motion to the solar globe which, being indifferent to circular motion, could easily be made to rotate. He introduced the following analogy to illustrate his contention :

> A ship that had received some impetus through the tranquil sea, would move continually around our globe without ever stopping, and placed at rest, it would rest for ever if, in the first place, all extrinsic impediments could be removed, and, in the second place, no external cause of motion were added.

On the strength of this thought-experiment, Galileo made a bold generalisation, and concluded that if the sun were set in motion by the rotating medium it would go on revolving for ever, and that this would not alter the arrangement of the sunspots any more than the position of objects in the cabin of a ship is changed when a ship circles the globe : 'as far as the constitution of the parts is concerned, such movement is as if it did not exist'. This sentence takes us a long way on the road to the Newtonian principle of inertia but it stops short for two reasons. First, Galileo was unable to break away completely from experience : he maintained that real motion on spherical planets was circular and not linear. Secondly, he was reluctant to forego the idea of natural motion which he used to support his thesis about indifferent motion.

> This may be further confirmed for, beyond what has been said, it does not seem that any movable body can have a repugnance to a movement without having a natural propensity to the opposite motion, for in indifference there is non-repugnance. Hence anyone who would wish to give the sun a resistance to the circular motion of its surroundings would be giving it a natural propensity to circular motion in the opposite direction. But this cannot appeal to a well-balanced mind.[36]

Of equal interest is Galileo's experiment to prove that the earth, contrary to common doctrine, reflects the sun's rays as far as the moon. The text published in the *Third Letter* reads as follows :

> Furthermore, we should be convinced of the effectual terrestrial reflection when we see how much light is reflected into a dark room from

a wall opposite it that is struck by the rays of the sun. *Even if the reflected light enters by an opening so small, that from the place where it falls its visual diameter is not greater than that of the moon,* nonetheless this secondary light is so powerful that when it is reflected from the first room into a second one, it will still be stronger than the light from the moon. Of this we have a clear and easy experiment since it is easier to read a book by the second reflection coming from the wall than by the direct reflection coming from the moon.[37]

The precise indications in the passage I have italicised strongly suggest that the experiment was actually carried out, but Galileo's letter of 25 January 1613 to Prince Cesi, in which he replied to objections raised by his friend Luca Valerio, conveys a different impression.

The point that Signor Valerio raises is true : the same bright body illuminates more from near than from afar. But it is also true that bright bodies of different sizes but of the same luminosity do not illuminate equally well : from the same distance, a large body will give more light than a small one, and from a greater distance it will give as much light. Therefore, when I consider the reflection coming from a wall and compare it with that of the moon, it is true that the one from the wall is closer, but the moon is incomparably larger, and I always intended to compare the moon's reflection with that of a wall whose size is proportional to the distance of the moon, so that the dark room, where the reflection from the moon and the wall are allowed to enter, receives the light from the wall through an aperture not exceeding in appearance the visual diameter of the moon. So, to explain my intent more clearly, the following words can be added to the passage referred to. . . .[38]

The words that are added are the ones I have italicised in the preceding quotation from the *Third Letter.* It is clear, therefore, that Galileo never performed the experiment. Had he done so he would have realised (and mentioned, it is hoped) the difficulty in allowing only the reflection from the wall to enter a dark room. The reader anxious to repeat the experiment—and such a reader would have been rare in the seventeenth century —must have wondered how to isolate a wall struck by the midday sun in order to ensure that only its reflected light penetrated into a dark room through a narrow opening.

Galileo's Errors

Our discussion of Galileo's experimental procedure would be incomplete if we did not consider some of the errors he made and ask ourselves whether they were unavoidable. We shall examine four such cases.

(1) The sun's disc, as we normally see it in the sky, appears to be uniformly bright, but this impression is dispelled by even the most perfunctory telescopic observation which reveals that the brightness decreases from the centre towards the limb. Scheiner made this discovery but Galileo dismissed it as not 'habitually confirmed by experiment'. Luca Valerio, who also raised the matter, received the following reply :

> It is up to my opponent to prove that the rays from the central parts of the solar disc are stronger. Furthermore, the experiment that could be requested of me is not impossible nor even difficult, for looking at the rising and setting sun, it does not appear brighter in the centre than near the circumference, and when we look at the circle it traces on a piece of paper after passing through the telescope, we see that it is equally bright everywhere.[39]

Galileo naturally displayed a certain reluctance to admit a fact introduced by an opponent as evidence for a rival theory, and he instinctively demanded additional proof before giving it serious consideration. Yet his own experiments were quite unsatisfactory. The rising and setting sun is observed through a thicker atmospheric layer than the midday sun, and this makes it more difficult to notice the differences in brightness. Likewise judging the brightness of the sun from the projection of its shape on paper is inconclusive.

(2) A second source of difficulty was the sun's axis which is slightly inclined (7° 15′) from the perpendicular to the plane of the ecliptic, so that during the course of the annual circuit of the earth's orbit we view the sun, and the direction of its rotation, under a variety of slightly different perspectives. The line of intersection of the plane of the sun's equator and that of the ecliptic is so orientated that the earth crosses it at the beginning of June and December. At these times, the sun is seen exactly in profile, the spots describing straight lines parallel with the equator as the sun's rotation carries them around the disc. At intermediate times, the equator and the parallels of latitude appear more or less curved to the north or south as the result of the perspective of a spherical surface, while first one pole and then the other comes into view.

In the *Third Letter*, Galileo mentioned that the straight lines described by the spots were a 'necessary proof' that the sun's axis was perpendicular to the ecliptic. Scheiner was more cautious and did not venture to affirm that the motion of the spots was parallel to the ecliptic. It would be wrong, however, to conclude that Galileo's observations were inaccurate; he happened to observe the spots from May to July, approximately the time when the earth crossed the line of intersection of the planes of the sun's equator and the ecliptic, and, therefore, when the spots appeared parallel to the ecliptic.[40]

(3) A third error is related to the sun's motion on itself. The sun does not rotate as a solid body and the period of rotation depends on the latitude, becoming progressively longer from the equator to the pole, as the following table indicates :

Latitude	Period
0°	24.9
10°	25.0
20°	25.3
30°	25.9
40°	27.5

Galileo affirmed against Scheiner that all the spots, whatever their latitude, traversed the sun in the same time, which he estimated at 'slightly more than fourteen days'. Now even for the remotest spot observed by Galileo at 30°, the actual time is not quite thirteen days. G. B. Agucchi, Galileo's friend and admirer in Rome, gave the correct value, and added that Galileo's own diagrams did not allow for more than a little over thirteen days![41] It is by no means clear why Galileo should have added half a day to the times between the first and the last observation of the sunspots on the edge of the sun's disc, and his error remains quite baffling.

(4) It is generally agreed by modern astronomers that the spots are probably depressions in the photosphere. This is suggested by their changing appearance as a result of perspective; for example, they show the same features as the holes on the moon : the umbra indicating the bottom of the depression, and the penumbra the slanting wall. It is interesting that Scheiner should have entertained the possibility of this hypothesis, while Galileo resolutely discarded it as unworthy of serious consideration.[42]

The New Realism

It is obvious to the historian of ideas that the new science could have no ontological status in the old metaphysics, and no epistemological value in the old psychology. It is no less evident that the new approach to physical reality preceded its organisation in a coherent philosophy of human knowledge. Galileo was not consciously applying a new philosophy of nature, although he was quite deliberately using mathematics to interpret the motion of bodies in the heavens and on the earth. The precise stages in the development of his method are a moot question, but there can be no doubt that he was firmly committed from the outset to the ideas of order and simplicity. He rejected the hypothesis that the spots were congeries of stars, because this would have meant introducing in the heavens 'innumerable, irregular, tumultuous and uneven movements', which did not agree 'with any plausible philosophy'. He refused to accept that a star as bright as one of the first magnitude could vanish completely within ten days, and he affirmed that the same spot returned after one complete revolution because he was convinced that it could not decrease in size faster than it had increased. His belief in order and regularity even led him to make one of his most ill-fated predictions : having failed to detect any variation in the movement of Saturn and its companion-stars (actually Saturn's rings), he wrote in the *First Letter* that 'reason, based upon our experience of all other stellar motions, renders us certain that none will ever be seen'. Yet by the time he wrote the *Third Letter*, seven months later, the companion-stars had not only moved, they had vanished entirely![43]

Galileo was prepared to state that the constitution of the universe was 'unique, true, real', that it could not be otherwise, and that nature was not only orderly, but immutable in its laws :

> We must remember that nature, deaf to our entreaties, will not change the course of its events, and that the things we investigate now (and later will attempt to convince others of) do not appear once and then fade away. They follow their course, and they will be seen and observed by many people to do so for a long time.[44]

These views, as such, were neither original nor peculiar to Galileo. Granted that the system of the world is unique, one was still justified in asking whether it could be known. The astronomers of the day were skilful in predicting eclipses and conjunctions with the aid of deferents and epicycles and other mathematical devices. They agreed that there existed one system of astronomy, but few, if any, would have ventured to affirm that their particular cosmic model was real. This was not only the view of Galileo's stiff-necked opponents. It was shared by Giulio Cesare Lagalla, the professor of philosophy at the Sapienza in Rome with whom Galileo was on good terms. Jacopo Mazzoni, the sensitive mind that mirrored the conflicting tendencies of the period, was also agreed that mathematicians were philosophical instrumentalists. In his *In Universam Platonis et Aristotelis Philosophiam Praeludia*, he contended that the astronomer (*mathematicus*) and the natural philosopher (*physicus*) discussed the moon's apogee and perigee, and the paths of Mars and Venus, from completely different standpoints. While the astronomer gave a purely formal interpretation of these motions, the natural philosopher studied their physical nature.[45]

Galileo would have none of this distinction, as can be gathered from his indictment of Scheiner for retaining eccentrics, deferents, equants, epicycles and the like, as though they were true, real and distinct things. These were assumed by pure astronomers [*i puri astronomi*] in order to facilitate their calculations. They are not retained as such by philosophical astronomers [*astronomi philosophi*] who, going beyond the requirement that appearances be saved, seek to investigate the true constitution of the universe—the most important and admirable problem that there is. For such a constitution exists; and it is unique, true, real and cannot be otherwise, and should on account of its greatness and dignity be considered foremost among the questions of theoretical interest.[46]

But the crucial question remained. How was this programme to be implemented? Basically, by reading the book of nature, instead of 'staring night and day at a world printed on sheets of paper without ever raising them to the true and real one, made by God's own hands, which is always open before our eyes for our instruction.'[47] No-one in his right mind would query this kind of general principle, and, of course, no-one did. Everyone is enough of an empiricist to believe that something can be learned by looking at the world around him. Real knowledge is possible, but what kind of knowledge? The Aristotelians claimed real knowledge too, but by this they meant penetrating to the 'essence' of things and interpreting their nature in terms of the four basic elements. Galileo leaned backward to avoid creating the impression that he accepted such a facile view of science :

> I know full well that the substance of the spots might be any of a thousand things unknown and unimaginable to us. The properties we observe in them, namely their shape, their opacity and their movement, because they are common, can supply us with only very general knowledge, if any at all.[48]

This passage occurs in the *First Letter* and is followed by a comparison of the properties of the stars with those of the clouds tending to show that the sunspots are similar to the latter rather than to the former.

There was some inconsistency in Galileo's thought-processes at this point, for he appealed to the very 'accidents' he considered too general to establish the nature of bodies to prove that the spots were like clouds rather than stars, namely he argued from the shape, density and motion of the spots, and in the concluding paragraph of the letter he promised to send Scheiner accurate diagrams to help him in 'further speculating about their nature'. Galileo's reason for disparaging the value of the material he himself employed can perhaps be inferred from the original draft of the letter where the passage we are considering ended as follows :

> ... can supply us with only very general knowledge, if any at all, which

is hardly worth attending to, such as when I ask what the substance of the moon is, and someone answers that it is *a denser portion of the celestial region.*[49]

Galileo wanted to show that the inferences of his opponents were trivial and scientifically irrelevant, but in so doing he attacked the evidence itself, the basis of his own generalisation. He realised his tactical mistake and struck out the most incriminating passage from his letter, but it was only in the *Third Letter* that he arrived at a more consistent and subtly-stated position. It is here that we find his manifesto of 'critical realism', if this expression may be permitted.

We can either try to penetrate the true and intrinsic essence of material substances, or we can content ourselves with a knowledge of some of their properties. To try and reach the essence, I hold to be an impossible undertaking and a useless task with regard to the closest elemental substances as well as with regard to the more remote and celestial things. I know no more about the substance of the earth than I do about that of the moon, of the clouds and of the sunspots. Neither do I see that in understanding substances near at hand we have any advantage except the number of instances, but all equally unknown. We wander through them, passing from one to the other with little or no profit. If I ask what the substance of clouds is and I am told that it is moist vapour, I shall wish to know in turn what vapour is. Perhaps I shall be taught that it is water, which when attenuated by heat is resolved into vapour. Equally curious about what water is, I shall then seek to find that out, ultimately learning that it is the liquid that runs in our rivers and which we constantly handle. But this knowledge is no more intimate than the one I had about clouds in the first place; it is merely closer at hand, and dependent upon more of the senses. In the same way I know no more about the true essence of earth and fire than about those of the moon or the sun. This knowledge will be granted to us in the state of blessedness and not before.

But if we wish to fix our minds on understanding some of the properties of things, then it seems to me that we need not despair of our ability to acquire this kind of knowledge with regard to distant bodies as well as with regard to those close at hand—and some cases perhaps with greater accuracy in the former than in the latter. Who does not understand the periods and the movements of the planets better than those of the waters of our various oceans? Was not the spherical shape of the moon discovered long before that of the earth, and much more easily? Is it not still argued whether the earth is at rest or goes wandering, whereas we know positively the movements of many stars? Hence I infer that although it may be vain to try to determine the substance of the sunspots, it does not follow that we cannot know some of their properties, such as their location, motion, shape, size, opacity, mutability, generation and dissolution. These in turn may become the means by which we shall be able to philosophise better about other more controversial qualities [*condizioni*] of natural substances.[50]

Traditional Aristotelianism taught that the essence of terrestrial substances could be known, but that the moon and the celestial bodies were made of some 'quintessence' of which little could be said except that it was not subject to the vicissitudes of change. The revised Aristotelian position admitted that change did occur in the heavens, but maintained that it was merely accidental, i.e. the result of casual grouping, as in the case of starlets combining to create the impression of spots on the sun. On the face of it, it would seem that the Schoolmen had fitted—albeit at the price of increased complexity—the fresh data into the old framework. While essential knowledge remained limited to objects close at hand, accidental knowledge became possible with respect to some distant objects but without disclosing anything about their 'real' nature.

Galileo usually brushed aside Aristotelian categories as irrelevant. Here he took it upon himself to stand the Aristotelian position on its head and to vindicate the validity of 'accidental' knowledge for the whole realm of nature. In point of fact, he claimed that the 'essential' knowledge of the Aristotelians was really 'accidental' since it depended entirely on the contingent fact that certain things are more familiar than others. In other words, their distinction rested on a category mistake, on the confusion between operational familiarity and intellectual grasp. Galileo saw no basic difference between understanding what water is and knowing about sunspots, save that water could be handled with relative ease while sunspots could not be directly manipulated. Having said this much, Galileo proceeded to reverse the order of priorities : what really opens the way to knowledge is our grasp of the accidents : location, motion, shape, size, opacity and mutability. These measurable properties, deemed secondary in the old philosophy, become fundamental in the new one. Galileo did not introduce new evidence; he merely asked his readers to see the well-known and familiar facts in a new perspective. The consequences of this reversal are clear : if real and useful science is based on the apprehension of accidental properties, then our knowledge of celestial bodies may well be better grounded and more accurate than much of our understanding of terrestrial phenomena. Galileo drove this point home by giving three instances of assured astronomical facts : the periods of the planets, the sphericity of the moon and the movement of the celestial bodies.

It would be unwarranted to read an 'operationalist' meaning into

Galileo's words. As a matter of fact, he repudiated the Aristotelian account of essential and accidental knowledge on the ground that it was nothing more than a thinly disguised nominalism. He was unwavering in his belief that the true constitution of the world could be known. What he set himself against was the philosophy that precluded the possibility of discovering this real constitution. He was making room for science by dislodging not realism itself but a naïve version of it that purported to canonise for all time Greek science and medieval common sense.

NOTES

1. Galileo was received into the Accademia dei Lincei by its founder, Prince Federico Cesi, during his visit to Rome in the spring of 1611, when he was widely acclaimed for his celestial discoveries. 'If we were in the ancient Roman Republic', wrote Cardinal Francesco Maria del Monte, 'I am certain that a statue would have been erected in his honour on the Capitol' (Letter to Cosimo II, 31 May 1611, *Opere di Galileo*, **11**, 119)
2. Christoph Scheiner, *Tres epistolae de maculis solaribus* (Augsburg, 1612), *ibid.*, **5**, 26
3. Scheiner subsequently realised that whereas he had assumed that the tables indicated the beginning of conjunction, they probably gave the medium time. He asked Welser to send a note to those to whom he had forwarded the *Letters* indicating the alternative reading, and showing that even on this account a large spot should have appeared on the sun (*ibid.*, **5**, 32). This reflects on the science of the day: professional astronomers themselves could be in doubt as to the correct interpretation of their own tables
4. *Ibid.*, 30
5. Galileo, Johann Fabricus, Thomas Harriot, Christoph Scheiner and Domenico Passignani observed the spots independently (Antonio Favaro, *Oppositori di Galileo. III. Christoforo Scheiner* [Venice: Carlo Ferrari, 1919], 57 ff.)
6. Christoph Scheiner, *De maculis solaribus et stellis circa Jovem errantibus accuratior disquisitio* (Augsburg, 1612), *Opere di Galileo*, **5**, 46. Scheiner dedicated his new satellite to Welser. Giovanni Tarde and Charles Malapert were later to dedicate even more fanciful sunspot-stars to the reigning families of France and Austria (G. Tarde, *Borbonia Sidera, id est planetae qui solis limina circumvolitant motu proprio ac regulari, falso hactenus ab helioscopis maculae solis nuncupati* [Paris, 1620], and C. Malapertius, *Austriaca sidera heliocyclica astronomicis hypothesibus illigata* [Douay, 1633])
7. These luminaries included Cardinal Borromeo, Andrea Chiocco, G. A. Magini, Angelo Grillo, Ottavio Brentoni, Leonardo Ceronico, Reinhard Ziegler, Simon Stevin, Johann Kepler, John Pretorius and J. G. Brengger (Scheiner, *Accuratior disquisitio*, *Opere di Galileo*, **5**, 62)
8. *Ibid.*, 67, italics mine
9. *Ibid.*, 68–69. Scheiner did not give a precise reference, but he probably had in mind the concluding section of the last edition of Clavius' *Commentary on Sacrobosco's Sphere* (Christopher Clavius, *Opera Omnia*, vol. III [Mainz, 1611], p. 75 of the separately paginated *Commentarium in Sphaeram Joannis de Sacro Bosco*)
10. Letter to F. Cesi, 4 November 1612, *Opere di Galileo*, **11**, 426
11. Galileo, *Istoria e dimostrazioni intorno alle macchie solari e loro accidenti*

(Rome, 1613), *Opere di Galileo*, **5**, 95. These letters on the sunspots are partly translated by Stillman Drake, *Discoveries and Opinions of Galileo* (Garden City: Doubleday, 1957)

12. *Ibid.*, 102
13. *Ibid.*, 108
14. *Ibid.*, 116
15. *Ibid.*, 117
16. *Ibid.*, 118
17. *Ibid.*, 119
18. *Ibid.*, 121
19. *Ibid.*, 124
20. *Ibid.*, 140, critical apparatus to line 26. Galileo never developed his conjecture that the sunspots were caused by the planets. In 1615, he speculated on the nature of the sun, and described it as the receptacle of the universal and subtle substance that pervades all living beings (letter to Piero Dini, 23 March 1616, *ibid.*, 301). He also compared the sun with the human heart, and linked the revolution of the planets with the sun's rotation on its axis (*ibid.*, 304; letter to Christina of Lorraine, 1615, *ibid.*, 345)
21. For instance, a geometer merely has to be told that the square on one side of a triangle is equal to the sum of the squares on the other two sides to know that the triangle is right-angled. To the uninitiated, this information is only a statement about the lengths of the sides and discloses nothing about the form of the triangle
22. Galileo, *Istoria e dimostrazioni, Opere di Galileo*, **5**, 105
23. *Ibid.*, 139–140
24. *Ibid.*, 128–129
25. *Ibid.*, 204–205
26. *Ibid.*, 216
27. *Ibid.*, 195, 140
28. *Ibid.*, 113. The pupil who taught Galileo how to draw the diagrams of the sunspots by projecting their image from the telescope on to a sheet of paper was Benedetto Castelli(*ibid.*, 117)
29. Lacking the telescope, Copernicus was compelled to affirm that Venus was either self-luminous or transparent
30. Galileo, *Istoria e dimostrazioni, Opere di Galileo*, **5**, 227
31. *Ibid.*, 232
32. *Ibid.*, 225
33. *Ibid.*, 106
34. *Ibid.*, 109
35. The expression 'book of nature' was an old cliché (see E. R. Curtius, *Europäische Literatur und lateinisches Mittelalter* [Bern: A. Francke, 1954], 323–329), and its origin is probably biblical. Galileo quotes two passages from Scripture in his *Juvenilia*: 'Caeli sicut liber complicabuntur' (*Is.*, **34**, 6), and 'Caelum sicut liber involutus recessit' (*Rev.*, **6**, 14), (*Opere di Galileo*, **1**, 64). Campanella in his *Apologia pro Galileo* published in Frankfurt in 1622 also speaks of 'the world which is the book of God' (20, 24). The convergence between Campanella and Galileo is merely apparent however. What is decisive in this metaphor are the characters in which one assumes that the book of nature is written. For Campanella these characters are the figures and shapes of the Constellations while for Galileo they are strictly mathematical relationships. Eugenio Garin criticises E. A. Curtius for failing to distinguish the different contexts in which the expression 'book of nature' is used (Eugenio Garin, *La cultura filosofica del Rinascimento* [Florence: Sansoni, 1961], 451–465). There is no doubt, however, that the expression became a rallying cry for the new philosophy at the time of Galileo, as can be seen in the letters of Orazio Morandi and G. B. Baliani (*Opere di Galileo*, **11**, 530; **12**, 18)
36. Galileo, *Istoria e dimostrazioni, Opere di Galileo*, **5**, 227
37. *Ibid.*, 223, italics mine

38. Letter to Cesi, 25 January 1613, *ibid*, **11**, 467
39. *Ibid.*, 466
40. Galileo subsequently discovered his error and used the declination of the spots in his *Dialogue on the Two World Systems* as an argument for the earth's annual revolution around the sun (*ibid.*, **7**, 373–382). See below, chapter 6, pp. 147–48. Stillman Drake has argued convincingly that Galileo probably realised his error when he read Francesco Sizzi's letter to Orazio Morandi which the latter forwarded to him in the summer of 1613 (Drake, *Discoveries and Opinions of Galileo*, 125, n. 14)
41. 'You suppose that the spots sometimes cross the sun's disc in approximately fifteen days, but I have never seen them for more than a little over thirteen days'. In the margin of the letter Agucchi added: 'The diagrams of your own observations do not allow for more than a little over thirteen days' (letter to Galileo, 1 December 1612, *Opere di Galileo*, **11**, 442). This was the second time Agucchi gave a better interpretation of Galileo's observations than Galileo himself. Previously, he had determined the periods of Jupiter's satellites from the diagrams published in the *Sidereus Nuncius* (letter to Galileo, 29 October 1611, *ibid.*, **11**, 225)
42. Scheiner, *Accuratior disquisitio, ibid.*, **5**, 51; Galileo, *Istoria e dimostrazioni, ibid.*, 202
43. Galileo, *Istoria e dimostrazioni, ibid.*, 110, 227
44. *Ibid.*, 218–219
45. Jacopo Mazzoni, *In Universam Platonis et Aristotelis Philosophiam Praeludia* (Venice, 1597), 160
46. Galileo, *Istoria e dimostrazioni, Opere di Galileo*, **5**, 102. This passage probably prompted the following apology from Sagredo: 'Although in the letters I wrote I distinguished between philosophers and mathematicians (to which you take objection), I want you to know that I employed these words according to common usage among ordinary folk, who call philosophers those who do not and cannot understand nature, yet who pretend to be nature's secretaries, and who use this reputation to trouble men's senses, and even to deprive them of their intellect' (letter to Galileo, 18 August 1612, *ibid.*, **11**, 379). In the *Dialogue on the Two World Systems*, Galileo again distinguished the '*astronomo puro calcolatore*' from the '*astronomo filosofo*' (*ibid.*, **7**, 369)
47. Galileo, *Istoria e dimostrazioni, ibid.*, **5**, 96, critical apparatus to line 19.
48. *Ibid.*, 105–106
49. *Ibid.*, 106, critical apparatus to line 3, italics mine
50. *Ibid.*, 187–188. In this perspective, tables of presence and absence become significant. The following one merely tabulates the data Galileo contrasts.

	Stars	*Sunspots*
1.	regular shape	irregular shape
2.	consistent in size and shape	always unstable and changing
3.	permanent	produced and dissolved
4.	always luminous	always dark
5.	motionless or moving on a fixed course	moving together but each affected by irregularities
6.	arranged at various distances from the sun	contiguous to, or imperceptibly removed from the surface of the sun
7.	visible only if to one side of the sun	visible only if in line with the sun
8.	probably dense and opaque	rarefied in the manner of clouds and smoke

4. THE CHALLENGE OF THE COMETS

In the autumn of 1618, three comets appeared in rapid succession. The last was of unusual size and brilliance, remaining visible from November until January of the following year. It was greeted (like any celestial novelty, be it a quasar or an orbiting station) with considerable interest, and Galileo was urged by his friends to swell the mounting tide of books and pamphlets that were flooding the astronomical and astrological market. Unfortunately, Galileo was bedridden with arthritis at the time and he was unable to make any observations. Yet he was free to speculate, and his admirers wanted not so much an accurate description of the size, position and motion of the comet as an authoritative pronouncement—an oracular verdict—on its nature. His literary friends, siding with the 'moderns' against the 'ancients' in the current debate on poetry, were only too willing to embrace Galileo's 'modern view' whatever it might be. Out of the scores of pamphlets which appeared, Galileo selected a lecture delivered by Fr. Orazio Grassi, the Professor of mathematics at the Roman College, and published anonymously in 1619. Grassi interpreted the new comet the way Tycho Brahe had accounted for the one of 1577, and concluded that the small parallax made it necessary to locate it somewhere between the sun and the moon. His tone was serene and he said nothing that was deliberately offensive to Galileo whose name was not even mentioned. It is puzzling why Galileo should have singled out this perfectly honest and unassuming address for special attention and criticism. He was, of course, fond of polemics, and it is possible that Giovanni Battista Rinuccini pricked his pride when he informed him that the Jesuits were publishing something on the comet and added, in the same breath, that some people considered that it discredited Copernicanism altogether. 'The Jesuits', he wrote from Rome, 'discussed the comet in a public lecture now in press, and they firmly believe that it is in the heavens. Some outside the Jesuit Order are spreading the rumour that this is the greatest argument against Copernicus' system and that it knocks it down'.[1]

Galileo welcomed the opportunity of briefing one of his disciples, Mario Guiducci, who had recently been elected Consul of the Florentine Academy and was anxious to create a favourable impression by giving his inaugural address on what had become the current topic of discussion in the learned world. Guiducci delivered a series of three lectures which were published under his name as the *Discourse on the Comets*. The manuscript, examined by Antonio Favaro, the editor of the National

Edition of Galileo's Works, is largely in Galileo's own handwriting, and the sections drafted (or perhaps merely copied) by Guiducci show signs of revision and correction by the master.

As Guiducci was a lawyer and enjoyed no scientific reputation, it was clear to Grassi that Galileo was the real author, and he prepared a rejoinder which appeared in print in the autumn of 1619 as the *Libra Astronomica ac Philosophica*. Galileo was incensed and prepared a point by point rebuttal which he completed in 1621, but it went through lengthy delays and only appeared in 1623 when Galileo dedicated it to the new Pope, Urban VIII, a Florentine like himself, and a patron of the arts. The *Saggiatore* (*The Assayer*) is a masterpiece of style and was wildly acclaimed not so much by scientists as by gentlemen of the literary world.

In an age which witnesses the demythologising of the heroes of the scientific revolution, twentieth-century admirers of Galileo can rest assured that his prose will remain one of the finest achievements of Italian Baroque, and his *Assayer* a model of brilliant wit and devastating irony. It is in this context that Galileo is reputed by some historians of science to have set out with unparalleled clarity the nature of his scientific method. It is here that we find the brilliant passage on nature written in the language of geometry, and the portentous analysis of sensations as subjective occurrences in the sentient rather than objective qualities in the bodies perceived. Grassi felt that Galileo had earned himself a reply, and in spite of opposition from his religious superiors, he published a retort, the *Ratio Ponderum Librae et Simbellae*, in 1626. Galileo, on the advice of his Tuscan friends, thought that the polemic had been sufficiently protracted. In any case, by that time he had greater things to attend to : he was busy writing his most famous work, the *Dialogue on the Two World Systems*, which he was to complete in 1632.

I THE DISCOURSE ON THE COMETS AND THE LIBRA

The structure of the first part of the *Discourse on the Comets* is typical of medieval and Renaissance commentaries on Aristotle. The opinions of the ancients recorded in the *Meteorologica* are enumerated, Aristotle's appraisal is discussed, and, finally, Galileo's personal interpretation is put forward.

In the *Meteorologica*, Aristotle discusses three theories about the comets, and dismisses them in favour of a fourth which he proposes as his own.

On the first theory, ascribed to Anaxagoras and Democritus, comets are considered clusters of wandering stars because stars are sometimes observed when comets disintegrate. Aristotle objects that the dissolution of comets is not always accompanied by the production of stars, and, furthermore, that stars appear as indivisible points which, however numerous, can never produce a continuously extended body such as a comet. Galileo comments that Aristotle confuses indivisibility with invisibility, that he fails, in other words, to grasp the distinction between a mathematical point and a physical dot. But if Aristotle's criticism is inept, Galileo does not feel that Anaxagoras and Democritus are thereby vindicated, for planets are often seen in conjunction without any comet appearing, and, furthermore, conjunctions are too brief to explain the lengthy duration of comets.

On the second theory, attributed to certain Pythagoreans and Stoics, comets are identified with planets that become visible when they approach the earth, and invisible when they recede from it. Aristotle reasons that the comets are not planets because they do not travel within the zodiacal band like all the known planets. Galileo irked by this kind of argument asks: 'Who places these limits upon the stars? Who encloses divine creations and marvels within such narrow bounds?' His own criticism of this second theory is that the comets did not increase in apparent size until they reached a maximum, and then decrease at the same rate as planets. They were already large when they first appeared, and after increasing in size for a brief period, they decreased steadily for the remainder. An exceptionally large orbit could be postulated, but this would not account for the considerable change in the apparent magnitude of the comet of 1618 over a period of only forty days. Furthermore, in order to make room for such a celestial body—which Galileo assumes could be none other than the comet of 1577 returning in 1618—the universe would have to be vastly expanded. His mind recoils at the thought of the size of the world that would be required:

> If so many years are necessary for it to complete one revolution of its own, then in the forty days during which it was seen by us it cannot have travelled even one degree in its orbit; yet it apparently passed over more than one-fourth of a great circle in the celestial sphere. How many times would the world have to be expanded to make enough room for an entire revolution when one four-hundredth part of its orbit takes up half of our universe?[2]

The reader may well ask, who is now setting bounds to God's creation?

On the third theory, associated with the names of Aeschylus and Hippocrates of Chios, comets are said to be planets which attract vapour and moisture when they pass close to the earth. Galileo points out that it suffers from the same difficulties as the preceding theory.

Aristotle himself suggests the following hypothesis. Hot and dry exhalations rise from the earth and are carried around by the motion of the sky. When they are sufficiently warmed by motion they catch fire, and burn either rapidly as in the case of shooting stars, or slowly as in comets when the fire is fed and fanned by a warm breeze from the lower regions. Galileo considers this interpretation gratuitous :

> Unless I am mistaken, Aristotle's reasoning is filled to the brim with assumptions which, if not obviously false, stand much in need of proof, whereas what is assumed in science should be perfectly evident [*e pure quel che si suppone nelle scienze, doverrebbe esser manifestatissimo*].[3]

More specifically, Galileo argues against Aristotle that it is impossible to maintain that a comet is an incandescent body and yet locate it under the moon, *'this being repugnant to its small parallax as observed by so many excellent astronomers with extreme care'*. He concludes :

> These, o Academicians, are the most famous opinions concerning comets that have thus far come to my attention. Among these, I accepted as highly probable the Pythagorean view that a comet was a refraction of our vision to the sun, and I considered its location far above the moon as having been conclusively demonstrated by astronomers, when further questions suggested to me by our oft-mentioned Academician led me into more doubts and difficulties than before.[4]

These doubts arise from a consideration of Tycho Brahe's use of parallax to determine the height of comets.

The Relevance of Parallax

The phenomenon of parallax refers to the shift in view that occurs when the same object is seen from different positions. For instance, if one holds a pencil in front of one's face and looks at it with one eye closed, then with the other eye closed, the pencil will seem to have moved. The greater the distance of the pencil, the smaller the shift or parallax. When the moon is observed from two points on the surface of the earth, it shows a small but definite parallactic displacement against the background of distant stars. Since the comet of 1577 showed a much smaller parallax, Tycho Brahe had inferred that it was well above the moon.

Galileo recognises that parallactic displacement is an accredited method of establishing distances, but he contends that it has been used indiscriminately when its usefulness is restricted to a particular class of bodies.

> There are two kinds of visible objects, the first are true, real, individual and immutable, while the others are mere appearances, reflections of light, images and wandering simulacra. These are so dependent for

their existence upon the vision of the observer that not only do they change position when he does, but I believe that they would vanish entirely if his vision were removed.[5]

Hence, the size of the parallax can be used to determine the distance of real objects but not of haloes, parhelia and rainbows. Galileo places the comets in the latter category and compares them to shafts of sunlight streaming through holes in the clouds at sunset, and to long luminous bands that stretch from an observer on the shore to the sun setting at sea. This last comparison is particularly important : it becomes Galileo's key-analogy :

> In this instance, the sun is above, and the surface of the sea is beneath, but if we imagine the sun to be below the horizon and some other surface than the sea's to be raised above it, we should perceive in it a reflection similar to that of the sun's light, everything else remaining indistinct from the sky itself, since even the surface of the sea is sometimes so confused with the sky that no distinction can be perceived between them.[6]

Galileo insists that those who wish to use parallactic motion to determine the position of the comet must first prove that it is a physical body and not an optical phenomenon. He thus passes on the burden of proof to his opponents, and assumes that he is free to suggest that the comets are merely the refraction of sunlight in vapours rising from the earth.

The Size of the Comet

In his lecture, Grassi had made a casual remark about the telescope enlarging objects that are near to a greater degree than distant ones. Galileo sets out to disprove this with the aid of three experiments. First, two neighbouring stars are observed through the empty tube of a telescope so that they just fall within the visual diameter. When the lenses are inserted, the telescope has to be moved to pass from one star to the other, which would not be necessary if very remote objects were not enlarged. Secondly, a black circle is placed at some distance from an observer, and a white circle is placed several times as far in the same direction so that the black one does not cover it entirely, but leaves a white rim exposed to view. When this arrangement is observed through a telescope, it remains unchanged, whereas if the black circle were enlarged more than the white one, the white rim would no longer be visible. Thirdly, an eclipse of the sun witnessed with the naked eye does not differ from the same eclipse seen through a telescope. On Grassi's theory, however, one would expect the eclipse to become total when observed through a telescope.

Galileo's refutation of Grassi, however, does not imply that he has a clear understanding of the properties of lenses. He confuses an increase in size with the formation of an image slightly out of focus, as appears from the following passage : 'Set a telescope to view some objects placed at a distance of one thousand yards, and without moving the telescope lengthen the tube by only an inch or two. Immediately a noticeable growth of the object will be seen'.[7]

It should not be forgotten that Grassi could claim experimental evidence for his position : stars observed with a telescope appear little larger than when observed unaided. Galileo tries to forestall this when he claims that irradiation is not a physical property of stars but results from refraction through the moisture on the pupil of the eye. He adduces as evidence that closing and compressing the eyelids makes the rays appear longer, and that people with bleary eyes see more irradiation than others.

> Such are our experiments and such are the conclusions that follow from the principles and the causes adduced from the science of optics [*prospettiva*]. If our conclusions are false and our experiments defective, then our foundations are weak. But if ours are true and theirs are false, let them agree that we can doubt the strength of the foundations of their own principles.[8]

Grassi was quick to point out in the *Libra* that if the cause of the rays were refraction at the surface of the eye, the telescope would not make the slightest difference. This is a cogent argument and Galileo's understanding of optics is too jejune for him to offer an adequate reply. Instead, he cleverly shifts his ground :

> Exactly the same thing happens to objects seen through the telescope as to those seen without it. For instance, the disc of Jupiter when seen with the naked eye is so small that it remains lost within the spread of its irradiation, but the disc of the moon does not, because it occupies in our pupil a much larger space than its radiant circle, and is therefore seen as shorn, and not as hairy.[9]

Galileo's reply, therefore, is that Jupiter has to be magnified to be freed of its adventitious rays, but that the moon is always large enough to be seen without them. This is an ingenious answer, but the question remains in its entirety for stars that receive no apparent magnification. The main cause, as we know today, is that the light of a star reaches us as a luminous point to which the telescope, especially if imperfect, may give the appearance of a disc. This is not magnification, but merely the result of failure to focus in a precise point. To the extent that this affects a larger area of the retina, the effects of irradiation and twinkling are reduced. Galileo was unaware of this and he attributed irradiation to defective lenses, while he assumed that telescopes that showed the stars as round bodies were perfect.

Motion of the Comet

The crucial issue in the debate on the comets is the problem of their motion. The famous comet of 1577 had appeared to move twenty times faster when it was first seen than when it disappeared. Tycho Brahe tried to reduce this irregular motion to uniformity by making the comet revolve around the sun, but in his attempt he committed what Galileo considers a methodological outrage.

> Although Tycho tries his best to reduce the motion to uniformity by assigning to the comets an orbit around the sun, nevertheless, he cannot gloss over the truth so completely as not to be forced to confess that he has to give it an irregular motion even within its own orb. He would even assume a non-circular orbit for it, concealing (in order to indulge this new fancy of his) that one of the main reasons why Copernicus and himself abandoned the Ptolemaic system was the impossibility of saving the appearances by means of perfectly circular and uniform motions in their own orbits and around their own centres. He also pretends not to see another extravagance, namely that although it is obvious in every system that all the planets move in the same direction, he introduces an orb designed for comets only and moving in the opposite direction, a most implausible conjecture.[10]

Tycho, therefore, sinned against two basic tenets of Galilean science : the principle of circularity and the principle of simplicity. As an alternative interpretation, Galileo suggests that the comet is merely a phenomenon of refraction not unlike the aurora borealis :

> In my opinion this effect has no other origin than that a part of the vapour-laden air surrounding the earth is for some reason unusually rarefied, and being extraordinarily sublimated rises above the cone of the earth's shadow so that its upper part is struck by the sun, and made to reflect its splendour, thus causing the aurora borealis.[11]

He adds that the sunspots prove the presence of wandering patches of vapour in the sky, and that just before the comets appeared the eastern region of the sky was more than usually full of luminous vapours.

Galileo contends that simple motion in a straight line accounts for the four basic observations concerning the comet : first, it appeared to move in a straight line; secondly, it continually slowed down as it got farther away, thirdly, it decreased in size, and finally, it seemed to move away from the sun. He illustrates his point with the aid of figure 9.

Let *ABC* be the terrestrial globe with the observer at *A*, and the line to the horizon *AG*, and let the straight line *DF* be the path of the comet marking off the equal segments $SO = ON = NI = IF$. It is immediately obvious that for the observer at *A*, the comet will appear to slow down progressively and to decrease in size as it moves from *O* to *F*.

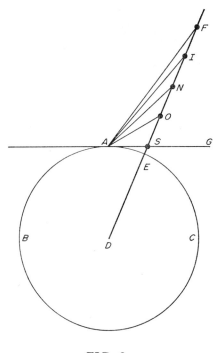

FIG. 9

Rectilinear vertical motion is mathematically clear and economical, but it also implies a consequence that cannot be avoided : if the comet had moved in a straight line perpendicularly to the surface of the earth it would always have appeared to be moving toward the zenith. Since this is contradicted by observational reports, Galileo's argument breaks down completely, as he is bound to acknowledge :

I shall not pretend to ignore that if the material in which the comet takes form had only a straight motion perpendicular to the surface of the earth (that is, from the centre to the sky), the comet should have seemed to be directed precisely toward the zenith, whereas, in fact, it did not appear so, but declined toward the north. This compels us either to alter what was stated, even though it corresponds to the appearances in so many cases, or else to retain what has been said, adding some other cause for this apparent deviation. I cannot do the one, nor should I like to do the other.[12]

Ockham's razor turns out to be a double-edged sword : it cuts at the root of Aristotle's unjustified assumptions, but it also severs Galileo's gratuitous chain of reasoning.

This leaves Galileo in a serious quandary, but instead of facing it, he immediately goes on to impugn Tycho Brahe's explanation of the tail of the comet, which he considers misguided because Tycho suggested that straight lines can appear curved : 'Concerning the tail, I do not find that anyone but Tycho has written, and he, I believe, no more correctly than of other particulars which depend on human conjecture. I shall therefore examine what he has written, and as this will surely be found inconclusive, I shall try to produce something plausible'.[13] Galileo's own interpretation is that atmospheric vapour refracts light the way a plano-convex lens does.

> In our case, since the eye is undoubtedly not at the centre of the vaporous orb, the comet, which in itself is really straight, never appears straight to us except when it is extended in a plane which passes through our eyes and the centre of the vapours, in other words, in a circle vertically above us. When it cuts these circles, we shall always see it more or less curved according as it cuts them more or less transversely.[14]

This passage raises two problems. First, how can Galileo affirm that the comet was really straight when he has already admitted that this would have required it to head for the zenith at all times? He rides roughshod over this difficulty by introducing the idea of refraction, but then, and this is the second problem, if atmospheric vapour acts as a lens for the rays of the sun, it should also distort light coming from other celestial bodies, which is not the case. And if, as Galileo suggests, the rays of the sun responsible for the production of the comets are more refracted near the horizon than near the zenith, the alignment of stars in a constellation should change considerably as they move from the zenith to the horizon, but no such distortion is observed.

The Libra Astronomica

In view of these weaknesses in Galileo's position, reaction to his discourse was swift. By the end of 1619, Grassi published his *Libra* in which he proposed to weigh Galileo's opinions. In deference to his religious superiors, ever wary of allowing their subjects to get entangled in public controversy, Grassi concealed his authorship under the pseudonym of Lothario Sarsi Sigensani, an anagram of Horatio Grassi Savonensi, and posed as one of his own pupils.[15] He denied following Tycho except in the application of the parallax method, but he added significantly enough:

> Let it be granted that my master followed Tycho. Is this such a crime? Whom instead should he follow? Ptolemy? whose followers' throats are threatened by the out-thrust sword of Mars now made closer. Copernicus? But he who is pious will rather call everyone away from him and will spurn and reject his recently condemned hypothesis. Therefore, Tycho remains as the only one whom we may approve of as our leader among the unknown courses of the stars.[16]

This is a good example of how the Decree of 1616 proscribing the heliocentric theory inhibited and vitiated scientific discussion. It was too convenient a tool not to be used, especially against an adversary who had taken it upon himself to launch an unwarranted attack. Grassi's reference to the condemnation of Copernicus set an unfortunate precedent that was only too willingly followed by lesser minds. It is particularly regrettable in view of the fact that his criticism of Galileo is on the whole penetrating and to the point. He was quick to spot Galileo's inconsistencies and to criticise him for decrying parallax and then using it against the Aristotelians,[17] and for admitting that his theory was wrong and then maintaining it in the teeth of contradiction. He reminded Galileo that Kepler had also sought to explain the path of the comets by a straight line and had come to grief. But it is mainly for claiming that comets are mere refractions in the atmospheric vapour that he took Galileo to task.

The Nature of the Comets

Grassi produced an impressive array of arguments to show that vapours could not explain the appearance and the motion of the comets. First, vapours would have to be endowed with contradictory properties: they would have to be opaque to reflect light, and, at the same time, transparent to allow stars to twinkle through them without suffering any apparent refraction. Secondly, reflections of the sun on the surface of the sea, and rainbows, which Galileo used as models for the comets, follow the motion of the sun while comets do not.[18] Thirdly, since the space occupied by the vapour must have been large, the comet ought to have appeared as a circle or a segment of a circle, as can be illustrated with the aid of figure 10.

Let the sun be at I, the eye at D and the comet at A. Join ID and DA, and produce ID to H.

$< IDA$ will be the angle under which the comet appears. Rotate the $< IDA$ along the axis ID to produce the circle BAC. Since any point on this segment will form with I and D an angle equal to $< IDA$, the comet should have appeared as a circle or a segment of a circle for precisely the same reason that a rainbow presents such an appearance.

Galileo's 'economical solution' of rectilinear motion was subjected to the same searching analysis. If the vapours rose from the equator, where evaporation was presumably greater than elsewhere, Grassi asked how they could have moved north since Galileo had dismissed the rotating

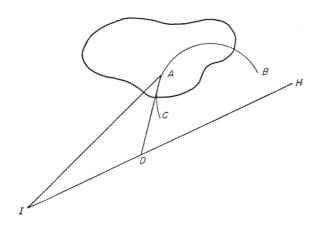

FIG. 10

celestial spheres that could have carried them. Furthermore, on Galileo's hypothesis, the apparent speed of the comet should have decreased in proportion to the size of the angle subtended (see figure 9). But the facts of the matter were different : during the first days the comet's speed had been nearly constant. Even the heliocentric theory provided no help; during the forty days that the comet was visible, the earth could hardly have covered 3°, a distance insufficient to account for the motion of the comet. It seemed to Grassi, therefore, that within the framework of the new as well as the old astronomy, Galileo's hypothesis failed to save even 'the appearances'.

II THE ATTACK ON TYCHO

The debates on the comets of 1618 show no significant advance in Galileo's appraisal of cosmic phenomena. The position he maintained— in the name of progress—was that of decadent Aristotelianism. It is the view put forward by men like Giulio Cesare Lagalla, the doting professor of the Sapienza, whom the young Jesuits at the Roman College ridiculed for mistaking smoke rising from a fire on the outskirts of Rome for a new comet.[19]

Tycho Brahe had vindicated the reality of comets and the usefulness of parallax in determining their distances. Galileo showed himself disinclined to grant Tycho recognition for his signal achievements.[20] This reluctance was probably prompted by the threat Tycho's system of astronomy presented to his own theory. Galileo was not prepared to admit this to himself, but he can hardly have been blind to the fact that his most competent adversaries were no longer disciples of Ptolemy but followers of the Danish astronomer. G. B. Baliani even wrote that Galileo's astronomical discoveries tended 'to prove the fluidity of celestial matter, and thus to make Tycho's hypothesis more probable'.[21] Galileo soon dispelled such an impression :

> In Tycho's hypothesis, I am left with those enormous difficulties which made me abandon Ptolemy, whereas in Copernicus there is not a single thing that raises the slightest doubt, and less than any other those objections against the motion of the earth that Tycho makes in some of his letters.[22]

Galileo's assertion that 'in Copernicus there is not a single thing that raises the slightest doubt' should not be taken as literal truth, and allowances must be made for the inflated language of propaganda. But the reference to Tycho Brahe's objections, and their dismissal as groundless, raises an interesting question : did Galileo have in mind the letters of correspondents other than Baliani? As early as 1611, Giovanni Lodovico Ramponi wrote to express the hope that he would find in Galileo's forthcoming book (the *Sistema Mundi* promised in the *Sidereus Nuncius*).

> the answer to a problem, which to my mind should be solved by those who hold the Copernican hypothesis or a similar one. It is the problem that was mainly responsible for Tycho abandoning this hypothesis, namely, comets have been seen in opposition to the sun but not distant enough (as the fixed stars) not to be subject to it, as he says in the first book of the *Letters*, page 149 . . . if this was true, as his exact observations convince us, *particularly in the case of the parallax*, it seems to me that the Copernican hypothesis would collapse if some other way of saving the appearances could not be found.[23]

Tycho did not suspect that comets move in parabolic curves greatly differing from the orbits of the planets and he took for granted that they followed a circular path around the sun. In the light of this assumption, he inferred that if the earth also revolved around the sun, the comets would display the stations and retrogressions that are observed in the planets. When in opposition, however, the comets do not move in a retrograde direction like the other planets. This strengthened Tycho in his belief that the earth was stationary and he produced a new astronomical system to replace both the Ptolemaic and the Copernican models.

The problem of the comets appeared relevant, therefore, to the great astronomical treatise that Galileo intended to write but kept deferring. If comets were real, then their path through space was a challenge to Copernicanism. The difficulty could be met, of course, by postulating a non-circular orbit, but Galileo was strenuously opposed to this idea. He chose rather to disclaim the existence of the comet and to reduce it to an optical phenomenon, to a case of refraction in vapours rising from the earth. This tenuous explanation stood little chance of being accepted unless he could show that Tycho had been completely wrong in what he stated about comets. He sought to achieve this by attacking Tycho on several fronts, and by using his consummate ability as a controversialist to destroy Tycho's prestige. Fear of a dangerous rival turned Galileo into a biased critic, and one wonders whether, in the heat of the debate, he hoped to dislodge the comet from the sky by demolishing Tycho's reputation on earth. He criticised him for falling from the high ideal of circularity and granting that the comet could move at an uneven speed along a non-circular path in a direction opposite to that of the other planets, but he glossed over the break-down of his own attempt to explain the progress of the comet by rectilinear motion. He deplored Tycho's failure to produce the work on astronomy that he had promised, but he did not mention that nine years had passed since he himself had announced in 1610 his intention of writing a treatise on the system of the world. He chided Tycho for thinking that earlier astronomers might all have been mistaken, 'perhaps from not possessing instruments as costly as his'. Yet a few pages earlier in the same *Discourse on the Comets*, he had appealed to 'the most accurate account of Tycho and others' to support his contention that comets usually move away from the sun.[24]

Galileo pursued his attack in *The Assayer* where he tried to show that Tycho was 'in need of learning the first elements of mathematics', because he had assumed that the rays extending from a star to the extremities of a terrestrial chord joining Uraniborg and Prague were parallel. Strictly speaking, Galileo's criticism was justified, but in the context of Tycho's argument this geometrical nicety was irrelevant as Kepler gently reminded him.[25]

The Price of Controversy

Galileo had to pay the price of a general offensive against the greatest astonomer of his age. His refusal to consider comets as real bodies cast him in the role of a conservative Aristotelian, and his explanation of their nature by refraction led to a host of inconsistencies : he used the parallax method against Aristotle, discarded it, and then resumed it to prove that comets were higher than lightning; he failed to notice that his theory of refraction entailed that the alignment of stars in a constellation should be distorted when they approached the horizon; he showed how the position of the sun determined the appearance of rainbows, haloes and parhelia, to which he likened comets, but he omitted to explain how the motion of the sun gave rise to the apparent path of the comet, which was the point at issue. Galileo also supposed that vapours could ascend to a great height, and when Grassi objected that strong winds would put the vapours off course, he replied : 'These reasons are useless for the fluctuation of the winds do not rise or extend to the height of some mountains'. Three years earlier, however, in his *Discourse on the Tides*, he had made much of the Trade Winds to prove the daily rotation of the earth on its axis, thus implying that strong winds could in fact be felt at the top of mountains.[26]

Galileo refused to entertain the possibility of non-circular orbits, and he was unwilling to consider enlarging the size of the universe. This last refusal meant that he stuck to the idea of a world small enough for the parallactic displacement of distant stars to be noticeable if the earth really moved. He was so intent on refusing Tycho that he failed to notice that he was pleading for a world where there would be no room for the heliocentric theory, for unless the stars were at an enormous distance, the absence of annual parallax became a cogent argument for the immobility of the earth.

III THE PROBLEM OF METHOD

Grassi's writings prove him to be Galileo's superior in scholarship, but he was a man fettered by his own erudition and not prone to query his sources if they were hallowed by time. Well versed in traditional logic, he was fond of casting his results in syllogistic form. Galileo treated him with withering scorn for criticising the loose terminology of the *Discourse on the Comets*, and attacked him for attempting to solve with logical arguments problems that could only be settled by empirical evidence and a knowledge of optics.

Galileo's attitude provides a clue to the influence of the movement originating in the circle of the *letterae humaniores* on the birth of modern science. Galileo was not a disciple of the Paduan logicians, but a follower of the Florentine Humanists who rebelled against the jargon of the schools.[27] Their contempt for scholastic distinctions had both a liberating and a dissipating effect on the culture of the day. It made room for free thought and original research but it also allowed rhetoric to pass muster for rational argument. For instance, when Virginio Cesarini, one of Galileo's literary friends, contrasts 'obstinate lovers and worshippers of old things' with 'minds that have the courage to consider new ideas', novelty seems a value in itself.[28] What raised Galileo above the throng of writers who deplored the literal-mindedness of the Aristotelians was his faith in, and his dedication to, mathematics. Herein lay his originality.

The Book of Nature

By early seventeenth-century standards, Grassi and Galileo were both first-rate mathematicians, but Galileo was more radical in his commitment to the mathematical method. Whereas Grassi used mathematics as a convenient tool, Galileo equated understanding the nature of physical reality with knowing its geometrical structure. In the autobiographical sketch at the beginning of *The Assayer*, Galileo recalled the attacks on his *Discourse on Floating Bodies* in words that left no doubt about his conviction that mathematics was the inroad to true and certain knowledge :

> I set down on paper beyond the teachings of Archimedes all that occurred to me, which is perhaps as much as may be truly said on the subject. And behold! Immediately the whole press was filled with attacks upon my *Discourse*. Without the least regard for the fact that what I had set forth was supported and proved by geometrical demonstrations, they contradicted my opinions, and such is the strength of men's passions that they failed to notice that to go against geometry is to deny truth in broad daylight ['*l contradire alla geometria è un negare scopertamente la verità*].[29]

Galileo expatiated on this point in the famous 'book of nature' passage, which he introduced by poking fun at Grassi's respect for authority :

> I believe Sarsi is firmly convinced that it is essential in philosophy to support oneself by the opinion of some famous author, as if when our minds are not wedded to the reasoning of some other person they ought to remain completely barren and sterile. Perhaps he thinks that philosophy is a book of fiction created by one man, like the *Iliad* or *Orlando Furioso*—books in which the least important thing is whether what is written in them is true. Sig. Sarsi, this is not the way matters stand. Philosophy is written in that great book which ever lies before our eyes —I mean the universe—but we cannot understand it if we do not first learn the language and grasp the symbols in which it is written. This book is written in the mathematical language, and the symbols are triangles, circles and other geometrical figures, without whose help it is

humanly impossible to comprehend a single word of it, and without which one wanders in vain through a dark labyrinth.[30]

This commitment to geometry helps to understand the recurrence of the 'Platonic' theme of circularity in Galileo's writings. Geometry could only be expressed in the language of regular forms, among which the circle occupied a prominent but by no means exclusive position. Galileo accused by Grassi of granting a unique ontological status to the circle, could retort :

It is not I who wants the sky, because it is the most noble body, to have the noblest shape, which is the perfect circle, it is Aristotle himself, against whom Sig. Mario argues *ad hominem*. As for myself, since I have never read the chronicles nor the particular titles of nobility of the shapes, I do not know which of them are more and which less noble, or which more and which less perfect. I believe that all of them are, in a way, ancient and noble; or, to put it better, that in themselves they are neither noble and perfect, nor ignoble and imperfect, except in so far as for building walls the square shape is more perfect than the circular, while for rolling or for moving wagons I deem the circular more perfect than the triangular.[31]

When Grassi feebly replied that in the biblical account of creation heaven and earth were given a circular shape, Galileo commented : 'The sphere, the cube, the pyramid etc., are equally eternal and prior to the creation of heaven and earth, and therefore, in this respect, they are equally noble'.[32] A genuine scientific conclusion had to be absolutely certain because it expressed the eternal truth of the mathematical structure of the universe. This was not to say that there was no room for tentative hypotheses in science; on the contrary, it implied that most theories were merely provisional. The Schoolmen affirmed too much because they rested their arguments on subjective qualities instead of reasoning from the objective geometrical structure of matter. Galileo was utterly convinced that nature was geometrically structured, but what particular structure obtained in this or that case he viewed as a matter for mathematical analysis and empirical confirmation. Under the best conditions, it was a difficult task, and the number of assured conclusions could only be small.

There was a tension in Galileo's mind between the certitude he claimed for geometrical demonstrations and his awareness of the hypothetical nature of his own speculations. On the one hand, he frequently insisted that mathematical reasoning could settle an issue unequivocally, as when he wrote : 'To reduce oneself to the rigour of geometrical demonstrations is too dangerous an experiment for anyone who does not know thoroughly how to manage them; for just as in nature itself there is no middle ground between truth and falsehood, so in rigorous proofs one must either establish his point beyond doubt or else beg the question inexcusably. There is no chance of keeping one's feet by invoking limitations, distinctions, verbal distortions or other mental acrobatics. One must with a few words and at the first assault become Caesar or nothing at all'.[33] On the other hand, he often reminded his reader that his own explanations were tentative : 'I shall bring before you, not positively but only probably and tentatively, as I think should be done in so obscure and doubtful a matter, those conjectures which have been received by our Academician Galileo'.[34] 'I frankly confess (as I always have) that I am dazzled and almost totally blind when it comes to penetrating the secrets of nature. I certainly desire to achieve some small knowledge of those secrets, but nothing is more contrary to my intention than hypocrisy and feigning. Sig. Mario in his essay has never feigned anything, nor did he have to do so, for whatever he has adduced that is new, he has always set forth tentatively as a conjecture, nor has he sought to make others accept as certain that which he and I consider open to doubt and, at best, only probable. This we have submitted to the consideration of people more knowing than ourselves in order with their help either to confirm some true conclusions or to exclude completely the false ones'.[35] Nor is Galileo's reply to Grassi, who accused him of hedging, entirely satisfactory : 'We are not departing from our custom of declaring nothing as certain except what we know beyond doubt, for this is what our philosophy and our mathematics teach us'.[36]

Galileo realised that the human mind could not penetrate the secrets of nature unless it abandoned the preposterous philosophical claim to exhaustive knowledge. This is an important aspect of Galileo's intellectual revolution : the methodological shift from an attempt at understanding the parts of the universe by grasping their significance in the whole, to a more modest effort at comprehending the working of the different parts without waiting for an all-embracing world-view. Man's unrestricted desire to know had to be channelled, to be severely limited, in order to become productive. At this critical juncture, Galileo had to communicate a new notion of scientific inquiry; he had to impart a novel understanding of the correct attitude toward science. He responded to this task by using the graphic approach of a parable, and he invented the story of a man who found one day, to his considerable astonishment, that musical sounds were not only produced by birds. After investigating various sources of sound and feeling confident that he knew them all, he chanced to capture a cicada and found himself more baffled than ever. Neither by closing its mouth nor stopping its wings could he diminish its strident sound, and yet he could not see it move either its scales or any other parts. At length, he lifted up the armour of its chest and saw beneath this some hard ligaments, which he thought were the cause of the sound and he resolved to break them. But everything failed until, driving the needle too deep, he transfixed the creature, and took its life with its voice, so that even then he could not make sure whether the sound had originated in those ligaments. 'Thereupon he became so diffident about what he knew, that when asked how sounds are produced, he would reply quite frankly that although he knew some ways, he was certain that many more existed which were unknown and unimaginable.'[37]

The parable takes the student of sound through three successive phases of enlightenment. First, his intellectual curiosity is awakened by the discovery that sound can be produced in more than one way. Secondly, he enters an inductive phase in which facts are gathered until he is satisfied that the collection is exhaustive. Finally, he is roused by the startling discovery of yet another way of producing sound, and this leads to the most surprising discovery of all : all science is open to drastic reappraisal in the light of fresh evidence. There is no way of knowing whether nature's ways have been thoroughly investigated. It is only possible to anticipate that what will be known will be expressible in the language of mathematics.

The Compliance of Experiments

Facts do not speak unless interrogated, and the kind of question that is asked limits and determines the range of meaningful answers. Galileo and Grassi both called upon experimental facts to justify certain features of their own theories, but they never suggested that experiments gave rise to theories; they always assumed that they illustrated, confirmed or falsified existing hypotheses. The laboratory was for them not the breeding-ground but the testing-place of theories.

The debate on the comets of 1618 illustrates how experiments are performed and often prejudged in the light of a theory. This will be clear from three episodes in the war of experiments that Galileo and Grassi waged against each other on the influence of revolving spheres, the cause of heat and the nature of the comets.

The Influence of Revolving Spheres

Aristotle claimed that the vapours rising from the earth were carried round by the motion of the sky. Galileo denied that a light material such as air could be swept along simply by touching the surface of its container, and he proved this experimentally by placing a lighted candle in the centre of a hollow vessel and showing that when the vessel revolved the flame remained erect, and, therefore, that the air was at rest. Grassi retorted with a modified experiment. He moved the candle from the centre and placed it close to the internal surface of the vessel, triumphantly noting that the flame was deflected in the direction in which the vessel was twirled. A strip of paper hanging from a thread and suspended near the surface of the vessel was even more deflected, thus confirming that the air moved with its container. Galileo accepted the experimental challenge in *The Assayer*. This time he took two lighted candles, attached one inside the vessel an inch or two from the top, and held the other in his hand inside the vessel at the same height. The vessel was then set in motion. He reasoned that if the motion was imparted to the air as Grassi claimed, the flame of the candle attached to the vessel would not bend because it would move with the same speed as the air, whereas the flame of the candle that was not attached to the vessel would be deflected. Experiment, however, proved just the opposite : the flame of the candle held in the hand remained straight while the flame of the candle fastened to the rotating vessel was deflected. Galileo concluded that the most Grassi could claim for his experiment was that a very thin layer of air was carried round by the roughness of the surface of the vessel. In his rejoinder, Grassi argued that he had never asserted that the air rotated as swiftly as the sphere in which it was contained, and that Galileo's experiment was a distortion of the real empirical situation in which the flame of the candle fastened to the vessel met with resistance from the air, not because the air did not move but because it did not move as swiftly as the vessel itself. By shifting his ground, Grassi managed, therefore, to render Galileo's experiment innocuous.

The Cause of Heat

The Aristotelians attributed heat to motion and adduced as evidence that the tip of an arrow shot with great speed grew hot, and that forests and ships could be set on fire by very strong winds. Galileo did not deny the evidence, but he offered a different interpretation : he argued that strong winds set forests or ships on fire, not because of their great speed, but because they rubbed the planks of the ships or the dead timber of the forest together and warmed them. Likewise, he suggested that the tip of an arrow shot through a thick target became hot, not because of the speed of its flight, but because of friction in passing through the target.

Galileo carried his argument a step further and explained that friction produced heat by detaching some particles of matter. In the light of this theory, he saw the fume that rose when glass was scratched with a key as evidence that 'other more subtle sulphurous and bituminous parts which are invisible but which make themselves evident by their smell may also be rising'.[38] When Grassi objected that the fume that was seen when glass was scratched was a cloud of minute particles of glass that rose and soon fell, and that when a piece of glass was neatly broken no fume appeared, Galileo remained unperturbed. He merely reasserted his position, and introduced a subsidiary hypothesis to fit the evidence into the framework of his theory : 'When the glass is broken in two, the fume or exhalation rises, but it is invisible, because it does not carry with it the light dust by which it becomes visible; likewise wind becomes visible by the dust it lifts up, and the dust is not raised except by a turbulence in the air; in still air it falls to the ground'.[39] Grassi had avoided the consequences of Galileo's experiment with a candle by modifying his theory; Galileo now parried the blow of Grassi's criticism by postulating the existence of an invisible substance.

The fact that hard bodies such as diamonds did not grow hot when rubbed together was also open to various interpretations. For Galileo this was an indication that nothing was consumed from their surfaces, while for G. B. Baliani it proved that they adhered so closely together that there was no room left between them for the air to be volatised, leaving the bodies exposed to the ubiquitous celestial heat, which he considered the cause of warmth.[40]

Grassi had a good experimental flair but he was hampered by his readiness to believe ancient writers. For instance, he accepted on the authority of classical authors that projectiles and cannon-balls sometimes melted in mid-air because of their speed. He even gave as evidence for the production of heat by motion the legendary account of Babylonians cooking their eggs by whirling them in slings. This prompted one of Galileo's most celebrated and devastating comments :

If Sarsi wishes me to believe, on the word of Suidas, that the Babylonians cooked eggs by whirling them rapidly in slings, I shall believe it; but I shall say that the cause of this effect is very far from the one he attributes to it. To discover the true cause I reason as follows : 'If we do not achieve an effect which others formerly achieved, it must be that we lack something in our operation which was the cause of this effect succeeding, and if we lack one thing only, then this alone can be the true cause. Now we do not lack eggs, or slings, or sturdy fellows to whirl them, and still they do not cook, but rather cool down faster if hot. And since we lack nothing except being Babylonians, then being Babylonian is the cause of the egg hardening'. And this is what I wished to prove. It is possible that Sarsi in riding post has not observed that coolness brought to his face by the continual change of air? And if he has indeed felt this, can he prefer to believe things which happened two thousand years ago in Babylon, and are related by others, rather than present things which he himself experiences?[41]

Galileo recognised the significance of experiments, but the passage is a witty retort rather than a statement about method. What is affirmed is merely the priority of personal observation over time-hallowed descriptions. We should remember that if Grassi failed to criticise his sources, Galileo was not given to questioning the accuracy of his own experimental reports : cannon-balls melting in mid-air are no more preposterous than invisible fumes rising from broken glass !

The Nature of the Comet

Galileo dismissed the hypothesis that comets are incandescent bodies on the grounds that they cannot be observed through a flame, whereas stars can be distinguished through the tail of a comet. Grassi immediately accused him of turning a blind eye to the evidence : 'In regard to these matters, I am most astonished that a famous man, fond of experiments, can so confidently affirm what is easily refuted by obvious experiments.'[42]

Grassi defended Aristotle by pointing out that a lamp wick is visible in the middle of a flame, that half-burned pieces of wood can be seen in a burning pile, and that a printed page is legible through a candle flame. He concluded with heavy-handed irony that Galileo, in fact, reasoned as follows :

Flames are not transparent;
but the beard of the comet is transparent.
Therefore, the beard of the comet is not a flame.

It would be more appropriate, however, to say :

Luminous objects are not transparent;
the beard of the comet is transparent.
Therefore, the beard of the comet is not luminous.[43]

Galileo was not at a loss for a rebuttal : granted that a thin flame does not impede light altogether, it does not follow that a flame several hundred yards thick—as it would have to be in the case of a comet— would not obstruct the view of the stars. 'For instance, a cloud which does not prevent us from seeing a tree trunk when we are twenty or thirty yards away from it, can hide the sun altogether if it rises to a height of two or three hundred yards'.[44] Since the war of experiments is always fought on the battleground of interpretations, Grassi could produce yet another rejoinder : if it were true that what is transparent when thin becomes opaque when it increases in size, then large quantities of glass and air would impede sunlight !

Galileo sought to buttress his explanation of comets as refractions in atmospheric vapour by comparing them to haloes, rainbows, parhelia, rays of sunlight streaming through clouds and luminous strips on the surface of the ocean. Grassi pointed out that Galileo had disregarded the most important fact about these optical phenomena, namely that their position varied not only with the motion of the observer but also with that of the sun. Figure 11, used by Grassi, shows that the image cast by the sun on the surface of the sea withdraws as the sun moves away. Let *BI* be the surface of the sea and *A* the position of an observer on shore. Let *F, G, H* be the successive positions of the sun, and *D, E, I* the corresponding positions of the reflected images when the angles of incidence *ADB, AEB, AIB* are equal to the angles of refraction *FDE, GEI, HIO*.

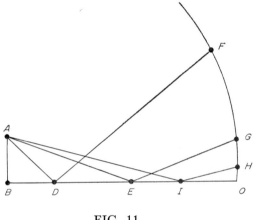

FIG. 11

It is clear that the reflected images will move in the same direction as the sun.

Using the analogy of sunlight reflected on the surface of water, Galileo modified Grassi's diagram to prove that the comet will appear to move away from the sun. Produce the arc *FGHO* to *N*, and extend lines *AI, AE* and *AD* to *L, M* and *N* (figure 12). Since the observer at *A* looks at the comet through a sea of vapour, when the sun is at *H*, its image is seen along the line *AI*, and hence the comet appears to be at *L*. Similarly, when the sun reaches *G*, its image is observed along the line *AE*, and the comet appears to have moved to *M*. Therefore, the comet seems to move in a direction opposite to that of the sun.

Grassi objected that this geometrical device did not tally with the facts. The comet of 1618 did not always move away from the sun. Furthermore, on Galileo's reinterpretation, the distances *OL, LM* and *MN* travelled by the comet are equal to the distances *OH, HG* and *GF* covered by the sun, but this was also contradicted by observation.

This disagreement between Galileo and Grassi is a reminder that facts and experiments do not exist in isolation : they are always part of a network which endows them with meaning and from which they derive their significance. Galileo did not believe that Grassi's objection heralded the ruin of his theory, but merely that it indicated the necessity of devising a new illustration, which he found in the reflection of candlelight on a carafe. In *The Assayer*, he described the construction of such a model. Oil

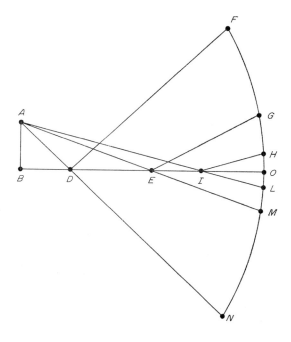

FIG. 12

is applied on the spot where a carafe reflects the light of a candle, and the carafe is rotated so that the image seems to emerge from the oily spot. A finger is run across the oil, and the straight ray thus formed is assumed to represent the tail of the comet. The carafe is moved again to place the reflection of candlelight in the unoiled part at the beginning of the ray. This stands for the head of the comet which always appears brighter than the tail. Galileo added that the same effect could be obtained if the carafe was fogged by breathing upon it, instead of using oil. He ended with a witty remark at Grassi's expense :

If you should mention this little diversion to Sarsi, I beg your Excellency to protest specifically and at length that I do not mean to imply by this that there is a huge carafe in the sky, and someone oiling it with his finger, and that thus the comet is formed. I merely offer this example (and I could give others, and perhaps there are many more in nature which we do not even dream of) as an illustration of nature's bountiful and varied ways of producing effects.[45]

Experiments as such cannot secure automatic solutions for basic issues, and those who rail at the wilfulness and blindness of minds fixed in habitual routine do so because they are committed and dedicated to a different—and not necessarily novel—way of looking at things. As Max Planck testified, a new scientific position gains general acceptance, not by making opponents change their minds, but by holding its own until old age has retired them from their professorial chairs.[46]

IV THE NATURE OF MATTER

The discussion on the ultimate constituents of matter begun in the debate on floating bodies was reintroduced in the controversy on the comets by Galileo's criticism of the Aristotelian position that vapour in the atmosphere is kindled by the rotation of the celestial orbs. He argued that motion as such produces no change, and that friction and compression are the sole agents of heat, which results from the dissolution of a body into very fine parts that penetrate our flesh and produce either the pleasant feeling of warmth or the pain of scorching and burning.[47] Very hard surfaces such as diamonds, or very smooth ones such as glass, do not become warm when rubbed together because no particle is detached from them.

Giovanni Battista Baliani complained in a letter to Galileo that it was not clear how small particles flying from incandescent bodies could produce an unpleasant feeling by moving swiftly, and a pleasant one by moving slowly. Nor did he see how Galileo explained the difference between fire in a burning body and the sensation of fire in the sentient. He noted furthermore that wood, wax and oil dissolve into vapour while iron and other metals do not. Galileo scribbled the following reply in the margin of Baliani's letter :

We have 1000 liquids like water, 1000 solid like earth, 1000 like air (which is manifest from the evaporation of 1000 scents), and why not 1000 like fire? Therefore, the heat we feel does not proceed from the substance, but from the shape, size and motion of the body reduced to very small parts. In order to cut meat, a knife does not have to be made of steel rather than copper, stone, bone or oak. It is enough that it should be sharp and cutting. Thus, that wax should dissolve into *minimi* substantially different from those into which iron dissolves is of no importance with respect to producing heat in us, as long as both are dissolved into very small, sharp and mobile parts, namely apt to penetrate the pores of our skin.[48]

The objection raised by Orazio Grassi, Galileo's main adversary, was less speculative, and it brought the discussion down to the level of the empirical and the quantitative. Grassi weighed a piece of copper on a sensitive balance, hammered it into a red-hot plate, weighed it again, and found that no weight had been lost.

If at this point someone were to say that the parts that are lost are so minute that even an exact balance does not reveal them, I would ask him whence he knows that such parts are lost, for I do not see how I could have examined the matter more properly and carefully. Also, if this loss of parts is so slight that it cannot be perceived by the senses, why did it produce so much heat? Furthermore, when iron is smoothed with a file it becomes hot, but less or certainly not more, than when it is struck very hard with a hammer, although more parts are lost through filing than by hammering.

In a postil, Galileo dismissed Grassi's interpretation : 'It is not surprising that the balance should reveal no difference : as much gold could be removed by half an hour of hammering as is removed from a ring that is worn for two months where the loss, however real, cannot be detected by a balance'. And to the question as to how we know that some parts are lost, he replied :

This we know because the bodies that lose nothing do not become warm while all those that are seen to lose some parts do. Therefore, it is reasonable to believe that in the bodies that become hot, some parts, albeit not perceptible, are lost.[49]

In *The Assayer*, Galileo added that the gold lost by a gilded button over a period of weeks remains imperceptible, and that a ball of amber can fill a room with scent for a fortnight without losing any of its weight.

Grassi's rejoinder is instructive because he cast himself in the role of the hard-headed experimentalist.

Granted that the fact that the weight remains the same when iron is hammered out does not destroy the argument that something might have flown away which is specifically lighter than iron, yet there is no reason—not even a hypothetical one—for saying that such a diminution did in fact take place. Unless reason points another way, we follow the lead of our senses to knowledge; the senses are on my side, and Galileo's reasoning or logical inference fell through at the very outset, as has been shown above.[50]

Galileo had adduced the fume rising from a piece of glass scratched with a key as evidence that what was detached was lighter than air. Grassi replied that when a plate of glass is neatly broken no fume appears, although on Galileo's theory a huge cloud of smoke should be seen because of the large number of pores that are opened. A slight scratch on a piece of glass, however, produces a considerable amount of fume, thus indicating that it is not some mysterious exhalation but merely the dust of glass. Galileo's rebuttal to this last objection is particularly interesting because he did away with experiments altogether, and took refuge in the unassailability of theory : 'When the plate is broken in two, fume or exhalation rises, but it remains invisible, because it does not carry with it the light dust by which it becomes visible.'[51]

Rousing the Senses

The debate on motion as the cause of heat thus led Galileo to postulate the existence of invisible particles of matter which impinge on the sense-organs and elicit a subjective response termed heat. This view clashed with the common-sense belief that heat was an intrinsic property of bodies, and Galileo devised one of his most epistemologically significant thought-experiments to refute this naïve realism.

> As soon as I think of a material object or a corporeal substance, I immediately feel the need to conceive simultaneously that it is bounded and has this or that shape, that it is big or small in relation to others, that it is in this or that place at a given time, that it moves or stays still, that it does or does not touch another body, and that it is one, few, or many. I cannot separate it from these conditions by any stretch of my imagination. But my mind feels no compulsion to understand as necessary accompaniments that it should be white or red, bitter or sweet, noisy or silent, of sweet or of foul odour. Indeed, without the senses to guide us, reason or imagination alone would perhaps never arrive at such qualities. For that reason, I think that tastes, odours, colours and so forth are no more than mere names so far as pertains to the subject wherein they seem to reside, and that they only exist in the body that perceives them. Thus, if the living creature were removed, all these qualities would be removed and annihilated.[52]

Galileo did not put nature to the rack; he passed it through the crucible of a mental experiment, and then called upon common sense and everyday experience to confirm the result. For instance, he noted that although the motion of a hand over a marble statue and over a living person is identical in as much as the hand is concerned, it can produce a tickling sensation in man only. Galileo argued that it would be as erroneous to affirm that tastes, odours and colours exist apart from the organs that are affected by them, as to attribute the property of tickling to the hand. What exists in the object that produces a sensation is matter in motion. Particles of various sizes, shapes, number and speed impinge against the organs of sense and give rise to the different sensations. More specifically, the elements in order of ascending immateriality; earth, water, fire, air and light affect the senses of touch, taste, smell, hearing and sight respectively.

This correlation was common among exponents of the correspondence theory between the macrocosm and the microcosm, as a passage from Anton Francesco Doni's *Mondi celesti, terrestri et infernali* bears out :

> The macrocosm enters the soul of the microcosm through five doors, namely the five senses. The higher luminous and coloured bodies enter through sight, the solid and terrestrial ones by touch, the things of water through taste, those of air through hearing, and, through scent, those vapours that are made of water, air, flashes of light, or aromatic substances. Therefore, earth corresponds to touch, water to taste, air to hearing, fire to smell, and Quintessence (or the body) to sight, and so again we see the mutual love of these elements that combine so willingly.[53]

Assuming that the basic sensations of touch, smell, taste, hearing and sight, which appear to reside in external objects, have no reality outside the subject perceiving them, Galileo extended his investigation to heat. Fire, he affirmed, is merely a name for the multitude of minute corpuscles that strike the sense-organs. They cause a pleasant sensation when they assist the process of transpiration and an unpleasant one when they tear and scorch the flesh. In itself, fire is nothing in addition to the shape, motion, and penetrating power of its particles, but these cannot produce heat unless they are moving, and, in this sense, motion is the cause of heat. This last consideration seems prompted by the observation that quicklime does not produce heat except when dropped in water. Galileo's conjecture is that the fire-particles are held motionless in the constricted pores of the quicklime until they are opened by the action of the water.

Galileo's terminology is worth attending to. He avoided the word 'atom' throughout the entire discussion of primary and secondary qualities. The expressions he used are *corpicelli minimi, minimi, ignicoli, minimi ignei, i minimi del fuoco, minimi sottilissimi e volanti* and *i minimi quanti*. These *minimi* are the smallest parts of a natural substance, but they are not the ultimate constituents of matter since they can be divided. Galileo went on to suggest at the end of *The Assayer* that their ultimate resolution into atoms would entail a radical transformation of matter :

When the thinning and attrition stop at, or are confined within, the *minimi quanti*, the motion is temporal and the action calorific only, but perhaps when the ultimate and highest resolution into truly indivisible atoms is reached, light is created whose motion, or if we prefer expansion and diffusion, is instantaneous, and is capable of occupying immense spaces by its—I do not know whether to say subtlety, rarity, immateriality, or some other property different from all these, and unnamed.

Earlier in the same work, Galileo had speculated that 'a very subtle aethereal material diffused throughout the vast reaches of the universe through which the solid cosmic bodies travel of their own accord'.[54] These words echoed what he had written Piero Dini a few years prior :

It seems to me that there exists in nature a most tenuous, rapid and subtle substance, which is diffused throughout the universe and penetrates everything without impediment. It warms, vivifies and renders fertile all living creatures. Our senses themselves would seem to indicate that the main reservoir of this spirit is the sun, from which an enormous light expands throughout the universe, accompanied by this calorific spirit penetrating all vegetable matter and making it alive and fertile. We may reasonably believe that this is something more than light, since it penetrates and is diffused throughout all corporeal substances, albeit very dense, through which light does not penetrate in the same way. As we see and feel light and heat coming out of our fires (with heat passing through all bodies although opaque and very solid, while light is impeded by solid and opaque bodies), so the solar emanation is both luminous and calorific, and the calorific part is more penetrating.[55]

Galileo was not fixed on this point and he entertained several successive hypotheses. In his letter to Dini, heat was more basic than light; in *The Assayer* the order was inverted and light took precedence. The change seems to have been dictated by the realisation that if heat was caused by motion and motion occurred in time, heat could no longer be said to travel instantaneously, whereas this could still be asserted of light. Some years later, however, in the *Discourses Concerning Two New Sciences*, Galileo abandoned the idea of instantaneous propagation altogether and suggested an experiment to determine the speed of light.[56]

Grassi was not prepared to let matters stand, and he counterattacked on the levels of theology and scholastic philosophy. In theology, he appealed to the argument, common among Schoolmen since the Middle Ages, that the mystery of the eucharist implied a substantial change in the nature of the bread but the permanence of the sensibles species, such as colour, odour and taste. By pronouncing these qualities subjective and regarding them as mere names in the external object, Galileo imperilled the dogma of transubstantiation. This argument was unfair, not only because it set up a philosophical interpretation as a doctrine of faith, but because it carried the debate on grounds Galileo was not allowed to tread.

From a philosophical standpoint, Grassi rehearsed the customary Aristotelian objections to Democritus. If light is made up of indivisible atoms, they must be either finite or infinite. But they can be neither infinite, because there is no middle point between the extremities of a line consisting of an infinite number of points, nor finite, since mathematical difficulties would ensue. Furthermore, if different sensations were caused by the different shapes of particles in motion, an alteration in the shape of the particles would modify the nature of the sensation. But a naturally sweet substance, such as sugar, can be ground into a very fine powder without losing its taste.

The debate could have continued without bringing the opponents any closer. It merely serves to illustrate that the same doctrine takes on very different complexions against different intellectual backgrounds. Within the Aristotelian framework, the atomic theory leads through a sequence of deplorable errors into a sea of contradictions, while in the setting of Galileo's thought, it opens new vistas by by-passing the jungle of traditional questions.

Old Ideas Made New

Galileo's idea of resolution into *minima* and finally into *atoms* appears as the forward thrust of a current that had been swelling since the Middle Ages. Averroes had commented on Aristotle's passing remark on the smallest particles, and successive generations of followers entered more frequently into the theory of natural *minima*. Agostino Nifo and Jacopo Zabarella, the Paduan Averroists, discussed the problem at length, and attributed to the *minima* an independent reality and a role in physical and chemical reactions. Andrew van Melsen sees this as an important step in the formation of the modern scientific outlook :

> Because the *minima* had acquired more physical reality, it became necessary to examine how the properties of the *minima* could be reconciled with the sensible properties of the substance. This necessity produced a certain mentality which was not so much concerned with possible divisibility as with concretely observable properties.[57]

The Averroists discussed the problem within the rigid framework of Aristotelian physics and in terms of matter and form but the fact that they granted actual reality to the *minima* and applied the concept to quality helped to prepare the revival of atomism in the seventeenth

century. Zarabella died before Galileo arrived in Padua, and it is difficult
to know to what degree his school may have influenced the young lecturer
in mathematics. Galileo read very little, but he revelled in discussion, and
in a small academic circle this was sufficient to keep a man abreast of
recent developments and current views. It makes it impossible, however,
to know how Galileo used his sources for his own purposes, or how much
he borrowed from the lively minds of his colleagues, especially those who
did not bother to publish. In any case, Galileo would have been familiar
with the atomic theory through the works of Galen which he read in Pisa,
and he may well have discussed it with his friend Mazzoni who mentions
it in his *In Universam Platonis et Aristotelis Philosophiam Praeludia*.[58]

Even the radical distinction between primary and secondary qualities
was not unheralded. Medieval and Renaissance Schoolmen distinguished
between the *sensibilia propria*, the objects of the five senses, and the
sensibilia communia, size, shape, number, motion and rest.[59] The *sensibilia
propria*, the secondary qualities of a later terminology, were granted an
objective status because they affected the senses directly. The *sensibilia
communia*, roughly the primary qualities, were assigned a lower epistemological rank because they could only reach the senses through the
secondary qualities. Within the Aristotelian scheme, therefore, perception
meant penetration of the senses by the real qualities of the things themselves, a participation of consciousness in the objective reality of the
physical world. Thus the senses could not be deceived about tactile
properties, colours, tastes, sounds and scents, but they could err about the
'inferred' primary qualities. For the atomist, however, perception was no
longer a vicarious sharing in the reality of the world, but a subjective
interpretation of the physical arrangement of the atoms that assailed the
sensory apparatus. Atoms composed nature, but they could not be perceived directly, nor could one hope to demonstrate their existence
empirically; by definition, they lay below the dimensions of sense. Why
then must they be inferred from the visible world? Galileo never raised
the question in quite those terms, but at a later late, in the *Discourses
Concerning Two New Sciences*, he sought to demonstrate that atoms were
necessary to make objective mathematical reasoning possible.[60]

But if the world comes to us as a puzzle to be pieced together, how are
we to know what parts fit into each other? How are we to organise the
congeries of discrete entities? The newly enlisted concept of the atom
makes another step imperative : the conception of the mind as an instrument for sorting out discrete impulses. Galileo did not take this step nor
does he seem to have been aware of its inevitability, but the distinction
he drew opened a whole world of new questions : what is the difference
between inner experience and outer world? How can we be sure of sense
data? What is the distinction between private reality and public truth?

The fact that philosophers are still grappling with these problems today is a measure of the revolutionary and generative power of the revival of atomism in the seventeenth century. It is also a tribute to Galileo's daring.

Galileo's great ambition, the book he longed to bequeath to the world, was the definitive validation of the heliocentric theory, demonstrated by Copernicus and obvious to mathematicians but still in need of proof for the man in the street. For several years, he had been wrestling with Tycho's objection : if the sun is at the centre of the universe, the orbit and the speed of comets must be irregular. G. L. Ramponi reminded him of this difficulty, and with the unconscious cruelty of the fervent admirer repeated his assurance that Galileo would solve the problem. Galileo did more than that : he abolished it. The unwieldy path of the comet was a menace only if it was real; if it could be shown to be merely a phenomenon of refraction in the atmosphere, it would cease to be a threat to Copernicans. But the incriminating evidence kept rearing its ugly head, and Galileo shifted his ground until he landed himself in a contradiction : the path of the comet could not decline to the north and still be per- pendicular to the surface of the earth as his theory required. But Galileo remained undaunted, not out of bravado, but because he was sure that however difficult it might prove to turn the lock, he, and not his opponents, had the key to knowledge. He felt assured that the language of nature was mathematically clear and aesthetically pleasing. The Pythagoreans had hit upon the notion that nature was made of numbers and that numbers had a definite shape. Galileo left the number-juggling aside and assumed that shape was the underlying principle of reality. Lines, triangles, squares, cubes and circles were the building blocks of the world, and, because they were economically organised, the simplest figures, the line and the circle, were to be preferred over more complicated ones such as the ellipse.

A further implication was obvious : since the nature of bodies could never be fully understood from what was perceived of their behaviour, uninterpreted (that is, non-geometrised) facts were only the raw material of science. The senses were no longer reliable guides to knowledge, and the role of experiment was to conform or refute what had been deduced from geometric considerations. It is at this point that Galileo went beyond the Humanists who also clamoured against traditional philosophy. They were opposed to the Scholastic style, but they replaced its dialectical reasoning and syllogistic deduction by a flow of rhetoric. The letters of Galileo's literary friends are full of repetition and conceptual imprecision. Instead of proof or demonstration, they pile assertion upon assertion. Instead of producing arguments for a proposition they recommend, they embellish it with yet another metaphor. Galileo replaced this discursive effusiveness with the rigour of geometry, if not in practice, at least in principle. Had he not done so, his attack on authority would have been no more than a half-heroic, half-petulant and wholly futile revolt. He took the Aristotelian citadel by storm when he declared that a scientific account of the behaviour of things should refer to mathematically analysable properties such as shapes and motions. From then on the campaign was won, and the subsequent history of science in the seventeenth century may be seen as the prolonged task of mopping up, of organisation and of consolidation.

NOTES

1. Letter to Galileo, 2 March 1619, *Opere di Galileo*, **12**, 443
2. Galileo [and Mario Guiducci], *Discorso delle comete* (Florence, 1619), *ibid.*, **6**, 51. Translation by Stillman Drake, *Discourse on the Comets*, in Galileo Galilei *et al.*, *Controversy of the Comets of 1618* (Philadelphia: University of Pennsylvania Press, 1960), 27. The reader is reminded that English translations quoted in this book have often been altered for the sake of emphasis
3. *Ibid.*, 53. (Drake trans., 29)
4. *Ibid.*, 63–64, italics mine. (Drake trans., 36)
5. *Ibid.*, 65–66. (Drake trans., 37)
6. *Ibid.*, 69. (Drake trans., 38)
7. *Ibid.*, 83 (Drake trans., 46)
8. *Ibid.*, 85 (Drake trans., 48)
9. Galileo, *Il Saggiatore* (Rome, 1623), *Opere di Galileo*, **6**, 362. (Translation by Stillman Drake, *The Assayer* in Galileo, *Controversy of the Comets of 1618*, 324–325)
10. Galileo, *Discorso delle comete*, *Opere di Galileo*, **6**, 88–89. (Drake trans., 50)
11. *Ibid.*, 94. (Drake trans., 54)
12. *Ibid.*, 98. (Drake trans., 57.) Giovanni Battista Baliani noted that Galileo was caught between the horns of a dilemma. On the one hand, if AE (see figure 9) is small, then the comet at S was very close to the earth, and therefore, it should have decreased in size much more than was observed as it ascended towards F. On the other hand, if AE is large, the comet, in order to account for the large angle FAS that was observed, must have risen to a much greater height than Galileo was willing to grant (letter to Galileo, 8 August 1619, *ibid.*, **12**, 477)
13. *Ibid.*, 98. (Drake trans., 57)
14. *Ibid.*, 102. (Drake trans., 61)
15. Grassi did not conceal his identity from Galileo's Roman friends. Giovanni Ciampoli informed Galileo that 'Fr. Grassi, a Jesuit, who has recently returned from Perugia, brought his *Discourse* on the comet this evening . . . The Father told me that he presented his arguments as well as he could but that he always spoke respectfully of you' (letter to Galileo, 18 October 1619, *ibid.*, **12**, 494)
16. Orazio Grassi, *Libra astronomica ac philosophica* (Perugia, 1619), *ibid.*, **6**, 116. (Translation by C. D. O'Malley, *The Astronomical Balance* in Galileo, *The Controversy of the Comets of 1618*, 71.) In Ptolemy, Mars cuts across the path of the sun. This was generally recognised as a serious shortcoming of the Ptolemaic system

17. *Ibid.*, 118. (O'Mally trans., 73.) Giovanni Remo noted the same inconsistency in his letter to Galileo of 24 August 1619 (*ibid.*, **12**, 485)

18. *Ibid.*, 140–142. (O'Mally trans., 91–94.) Giovanni Battista Baliani pointedly observed in his letter to Galileo of 8 August 1619: 'I do not see how you can use this to determine what the comet is, for such a luminous strip on the sea always and necessarily lies on a straight line between our eyes and the sun . . . Now not only the tail of the comet but the comet itself does not lie in a straight line between ourselves and the sun except accidentally. It cannot therefore be produced in the same way as a luminous strip on the surface of the sea' (*ibid.*, **12**, 477)

19. Lagalla wrote to Galileo to express his approval of the *Discourse on the Comets*: 'I have been confirmed in the opinion that I have always held . . . that the comets are not igneous exhalations, but refractions of sunlight in vapours and in some denser parts of the heavens'. He recounted himself how the Jesuits maintained that the comet he claimed to have observed was nothing but 'smoke rising from a fire outside the Porta d'Cavalliggieri' (letter to Galileo, 21 December 1619, *ibid.*, 500–501)

20. In *The Assayer*, Galileo praised Scipione Chiaramonti's *Anti-Tycho* (Venice, 1621) before reading it because he assumed that it was a refutation of Tycho in the light of Copernicus' system (*ibid.*, **6**, 231). When he subsequently read the work, he was sorely disappointed, and he singled it out for vituperation in his *Dialogue on the Two World Systems* (*ibid.*, **7**, 77)

21. Letter to Galileo, 31 January 1614, *ibid.*, **12**, 21

22. Letter to G. B. Baliani, 12 March 1614, *ibid.*, 35

23. Letter to Galileo, 23 July 1611, *ibid.*, **11**, 161–162, italics mine. The reference is to Tycho Brahe's *Epistolarum astronomicarum libri* (Uraniborg, 1596), in Tycho Brahe's *Scripta Astronomica*, ed. I. L. E. Dreyer, 14 vols. and index (Copenhagen, 1913–1929), **5**, 179. Galileo probably did not reply for we find Ramponi repeating the following year his query 'concerning the solution to the problem of the comets in opposition to the sun, which was powerful enough to dislodge the Copernican hypothesis from Tycho's mind' (letter to Galileo, 21 May 1612, *Opere di Galileo*, **11**, 300)

24. Galileo, *Discorso delle comete, Opere di Galileo*, **6**, 102–103, 92. (Drake trans., 62, 52)

25. *Ibid.*, 229. (Drake trans., 181.) See Tycho Brahe's *De mundi aetherei recentioribus phaenomenis liber secundus* (Uraniborg, 1588), in *Scripta Astronomica*, **4**, 107–112. This criticism was originally levelled at Tycho by Scipio Chiaramonti in his *Anti-Tycho* (Venice, 1621), 218–219. Kepler's remark occurs in his *Tychonis Brahi Dani Hyperaspiates*, in Kepler, *Gesammelte Werke*, ed., F. Hammer *et al.*, 18 vols. to date (Munich: C. H. Beck, 1938), **8**, 413–414

26. Galileo's postil to Grassi's *Libra, Opere di Galileo*, **6**, 136, postil 78; *idem, Discorso del flusso e reflusso del mare, ibid.*, **5**, 393–394

27. For a different interpretation, see John Herman Randall Jr., *The School of Padua and the Emergence of Modern Science* (Padua: Antenore, 1961). Randall establishes that the Paduan logicians were interested in the logic of science in general, but he fails to show that they influenced Galileo or that their definition of science tallied with his

28. Letter to Galileo, 7 May 1622, *Opere di Galileo*, **13**, 88

29. Galileo, *Il Saggiatore, ibid.*, **6**, 214. (Drake trans., 163–164)

30. *Ibid.*, 232. (Drake trans., 183–184)

31. *Ibid.*, 319. (Drake trans., 279)

32. Galileo's postil to Orazio Grassi's *Ratio ponderum librae et simbellae* (Paris, 1626), *ibid.*, 462, postil 113. Nevertheless, among regular lines, Galileo considered the circle 'more regular so to say, than any other' (*ibid.*, 244)

33. Galileo, *Il Saggiatore, ibid*, 296. (Drake trans., 252)

34. Galileo, *Discorso delle comete, ibid.*, 47. (Drake trans., 24)

35. Galileo, *Il Saggiatore, ibid.*, 303. (Drake trans., 261)

36. *Ibid.*, 279. (Drake trans., 233–234)
37. *Ibid.*, 281. (Drake trans., 236.) Galileo drew the moral of the story: 'The difficulty of understanding how the cicada's song is formed even when we have it singing to us right in our hand is more than enough to excuse us for not knowing how a comet is formed at such an enormous distance' (*ibid.*)
38. *Ibid.*, 334. (Drake trans., 294)
39. Galileo's postil to Grassi's *Ratio., ibid.*, 480–481, postil 137
40. Letter to Galileo, 8 August 1619, *ibid.*, **12**, 475
41. Galileo, *Il Saggiatore, ibid.*, **6**, 340. (Drake trans., 301)
42. Grassi, *Libra, ibid.*, 173. (O'Malley trans., 127–128)
43. *Ibid.*, 176 (O'Malley trans., 130)
44. Galileo, *Il Saggiatore, ibid.*, 365. (Drake trans., 328)
45. *Ibid.*, 291. (Drake trans., 246–247)
46. Max Planck, *Scientific Autobiography and Other Papers*, ed. and trans. F. Gaymor (London: Williams and Norgate, 1950), 33–34
47. Galileo, *Discorso delle comete, Opere di Galileo*, **6**, 56. (Drake trans., 32.) The ancestry of this theory extends at least as far back as Plato: 'We call fire "hot" by noticing the way it acts upon our bodies by dividing and cutting' (*Timaeus* 61d)
48. Postil to G. B. Baliani's letter to Galileo, 8 August 1619, *Opere di Galileo*, **13**, 475
49. Grassi, *Libra, ibid.*, **6**, 161–162. (O'Malley trans., 117)
50. Grassi, *Ratio, ibid.*, 479–480
51. *Ibid.*, 480, postil 137
52. Galileo, *Il Saggiatore, ibid.*, 347–348. (Drake trans., 309)
53. Anton Francesco Doni, *Mondi celesti, terrestri et infernali* (Venice, 1567), 50–51
54. Galileo, *Il Saggiatore, Opere di Galileo*, **6**, 352, 317. (Drake trans., 313, 276)
55. Letter to Dini, 23 March 1615, *ibid.*, **5**, 301. Benedetto Castelli had written to Galileo on 8 May 1612: 'A luminous body is nothing but a body that continuously vibrates and therefore continuously throws out very fast corpuscles' (*ibid.*, **11**, 295). Galileo himself never used this idea of a pulsating source of heat and light
56. Galileo, *Discorsi intorno a due nuove scienze* (Leiden, 1638), *ibid*, **8**, 87–89
57. Andrew van Melsen, *From Atomos to Atom* (New York: Harper, 1960), 66. W. Subow mentions the possible influence of Paduan physicians who by the end of the sixteenth century began to explain contagion in terms of minute particles (W. Subow, 'Zur Geschichte des Kampfes Zwischen dem Atomismus und dem Aristotelismus im 17. Jahrhundert' (*Minima naturalia und Mixtio*, in N. A. Figurowski *et al.*, eds., *Sowjetische Beiträge zur Geschichte der Wissenschaft* [Berlin: VEB Deutscher Verlag der Wissenschaft, 1960], 181–182)
58. Mazzoni refers with approval to Proclus who explained the sensations of warmth and cold by appealing to atoms: '*Proclus ergo pro defensione Platonis scribit ante quatuor elementa qualitatibus activis, et passivis imbuta, posuisse parva quaedam corpuscula regularia, ut indicaret calorem, et frigus pendere ab acumine, et obtusitate angulorum, et a subtilitate, et crassitie laterum. Quodquidem (meo quidem judicio) magna probabilitate dicitur. Et ante Platonem, et Phythagoram fuit etiam a Democrito et Leucippo et Epicuro creditum*' (J. Mazzoni, *In Universam Platonis et Aristotelis Philosophiam Praeludia, sive de Comparatione Platonis et Aristotelis* [Venice, 1597], 189, emphasis mine). It is noteworthy that this kind of atomism is explicitly considered by Mazzoni as a defence of Plato's doctrine
59. For instance, Thomas Aquinas, *Summa Theologiae, prima pars*, qu. 78, art. 3, *ad* 2m. The distinction between proper and common sensibles is already clearly spelled out in Aristotle's *De Anima*, bk. 2, ch. 6, 418a, 8–22
60. Galileo, *Discorsi, Opere di Galileo*, **8**, 72–81

5. THE END OF THE ARISTOTELIAN COSMOS: THE FIRST DAY OF THE *DIALOGUE*

Nicolaus Copernicus' epoch-making *De Revolutionibus Orbium Caelestium* was published in 1543, and when Galileo, some fifty years later, became interested in astronomical problems, the heliocentric theory was no longer a novel idea. It was common knowledge in educated circles that several Humanists had tried to establish the genuine world-picture by returning to the Ancients. They had sought help from Ptolemy, and when he had failed to give them the required assistance, they had taken the next step of examining those notions of Greek astronomy which the Ptolemaic system had replaced. Thus, while Copernicus had returned to Aristarchus, Fracastoro had reverted to Eudoxus and Aristotle, and Tycho Brahe (without explicitly acknowledging it) had revised the views of Heraclides of Pontus. The great astronomical controversy of the sixteenth century was fought by scholars over ideas which they often believed daring and revolutionary but hardly ever original.[1]

Copernicanism, however, became a rallying-cry for those who reacted against the forces of academic conservatism entrenched in the universities. Seeking escape from what they regarded as the trammels of Scholastic Aristotelianism, radical thinkers of the sixteenth century turned eagerly to any theory supporting their desire for innovation. 'Many discussions of Copernicanism', writes Marie Boas Hall,

> are set within the framework of anti-Aristotelianism, and one sometimes gets the impression that the defense of Copernicanism is partly a response to the intellectual delights of novelty and perversity. If one wanted to attack Aristotle in any case, what better way than to upset the cosmological basis of his natural philosophy? This anti-Aristotelianism explains why so many favourable references to Copernicus were made by men who were not astronomers, or even scientists at all, as well as why it is often associated with free thought and the wilder reaches of Lucretian Epicurianism.[2]

Galileo's literary friends, Virginio Cesarini and Giovanni Ciampoli, albeit innocent of any scientific knowledge, embraced the 'new' cosmology as the counterpart of their 'new' poetry.[3] They sang the praises of Copernicanism and recommended it with laudatory metaphors, but they seemed unable to discuss any rational argument in favour of the system they so strongly advocated. We can understand why philosophers, who grappled with the difficult problem of motion, and practical astronomers, who were interested in computing accurate tables, became impatient with the adolescent outcries of the young rebels. All they could see in their protest was the immature and wholly self-conscious revolt of a rising generation against the authority of their elders. They were convinced that in time these young men would come to see the light, especially after they had read Tycho Brahe's *Astronomical Letters* in which the latest Copernican claims had been laid to rest.

Tycho Brahe took care to summarise his arguments in non-technical language, and his work rapidly became a convenient handbook for the non-specialist who wished to quote an expert when attacking an opponent who believed in the motion of the earth. To the difficulties, already recognised by Copernicus, that the heliocentric theory would require Venus and Mercury to show phases like the moon, and the variations in the apparent diameters of Venus and Mars to be vastly greater than observed, Tycho added further objections. First, he argued that the earth's diurnal rotation would entail consequences that clashed with experience; for instance, it would imply that a ball of lead dropped from a high tower would not strike the ground at its foot but some distance to the west, and that a cannon-ball fired eastward would not carry as far as one shot westward. Secondly, he noted that the stars would have to be at least seven hundred times as far from the earth as Saturn is from the sun to account for the absence of stellar parallax. This, in turn, would require stars of the third magnitude, which appear one minute in breadth to the naked eye, to be as large as the orbit of the earth around the sun, a preposterous size in any astronomical system. More damning still were Tycho's own painstaking observations which had revealed that a circular path could not be assigned to the comets in the Copernican universe, and that no annual movement in the apparent positions of the stars due to the motion of the earth round the sun could be detected.

Yet, in spite of these serious difficulties, Galileo embraced Copernicanism. This is easier to understand if we recall that Tycho and Galileo represented not only rival theories, but different psychological—or aesthetic—orientations. Galileo was primarily a theoretical astronomer who made observations and used those of others, but he was far from expecting observational astronomy to provide exact measurements to which they would need to conform. Only men who valued mathematical neatness far more than quantitative accuracy could become convinced and militant Copernicans. The sun-centred universe did not speak to the utilitarian sense of the practising astronomer but to the aesthetic sense of the mathematician, who would be willing to substitute minor celestial harmonies for major terrestrial discord. The numerical predictions based on the new system were scarcely better than the ones known before, and even if they had been more accurate it would still have been possible— and intellectually respectable—to claim that the Copernican hypothesis was merely a computing device. Galileo himself brooded over the problem for several years. In 1597, however, he broke his silence, and in the course of two months wrote two letters professing his allegiance to Copernicanism. What prompted the end of his long reticence was the publication of Jacopo Mazzoni's *In Universam Platonis et Aristotelis Praeludia.*

Mazzoni's Challenge

Jacopo Mazzoni, Galileo's friend and former colleague at the University of Pisa, was an eclectic scholar who sought to reconcile the teachings of Aristotle and Plato. Covering a wide range of subjects, he was led to discuss the motion of the earth which he considered a major threat to the very foundations of Aristotle's doctrine, and to produce what he thought was a new argument against Copernicus. In point of fact, he merely restated the stock objection that the horizon would cut the sphere of stars unequally if the earth was not at the centre of the world, but he buttressed it with an 'observation' culled from Aristotle's *Meteorologica,* where Mount Caucasus is said to be so high that its summit is sunlit for one-third of the night. Mazzoni assumed that this meant that from the top of the Caucasus one could see two-thirds or perhaps even three-quarters of the heavens, and he concluded that at least as much of the stellar sphere would become visible if the earth moved.

Galileo immediately saw a flaw in his friend's reasoning, and he sent him a letter in which he suggested a different interpretation. Assuming, from contemporary tables, 3035 miles as the radius of the earth, 1216 earth-radii as the distance of the sun, and 45225 earth-radii as the distance of the stars, Galileo produced the following argument.

In figure 13, let *BFE* be the sphere of stars, *IC* the diameter of the earth, and *L* a point in space as far from the earth as the sun. Therefore LC = 1216 earth-radii, and BL = 45208 earth-radii (this is the value given by Galileo, the correct value should be 45211).

Join *ICL*, draw *BLE* perpendicular to *ICL*, and *DIH* parallel to *BLE*. Draw *BOA* tangent to circle *IG* at *O*, meeting the extended line *LC* at *A*, the summit of a high mountain. The horizontal plane at *I*, the foot of the mountain, is *DIH*, but an observer at *A* surveys the entire arc *BFE*. Now if the earth moved to *L*, a distance equal to the radius of its orbit around the sun, the horizontal plane *BLE* would cut the same portion of the heavenly sphere, *BFE*. Hence the additional amount of stellar sphere which would become visible if the earth moved around the sun would not be greater than what can be seen from the summit of a high mountain.

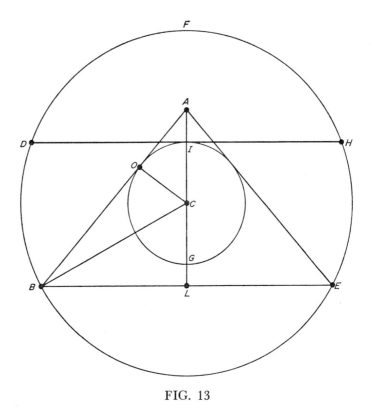

FIG. 13

The next step involves establishing the height of the mountain IA. Since triangles BCL and COA are similar, and the values of BC, BL, and LC, and CI are known, it is a matter of simple geometry to determine that IA is equal to 1.141 miles. Now the additional amount of stellar sphere that is visible from the top of such a mountain is only 1° 32′, a difference that is too small to be detected, at least with the naked eye. Hence Galileo could conclude that the revolution of the earth around the sun would not entail a perceivable difference in the amount of stars visible.[4]

This argument calls for two comments. First, Galileo was preparing the shift from the geocentric to the heliocentric universe by supposing that the line BE, marking the limit of the visible stellar sphere, is tangential to the circle which is the sun's (apparent) orbit around the earth. If we admit this, then Galileo's remaining argument follows as a near enough approximation, but it is clear that his assumption is gratuitous if the geocentric hypothesis is retained. Secondly, Galileo suggested the change from Ptolemaic (earth-centred) to the Copernican (sun-centred) universe, but he failed to work it out. Evidently, as the earth revolved around the sun, the proportion of the stellar sphere seen from the mountain top A would change slightly (but not observably since the radius LC of the orbit is merely $1/38 \times BC$), being sometimes less and sometimes more than the proportion seen in the Ptolemaic version. Alternatively, the height from which the same proportion of the stellar sphere could be seen would vary throughout the year. At this stage, however, Galileo was not concerned with the development of his own theory, and he made no attempts to articulate it in any detail; it was enough that he should be able to 'prove' Mazzoni wrong.

Galileo, along with a large number of his contemporaries, felt that Aristotelian cosmology had ended in a *cul-de-sac* and that it stood no chance of further development. Copernicanism offered an attractive alternative, but as a cosmological system its state was even more hypothetical than the geocentric theory. Before embarking resolutely on the Copernican venture, Galileo needed some assurance that it was worth the risk, and, at that, the risk of a mathematician who prided himself on the explanatory power of geometry. When he realised that he could use mathematics to dismantle the latest argument against the motion of the earth, he gained the necessary confidence to write Kepler a month later that he was a professed Copernican.[5] In this sense, the challenge of Mazzoni's argument may well have played a decisive role in the development of Galileo's ideas about the system of the world. For the time being, however, his commitment to Copernicanism had no special significance. Only fresh evidence could revive the debate of the heliocentric theory, and it was not forthcoming until 1610 when the telescope began to convey messages from the stars.

Evidence from on High

In 1610, Galileo published his *Sidereus Nuncius* in which he revealed the existence of unknown stars, the nature of the Milky Way, the rugged surface of the moon, and the presence of satellites around Jupiter. The striking similarities between the moon and the earth made the already dubious division between the sub-lunary and the celestial worlds even less plausible, and the fact that Jupiter could orbit with a train of four satellites provided Galileo with a reply to those who asked how the earth could rush through space without losing its moon. The telescope continued to bear witness to the truth of Copernicus' vision, and within a few months Galileo was able to verify that Venus had phases, and that the variations of the apparent diameters of Mars and Venus were in agreement with the heliocentric theory. By the end of 1610, the Copernican hypothesis had crossed the threshold of respectability. Even Clavius, the scholarly and prudent astronomer of the Collegio Romano went so far as to commend Galileo's discoveries in no uncertain terms.

But the battle was by no means won. A mere looking-glass could not dispel a theory about the structure of the world. The Aristotelians felt that Galileo would have to focus the eye of his mind on the real problems before he could persuade them to alter their convictions about the nature of the universe.

The opposition was led by Lodovico Colombo or delle Colombe, the witty and acute Florentine, who wrote a short treatise entitled *Against the Motion of the Earth*, which was not published but was widely circulated in manuscript. He acknowledged Galileo's celestial discoveries but tried to trivialise them by suggesting that they merely confirmed what the Peripatetics had always maintained, i.e. that the *novae* generated in the heavens were not 'real' stars of quintessential pedigree. Colombo repeated Tycho Brahe's objections, and his arguments lacked originality. They were representative, however, of the persistent doubts about the Copernican system among educated Florentines, and Galileo took pains to refute them at length in the Second Day of his *Dialogue on the Two World Systems*.

The crucial problem for Colombo and the followers of Aristotle was not whether Copernicanism could save the phenomena as well as the Ptolemaic sytsem. They were agreed that different and even mutually incompatible systems could be devised to account for the motion of planets. But granted that mathematicians could construct several equally satisfactory methods of predicting the course of heavenly bodies, granted in other words, an instrumentalist interpretation of astronomy, they argued that the burden of deciding which system was *true* rested not with astronomers but with natural philosophers. In this perspective, the basic issue became, *Can* the earth move? Does its nature allow or does it preclude the possibility of motion in space? Or, as Colombo put it :

> What architect ever sets out to execute a project elaborated in his mind without first examining the material he intends to use and whether the site is suitable? Philosophers, you must first examine whether the earth is a suitable subject of the Copernican system, and then enquire whether the mathematical constructions are true and do not give rise to inconsistencies.[6]

The debate, therefore, was ostensibly over correct scientific procedure. The Aristotelians objected to the substitution of ideal mathematical models for the empirically given reality; they would not allow abstraction to take precedence over fact. But the imaginative setting or the visual component of the model played a more important part than the logical arguments it purported to illustrate, and Colombo's thought-processes were guided by a vivid picture of the earth at rest in the middle of the universe. For instance, he reasoned that if the earth were not at the centre of the stellar sphere, the stars would appear larger to terrestrial observers on the side closer to the heavens. As Galileo pointed out, the argument presupposed 'the unconscious substitution of the terrestrial globe for the orbit of the earth around the sun'.[7]

Galileo interpreted the observational data on the rival assumption that the earth rotated on its axis and revolved around the sun. But the problem was to reconcile this view with common sense. When Colombo objected that birds would be unable to fly if the earth spinned like a top, Galileo replied that the air would follow the earth. He asserted this as self-evident, but it conflicted with the image of a stationary earth which formed the pictorial background of contemporary thought on astronomical questions. Birds could be 'carried along' by a strong wind in any system, including the Aristotelian, but this was not the 'carrying along' envisaged by Galileo. A more radical change was required : everyday experience had to be drastically reinterpreted. Galileo realised that the physical arguments of his opponents could not be conclusively disproved; at the most, they could be shown to be inconclusive because they were ambivalent and only acquired precise meaning within the context of a given theory. But Galileo also had to learn that whereas he could cope with the kinematics of the situation, the dynamics involved were actually too complex for the conceptual tools at his disposal.

In 1615, Galileo ventured to Rome on a Copernican pilgrimage. He held forth in the houses of several dignitaries, notably in that of Don Laurenzo Magalotti where he met with the opposition of Francesco Ingoli, the founder of the College of the *Propaganda Fide*. When the meeting broke up, Ingoli agreed to set down his objections on paper, and he subsequently forwarded them to Galileo. They were not original nor were they expressed in a particularly fresh or forceful manner, but they were characteristic of the conservative viewpoint prevalent in Rome. Ingoli believed that Scripture told against the heliocentric theory. How could a moving earth, he asked, be reconciled with the miracle of Josuah who stopped the sun or with the traditional location of hell at the centre of the universe? But Ingoli was also anxious to disprove Copernicanism on non-scriptural grounds, and he produced several stock objections of which the following is typical :

If the sun were located at the centre of the world, it would have a greater parallax than the moon. But this consequence is false, and so, therefore, is the premise. That the consequence is really entailed by the premise is clear : the further bodies are from the firmament, the greater their parallax.[8]

Like Colombo before him, Ingoli confused his coordinates and discussed the properties of the Copernican system while retaining a graphic representation of the Ptolemaic universe. Galileo made this clear in his retort :

You stuck to the idea that the earth is located at the centre of the universe, and then you inferred—as a necessary consequence—that because the moon is very close to the earth it is much further from the firmament than the sun . . . When you heard that astronomers observe a greater parallax in the moon than in the sun, you imagined that the cause of the greater parallax was the greater distance from the firmament. This reasoning assumes, however, that the earth, or more precisely the eye of the observer, is at the centre of the firmament. Hence you take for granted that the earth and not the sun is at the centre of the universe. But this is precisely what is in question ![9]

Copernicans and Anti-Copernicans could cite the same arguments, ostensibly based on direct observations and experiments, to demonstrate the validity of their diametrically opposed theses. The crucial factor in the disagreement over how the empirical data should be interpreted was the *a priori* constructions of both parties. Far from being decisive, the variously interpreted experiments merely reflected the already obvious positions of their proponents.

In the second decade of the seventeenth century, therefore, the heliocentric theory was still a lively issue. Unfortunately, the debate came to a halt in 1616 when Copernicus' *De Revolutionibus* was placed on the Index of proscribed books by the Roman authorities. Galileo had practically resigned himself to silence, when, in 1623, Cardinal Maffeo Barberini, a Humanist and a patron of the arts, was elected to the papacy and took the name of Urban VIII. At the suggestion of his friends in the Vatican, Galileo journeyed to Rome in the spring of 1624, and he was received six times by the Pope in the course of six weeks. He failed in his attempt to have the ban on Copernicanism lifted, but he nevertheless derived the impression that he was free to write in support of the heliocentric theory as long as he 'kept out of the sacristy' as Monsignor Piero Dini had advised him. Thus encouraged, he embarked, at the age of sixty, on his epoch-making *Dialogue on the Two World Systems* which he completed in 1630, and saw through the press two years later.

THE FIRST DAY OF THE DIALOGUE

The three interlocutors of the *Dialogue* are the Florentine Filippo Salviati (1583–1614), the Venetian patrician Giovanfrancesco Sagredo (1571–1620), and the Aristotelian Simplicio, an imaginary character. They are presented as having gathered in Sagredo's palace at Venice for four days to discuss the arguments for and against the heliocentric system. Salviati is a militant Copernican, Simplicio an avowed defender of geocentrism, and Sagredo an intelligent amateur already half-converted to the new astronomy.

The First Day belongs to the long history of Anti-Aristotelianism. Galileo, as we might expect, borrowed extensively from his predecessors' criticism of Peripatetic philosophy. What must be considered significant about his attack, however, is the skill with which it was conducted. Never before had any critic of Aristotle been so gifted as a writer, so apt at convincing an opponent by the sheer brilliance of his presentation, and so masterful at laughing him off the stage when he refused to be persuaded. Galileo drew from the literary resources of his native Italian to convey insights and to stimulate reflection, but his style did not possess the bare factualness of the modern laboratory report or the unflinching rigour of a mathematical deduction. Words are more than vehicles of pure thought. They are sensible entities, they possess associations with images, memories and feelings. Galileo knew how to use these associations to attract, hold and absorb attention. He did not present his ideas in the nakedness of abstract thought, but clothed them in the colours of feeling, intending not only to inform and to teach, but to move and to entice to action. He wished to bring about nothing less than a reversal of the 1616 decision against Copernicanism, and the dialogue form seemed to him most conducive to this end. It is true that the written dialogue is deprived of the eloquence of facial expression and the emphasis of gestures, of the support of modulated tone and changing volume, but it retains the effectiveness of pauses, the suggestiveness of questions, and the significance of omissions. Galileo made most of these techniques, and it is important to keep this in mind when assessing his arguments, for too often passages of the *Dialogue* have been paraded without sufficient regard for their highly rhetorical content.

A serious threat to understanding also arises from the vantage point of our more developed knowledge. The consequences of certain laws appear obvious to us, and we naturally expect Galileo to have seen them. Our innate desire for coherence makes us prone to mistake the laws of logic for the laws of thought, and to create a Procrustean bed into which the documents must fit. As all reading involves interpretation, there follows automatically the imposition on texts of meaning and implications that 'logically' they should possess but in fact do not bear. The present writer is sanguine enough to believe that we can guard against this danger, but the conflicting interpretations of Galileo's *Dialogue* are a constant reminder that there is no royal road to Galilean scholarship.

The Critique of Aristotle

In the Aristotelian system, the spherical earth is fixed at the centre of the universe, and surrounding it concentrically are the elemental and heavenly spheres arranged like the skins of an onion. The sphere of the moon divides the universe into two sharply distinct regions, the terrestrial and the celestial. Bodies in the latter are composed of a fifth element or quintessence which is ingenerable and incorruptible and undergoes only one kind of change, uniform motion in a circle. Bodies between the earth and the moon are subject to all kinds of change, and the kind of motion natural to them is rectilinear motion towards their natural place in the sphere of the element of which they are composed. Evidence for this view can be seen in the unconstrained motion of bodies to and from the centre of the earth : in fire which moves straight up or in earth which falls straight down.

In order to replace this *double-tiered* cosmos by the Copernican *uni-verse*, Galileo had to show that Aristotle's analysis was logically inconsistent and void of real empirical foundation. He did this by attacking the apparently natural distinction between rectilinear and circular motions upon which Aristotle rested his case. 'This is the cornerstone, basis and foundation of the entire structure of the Aristotelian universe . . . Now whenever some defect is discovered in the foundations it is reasonable to doubt the soundness of what is built upon them'.[10]

Salviati, Galileo's spokesman, argues that in a well-ordered universe rectilinear motion cannot be natural because what moves in a straight line is not in its proper place when it starts moving, and if it continues to move forever, it will head for an indefinite destination. Circular motion alone preserves the cosmic order by keeping moving bodies in the same relative position. It follows that what does not naturally move in a circle must naturally be at rest. In the new model, natural motion in a straight line loses its privileged status, and after the Second Day, in which Salviati demonstrates that the path of a body falling from a tower is really circular, it vanishes altogether. This is an over-compensation for Aristotle's exaggerated emphasis on the naturalness of rectilinear motion. The triumph of circularity is complete, but it is purchased at the price of excluding the possibility of rectilinear inertia.

Since the immutability and incorruptibility of the heavens was said to result from their perfect motion in a circle, now that all bodies are naturally endowed with circular motion, it follows that

> either the earth itself is ingenerable and incorruptible, like the heavenly bodies, or the heavenly bodies, like the elemental, are generable and alterable; or this difference of motion has nothing to do with generation and corruption.[11]

The Aristotelian Simplicio makes an attempt to save the immutability of the heavens by introducing the hoary argument that circular motion has no contrary, and that corruption presupposes contrary motions. Salviati impatiently brushes this reasoning aside, but Sagredo intervenes to demonstrate that the very notion that the heavens are incorruptible implies that they are subject to corruption. Since celestial bodies are incorruptible, they must have their contraries in nature, and these can only be bodies that possess the opposed quality. But where there is contrariety, corruption is possible. Simplicio protests that this is a sophism : contrariety occurs between elements and not between celestial bodies. Is the contrariety to be found in the body that is corrupted or is it merely a relation? asks Sagredo. Simplicio replies that it is a relation but that it postulates some contact between the bodies. This is impossible in celestial bodies which can influence inferior ones but cannot be influenced by them. Sagredo is undeterred : the opposition of upward and downward motions, he urges, depends on the contrariety of light and heavy, which in turn depends on the contrariety of rarity and density. But rarity and density are found in the heavens where stars are said to be denser parts of the celestial matter. Simplicio has an answer to this one too. Rarity and density on earth depend on the primary qualities of hot and cold, but in the heavens they merely result from the greater or lesser quantity of matter. How does Simplicio know that rarity and density in the heavens do not depend on hot and cold? 'I know this', he replies, 'because those qualities do not exist among celestial bodies'. Sagredo has proved his point : Simplicio 'knows' because he *believes* in the coherence of the Aristotelian system. The implication is that all Scholastic philosophers behave in this fashion.

Simplicio shifts his ground and argues that the heavens are immutable because no change has ever been observed to occur in them. Salviati takes him up on this point. If this naïve empiricism were normative, how could Simplicio, who has only seen Europe, affirm that China and America are subject to change? If the Mediterranean Sea was created, as many maintain, by water rushing in from the Atlantic through the straits of Gibraltar, the flood could have been noticed from the moon. But the earth was obviously subject to generation and corruption before this happened. Hence why should the moon not be equally corruptible even though humanity has failed to record any appreciable change? The *novae* of 1572 and 1604, and the sunspots, Salviati adds, are indisputable evidence that change does occur in the heavens. But Simplicio discounts this last observation with suitable *ad hoc* hypotheses : the occasional rash of spots on the face of the sun, he says, can be explained by starlets or vapours that chanced to cluster between the earth and the sun.

Sagredo interjects that the whole conversation rests on the gratuitous assumption that what is unchangeable is perfect. Very hard metals are called precious because they are rare, but if the earth were one solid frozen mass it would be a useless lump in the universe. Simplicio does not contest that change is a good thing on the earth, but he denies that it would make sense in the heavenly bodies, 'which are ordained to no other use than the service of the earth, and need nothing more than motion and light to achieve their purpose', for 'we plainly see and feel that all generations, changes, etc. that occur on earth are either directly or indirectly designed for the use, comfort and benefit of man . . . Of what use to the human race could generations which might happen on the moon or on other planets ever be'?[12]

In the light of this anthropocentric conception, Simplicio appeals to experience and the principle of economy[13] to support the unchangeable character of the heavens. This can be met either by denying that man is the centre of all things or by postulating the existence of human beings on the moon. Sagredo prefers to disclaim the anthropocentric assumption altogether. Although it is true that we can only imagine what we have already seen or what we can piece together from our past experience, we should not allow ourselves to be fettered by our limited knowledge when thinking on a cosmic scale. 'Thus on the moon, separated from us by such a great distance and perhaps made of a very different material from the earth's, it might be the case that substances exist and actions occur, not merely remote from, but completely beyond our imaginings.' Sagredo compares our speculation about the moon to the kind of intellectual fantasy a person who had never seen a lake or a stream would produce if he were told that animals move without wings or legs in a world made of water. Under such circumstances, it is easier to disprove hypotheses than to confirm them. 'It seems to me that we can determine that some things do not and cannot exist on the moon, but we can only ascertain in a very general way what actually exists or can exist there'.[14]

But if this is the case, how can the hard and impenetrable celestial matter of the Aristotelians be falsified? Galileo recognises that it can only be ridiculed, as in the following witty exchange between Sagredo and Salviati.

    Sagr.   What excellent stuff, the sky, for anyone who could get hold of it for building a palace! So hard, yet so transparent!
    Salv.   Rather, what terrible stuff, being completely invisible because of its extreme transparency. One could not move about the rooms without grave danger of running into the doorposts and breaking one's head.
    Sagr.   There would be no such danger if, as some Peripatetics say, it is intangible; it cannot even be touched, let alone be bumped into.
    Salv.   That would be no comfort, for celestial matter, although it

cannot be touched because it lacks tangible properties, can nevertheless touch elemental bodies, and it would injure us as much, and more, by running into us as it would if we had run into it.

More interesting than Sagredo's and Salviati's devastating satire, is Simplicio's comment : 'The question you have incidentally raised is one of the difficult problems in philosophy'.[15] The question is, of course, perfectly sensible and legitimate in the Aristotelian framework, but it appears ludicrous in the new conceptual scheme. The world must not only be seen through the telescope, it must be looked at through a new set of intellectual categories.

The New World

If the universe is truly one, something can be known about the moon and the planets if they exhibit analogies with events with which we are familiar on earth. On the new Galilean model similarities between the moon and the earth acquire epistemological status. It becomes possible to infer that the moon is spherical, opaque and hard; more important still, that the moon and the earth illuminate each other, thus accounting for the moon's secondary light, a perplexing phenomenon on the Ptolemaic model. It can also be shown that the two bodies eclipse one another, thereby explaining the ruddy hue on the moon's surface during eclipses, an equally vexing problem in the old cosmology.

But is it necessary to go to such extremes, asks Simplicio. Could the new data not be fitted into the old framework by postulating that the moon reflects light because its surface is highly polished, that its secondary light is due to intrinsic luminosity, and that the apparent ruggedness of its surface is caused by the varying density of its parts? Salviati grants that these hypotheses are possible, but they must be tested by deducing the observational consequences they entail, and confronting them with experience. Hence, the analogy between a mirror and the moon must be discarded because the phenomena observed on the moon cannot be reproduced with either flat or spherical mirrors. This can be achieved, however, by rotating a dark ball with prominences and cavities proportional in size to those on the moon.

Out of the countless different appearances that are revealed night after night during one lunation, you could not imitate a single one by fashioning as you please a smooth ball out of more or less opaque and transparent pieces. On the other hand, balls may be made of any solid and opaque material which, merely by having prominences and cavities and by being variously illuminated, will display precisely the scenes and changes that are seen on the moon from one hour to the next.[16]

Models are instruments, and if it is necessary to establish their relevance, it is no less important to determine when they break down. Simplicio brings the issue to the fore by asking Salviati how far he is prepared to extend the parallel between the earth and the moon. Would he be willing to say, for instance, that the large spots on the moon are seas? Salviati replies with a brief lecture on models and analogies :

> If the only way two surfaces could be illuminated by the sun so that one appeared brighter than the other was by having one made of land and the other of water, it would be necessary to say that the moon's surface is partly land and partly water. But because several other ways of producing the same effect are known, and there are perhaps others we are not aware of, I shall not make bold to make such a statement.

Salviati is certain, however, that the darker parts are plains and the brighter ones mountain ranges because 'the boundary which separates the light and the dark part makes an even cut in traversing the spots, whereas in the bright part it looks broken and jagged'.[17]

The model is subject to further limitations. Salviati explains that life on the moon would be unlike anything known to us because of different climatic conditions. First, a lunar day is equal to a terrestrial month, and no earthly plant and animal could survive fifteen days of relentless and scorching heat. Secondly, the seasonal changes, which are considerable on the earth because of a variation of 47° in the rising and setting of the sun, are much less on the moon where the variation is only 10°. Finally, while oceans cover a large part of the terrestrial globe, the moon must be waterless since it has no clouds. Sagredo suggests that this last difficulty might be overcome by postulating storms or great dews during the night. Salviati's reply is again instructive :

> If from other appearances we had any indication that there were species similar to ours there, and that only the occurrence of rain was lacking, we should be able to find something or other to replace it, as the inundations of the Nile do in Egypt. But finding no property whatever that agrees with ours of the many that would be required to produce similar effects, there is no point in troubling ourselves to introduce one only, and even that one, not from sure observation but because of a mere possibility.[18]

In Aristotelian physics, terrestrial models were deemed irrelevant because celestial bodies were said to be composed of a substance entirely different from anything on earth. In Galileo's unified cosmos, analogies from familiar objects can be used to explain features of the moon and the planets, but the limitations of this method are made clear. Galileo's caution seems dictated, not so much by the prudence of the experimentalist, as by the mathematician's conviction that visual models are by themselves insufficient to generate adequate knowledge.

Galileo never questions the existence of 'natural' motion, but it acquires an entirely new significance at his hands. In the biological and teleological paradigm of the Aristotelians, natural motion discloses the basic dichotomy in the universe between the perfect and unalterable heavens and the imperfect and ever-changing earth. In Galileo's new cosmology, natural motion—which can only be circular motion—reveals the fundamental unity of the universe. Galileo assumes that all moving bodies obey the same laws, and that every kind of change, whether substantial or accidental, is merely a reorganisation of matter in motion. On this view, it becomes easier to know the course of the planets in the sky than the nature of generation and corruption on the earth. The underlying assumption is that all bodies move in mathematically describable paths and arrange themselves in geometrical patterns. Simplicio is frankly puzzled by this new kind of reasoning :

> Please put it down to my lack of practice in the mathematical sciences if I say freely that your arguments, based upon greater and lesser proportions and other terms which I do not understand sufficiently well, have not removed my doubt—or rather my incredulity.[19]

How can a ball of lead, he proceeds to ask, go through *all* the degrees of speed when it falls more than a hundred yards in four pulse-beats? Sagredo comes to his aid with an illustration : when a cannon-ball is shot vertically upward it decelerates until it reaches its highest point, and then accelerates again on its way down. But in order to reach the point of zero speed, just before beginning its descent, it must go through all the degrees of speed between its initial velocity and zero. Simplicio is satisfied : 'I can grasp this argument much more easily than the previous mathematical subtleties'. The irony is thinly disguised : for those who fail to grasp the significance of mathematical reasoning, sensible illustrations are mercifully provided.

Salviati stresses that genuine knowledge can only be secured through mathematics. While Aristotle was right in asserting that bodies are three-dimensional, he should have proved this instead of appealing to the consensus of the Pythagoreans and the fitting character of the number three :

> I do not believe that the number three is more perfect for legs than four or two, nor that the number four is imperfect for the elements, and that they would be more perfect if they were three. It would have been better for Aristotle to leave these tropes to rhetoricians and to prove his point with rigorous demonstrations as is required in the demonstrative sciences.

Simplicio expresses surprise and dismay. How can Salviati, a mathematician himself, ridicule the opinion of the Pythagoreans? Simplicio's astonishment serves a dual purpose. First, it discloses the authoritarian frame of mind of the Aristotelian scholar, an intellectual stance Galileo is always eager to expose. Simplicio views disagreements as incidents between warring schools of thought. He thinks, and he assumes that others reason, as the member of a school, as the disciple of some ancient master. Secondly, Simplicio's reaction provides Galileo with the opportunity of distinguishing the Pythagoreanism of the mathematicians from that of the astrologers and the alchemists.

> I know very well that the Pythagoreans held the science of numbers in high esteem, and that Plato himself admired the human intellect and considered it to partake of divinity simply because it understood the nature of numbers. I would not be far from making the same judgement myself. But I do not believe that the mysteries which caused Pythagoras and his school to have such veneration for the science of numbers are the follies that abound in the sayings and the writings of the common man.[20]

This statement, coming at the very outset of the First Day, sets the tone of the *Dialogue*. Galileo rejects the mystical number-juggling of pseudo-science, but he never doubts that the human intellect partakes of divinity because it understands mathematics, the language of nature.

Salviati then demonstrates that bodies can have no more than three dimensions because not more than three lines can be drawn at right-angles to each other (figure 14). Simplicio fails to see the cogency of the argument. He suggests that two other lines could be added by prolonging *AB* and *AD*, and Sagredo has to point out that these extensions would still belong to the same lines. Simplicio lacks the elementary training that would enable him to think rapidly and consistently—a quality that can only be acquired by studying mathematics. 'The art of demonstration is learnt by reading works which contain demonstrations. These are mathematical treatises, not books on logic'.[21]

At the end of the First Day, when the use of mathematics has been vindicated in a variety of ways, Salviati returns to the theme of 'divine' mathematical knowledge. The human mind is restricted in many respects, but it can attain certainty

> in the pure mathematical sciences, that is, geometry and arithmetic, of which the divine intellect indeed knows infinitely more propositions, since it knows them all. But with regard to the few that the human intellect understands, I believe that its knowledge equals the divine in objective certainty, for it succeeds in grasping their necessity.[22]

For God the apprehension of the essence of a thing means the immediate comprehension, without temporal reasoning, of all its infinite implications, but man must work his way from one conclusion to the next. Yet the unity of all things in the mind of God *'is not entirely unknown to the human intellect, but is clouded in deep and thick mist'*.[23] The haze is dispersed when a mathematical proposition is so firmly mastered that it can be run over rapidly and with ease. What the divine intellect perceives in a flash, the mortal mind fits together piece by piece.

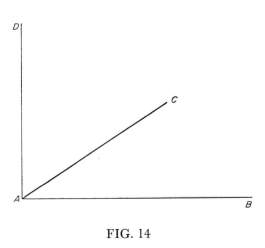

FIG. 14

Galileo owed this view partly to the Platonism which had been popular in Italy, and particularly in Florence, since the fifteenth century. As E. A. Burtt has stressed, the mathematical structure which makes science possible is ultimately grounded in a religious interpretation of the world. 'God by his immediate creative knowledge of nature, thinks into the world that rigorous mathematical necessity which we reach only laboriously through resolutions and demonstrations—God is a geometrician in his creative labours—he makes the world through and through a mathematical system'.[24] It is this basis of his philosophy that made Galileo bold enough to declare in a letter to the Grand Duchess Christina that doubtful passages in Scripture should be interpreted in the light of science rather than the reverse.

It seems to me that in discussing natural problems we should not begin from the authority of scriptural passages, but from sensory experiences and necessary demonstrations. Holy Scripture and nature proceed alike from the divine Word . . . Everything that is said in the Bible is not bound by rules as strict as those which govern natural events, and God

is no less excellently revealed in these than in the sacred pronounce-
ments of Scripture.[25]

Galileo's concept of nature implies a revolution in the very presuppositions of thought about the world. Against the Aristotelians who dismiss
mathematics as irrelevant and futile, he affirms that it is the divine feature
of the human intellect. The implication is clear: for centuries, Aristotelians
have ignored the divine principle in man. Salviati feels that time has
come to investigate the genesis of the real world. This does not mean performing new experiments but pushing for all it is worth a 'mathematical'
theory about the origin of the universe commonly ascribed to Plato.

We have seen that in order to establish a unified cosmos, Galileo
banished straight motion from the privileged category of 'natural' motion
and declared it strictly transitional. It merely serves to return bodies to
their natural place where they spontaneously resume their motion in a
circle. Unless, as Salviati suggests :

> we wish to say with Plato that these cosmic bodies, after their creation
> and their complete constitution, were for a certain time moved in a
> straight line by their Maker, and on reaching certain predetermined
> places, were set in rotation one by one, passing from straight to circular
> motion, in which they maintained themselves and continue to maintain
> themselves. A sublime concept and worthy indeed of Plato, which
> I remember having heard discussed by our friend, the Lincean
> Academician.[26]

Assuming that the globes were all created at the same place and fell
until they reached the speed proper to their orbit when their motion was
converted from rectilinear to circular, the Academician suggested that
their common point of departure could be determined by taking the sizes
of their orbits and their periods of revolution. Assuming that Mars, the
earth, Venus and Mercury also fell from the same place, their orbits and
periods could be calculated and confronted with the observational data
available. Salviati declares that the results 'agree so closely with those
given by computations that the matter is truly wonderful'. Sagredo is
delighted but he suspects that the calculations are long and tedious. 'The
task is indeed long and difficult', says Salviati, 'and I am not sure if I
could reconstruct it off-hand. Therefore we shall keep it for some other
time'.[27]

The calculations were indeed performed by Mersenne in his
Harmonicarum Libri and the conception expounded by Galileo shown
to be false.[28] The planets could not all have started from the same place.
Was this merely a jest, 'un capriccio et una bizzarria, cioè *jocularis
quaedam audacia*', as Galileo described his theory of circular motion to

Pierre Carcavy?[29] This has been suggested by Emil Strauss in his translation of the *Dialogue*, but there can be no doubt that it was a serious speculation (as, moreover, the circular theory probably was) for explaining the structure of the planetary system. First, Galileo not only mentions it twice in the First Day of the *Dialogue*, but he returns to the idea in the Fourth Day of the *Discourses on Two New Sciences*; secondly, he affirms that it is amenable to mathematical treatment; finally, and perhaps more decisively, he attributes this view to the Academician, namely to himself. When Salviati refers to the Academician it is always to stress that he was the first to make a major discovery.

There can be no doubt that Galileo was anxious to link his speculation with the name of Plato. But no-one has been able to find a passage in which Plato describes the cosmological ideas attributed to him.[30] On closer examination, furthermore, it appears that Galileo himself does not affirm that he has simply discovered the Platonic cosmology. Salviati in the *Dialogue* specifically says that he wishes to 'illustrate a Platonic concept' (*per adornare un concetto platonico*), and in the *Discourses*, Sagredo repeats the same expression, '*mi par che convenga adornar questo pensiero dell'Autore con la conformità del concetto di Platone*'.[31] In both works, therefore, we are told that the Academician has adorned, 'that is to say, embellished, developed, leaped to his own conception from the sublime idea of Plato'.[32] Sagredo, who seems so positive in his attribution to Plato of certain characteristic traits of the doctrine, adds that it was presented by Plato only under a mask, as a poetic allegory, and that it is the Academician who has revealed the foundations about which Plato was silent.

> This conception is truly worthy of Plato, and is all the more to be prized now that its underlying principles—about which Plato was silent, and which have been discovered by our Author, who removed from them their mask of their poetic dress—manifest it for what it really is (*lo scuoprono in aspetto di verace istoria*).[33]

If the theory is Galileo's own, why did he present it as Platonic? Was he only amused to cloak an ingenious idea with a prestigious name and to present it as coming from a great philosopher? This hardly agrees with what we know of Galileo's spirit of independence and his strong repudiation of authority in science. If he attributes the conception to Plato it is because he is convinced that at least the germ of the idea is to be found in his writings. More specifically, he is trying to show—and hence the insistence on the computations—that the genuine Platonico-Pythagorean science explains the actual structure of the universe and gives the true history of its origin. Hence also Sagredo's strong assertion in the *Discourses* that the Academician has discovered *la verace istoria* by lifting the poetic veil, by dispelling the mist surrounding human knowledge. Mathematics removes the cloud of unknowing and enables the human mind to ascend to the very threshold of eternity. It is no longer the philosopher but the mathematician who can claim to be a man of vision.

If this interpretation is correct, we are left with another problem : the claim made by Salviati in the *Dialogue,* and repeated by him in the *Discourses* that the Academician worked out the orbits and the periods of the planets by assuming that they all fell from one place. Did Galileo make the calculations or was he merely throwing out a bright mathematical idea? If we look at the context of the discussion in the First Day of the *Dialogue,* we notice that just before recalling the Academician's Platonic speculation, Salviati states, as a law of nature, 'that nature in conferring a definite speed to a body constituted at first at rest, gives it a straight motion through a certain time and space'. Now God, except in the case of miracles, does not break the laws of the world he created. Therefore, adopting the 'platonic' cosmology, namely introducing rectilinear motion prior to circular motion for the planets, results in an economy of supernatural action for God. It is important to stress this fact since from the viewpoint of Newtonian physics, which we naturally adopt, the reverse is true. For Newton the Platonic cosmology produces no gain.[34] Rather it implies two major miracles. First, it involves changing instantaneously the direction of the movement of the falling planets, which is as difficult as conferring instantaneously a determined velocity to a body. Indeed, in the natural order of things it is impossible. Secondly, it implies that the force of attraction of the sun is doubled at the very moment when a circular motion is substituted for a downward one. Neither of these considerations can be said to hold for Galileo. He considers the operation of conferring motion on a body at rest and that of changing its direction as altogether different. In the first case, something new has to be produced, but in the other the change is merely accidental. As to the doubling of the force of attraction, Galileo has no need for it whatsoever, since, first of all, circular motion is inertial and does not engender centrifugal forces, so that no force of attraction from the sun is necessary to make the planets describe their particular orbits and stay in them. Furthermore, Galileo does not work on the assumption that the sun attracts the planets; they move towards the sun by virtue of an inclination which has its origin in their bodies.

In the light of these principles which preclude the possibility of even suspecting the difficulties obvious in Newtonian physics, and in view of Galileo's belief in the explanatory power of mathematics, it seems likely that he did not carry out the calculations he mentions. He probably had no more than a strong hunch, which for him bordered on certainty, that if someone went through the drudgery of working out the paths and the

periods of the planets, he would find that his conjecture was right. Salviati
in the *Dialogue*, and Sagredo in the *Discourses* are pre-empting the fame
of the discovery for the Academician. Galileo's pride matched his genius
in breadth and scope. In both cases, he was only too capable of over-
reaching himself. For how else can we explain his boast that the
Academician 'once made the calculations and found them to correspond
most accurately with the observations', and the assurance with which he
writes : 'Should anyone wish to do likewise, he can by himself satisfy his
curiosity by means of the doctrine of the present treatise'.[35]

NOTES

1. Novelty in the sixteenth century is best summarised in the French proverb,
   reculer pour mieux sauter. Copernicus was usually referred to as the champion
   of the ancient doctrine of the Pythagoreans, for instance, in the title of
   Thomas Digges' astronomical treatise, *A Perfit Description of the Celestial
   Orbes according to the Most Aunciente Doctrine of the Pythagoreans, Lately
   Revived by Copernicus and by Geometrical Demonstration Approved*, pub-
   lished in 1576. Galileo himself extolled the ancestry of Copernicanism: 'No
   one will be able to call it ridiculous, unless he deems ridiculous and stupid
   Pythagoras and all his school, Philolaus, Plato's master, Plato himself (as
   Aristotle says in his book *On the Heavens*), Heraclidus of Pontus and
   Ecphantus, Aristarchus of Samus, Nicetas, and the mathematician Seleucus'
   (*Consideration on the Copernican Hypothesis* (1616), *Opere di Galileo*, **5**, 352)
2. Marie Boas Hall, *The Scientific Renaissance 1450–1630* (London: Collins,
   1963), 96–97
3. Virginio Cesarini compared Giovanni Ciampoli's 'new' poetry to Galileo's
   'new' astronomy: 'you will deign to entertain the suggestion that just as you
   found many faults in Ptolemy, so others perhaps have detected imperfections
   in the Tuscan poets who have written thus far' (letter to Galileo, 1 October
   1618, *Opere di Galileo*, **12**, 415)
4. Letter to Jacopo Mazzoni, 30 May 1597, *ibid.*, **2**, 197–202
5. Letter to Kepler, 4 August 1597, *ibid.*, **10**, 68
6. Lodovico Colombo, *Contro il moto della terra* (1610), *ibid.*, **3**, 255
7. *Ibid.*, 282, postil 36
8. Francesco Ingoli, *De situ et quiete terrae contra Copernici systema*, *ibid.*,
   5, 404
9. Letter to Francesco Ingoli (1624), *ibid.*, **6**, 516–517
10. Galileo, *Dialogo sopra i due massimi sistemi del mondo tolemaico e coper-
    nicano* (Florence, 1632), *ibid.*, **7**, 42. In the English translation by Stillman
    Drake, *Dialogue Concerning the Two Chief World Systems* (Berkeley and
    Los Angeles: University of California Press, 1962), 18; in the Thomas
    Salusbury translation revised by Giorgio de Santillana, *Dialogue on the Great
    World Systems* (Chicago: The University of Chicago Press, 1953), 22
11. *Ibid.*, 63. (Drake trans., 39, Salusbury trans., 47)
12. *Ibid.*, 84–85. (Drake trans., 59–61; Salusbury trans., 70–71)
13. '*Natura nihil frustra facit*' says Simplicio (*ibid.*, 85; Drake trans., 60;
    Salusbury trans., 71). Galileo poked fun at the bookish knowledge of the
    Aristotelians by having Simplicio use Latin works and phrases, a practice
    avoided by the other two interlocutors. When Salviati uses an Aristotelian
    axiom to his own advantage, he quotes or paraphrases it in Italian
14. *Ibid.*, 86. (Drake trans., 61–62; Salusbury trans., 72)

15. *Ibid.*, 94. (Drake trans., 69; Salusbury trans., 80)
16. *Ibid.*, 111–112. (Drake trans., 86; Salusbury trans., 97)
17. *Ibid.*, 124–125. (Drake trans., 99; Salusbury trans., 110–111)
18. *Ibid.*, 126. (Drake trans., 101; Salusbury trans., 112)
19. *Ibid.*, 54. (Drake trans., 30.) This passage was added by Galileo in his copy of the *Dialogue*, and is omitted in the Salusbury translation
20. *Ibid.*, 35. (Drake trans., 11; Salusbury trans., 14–15)
21. *Ibid.*, 60. (Drake trans., 35; Salusbury trans., 43)
22. *Ibid.*, 128–129. (Drake trans., 103; Salusbury trans., 114)
23. *Ibid.*, 129, italics mine. (Drake trans., 104; Salusbury trans., 115)
24. E. A. Burtt, *The Metaphysical Foundations of Modern Physical Science*, 2nd ed. rev. (London: Routledge and Kegan Paul, 1964), 71–72
25. Galileo, *Lettera a Madama Christina di Lorena* (1615), *Opere di Galileo*, **5**, 316–317
26. Galileo, *Dialogo, ibid.* (Drake trans., 20; Salusbury trans., 25)
27. *Ibid.*, 54. (Drake trans., 29–30; Salusbury trans., 36)
28. Marin Marsenne, *Harmonicarum Libri* (Paris, 1636), t.I, Praefatio, prop., 2 (not paginated) where he refers to the detailed calculations in his *Harmonie Universelle*, Seconde Partie, Traitez de la nature des sons, et des mouvements de toutes sortes de corps (Paris: Pierre Baillard, 1637), 103–107
29. Letter to Pierre Carcavy, *Opere di Galileo*, **17**, 89
30. 'However sublime it may be, the theory in question is not in Plato' (Alexandre Koyré, *Newtonian Studies* [London: Chapman and Hall, 1965], 218). The passage in the *Timaeus* 38–39 bears only a remote analogy to what Galileo is asserting. Neither can the text 30a discussed by Aristotle (*On the Heavens*, bk. 3, ch. 2, 300b 16) be said to be more closely related. Marin Mersenne wrote to Niccolò Fabri de Peiresc on 4 December 1634 asking him to inquire from Gassendi or someone else where Plato stated what Galileo attributed to him (Cornelis de Waard, ed., *Correspondence du P. Marin Mersenne*, **4** [Paris: Vrin, 1955], 403–404). Peiresc replied on 19 December 1634 that Gassendi 'n'a pas de souvenance d'en avoir rien leu dans le texte mesmes de Platon, lorsqu'il en a fait la lecture de bout à aultre de toutes les pièces qui s'en trouvent assemblées en un corps, et faut que ce soit dans quelque aultre autheur ancien qui l'aye veu en d'aultres oeuvres de Platon de celles qui ne se trouvent plus, dont il faudra faire la recherche plus à loysir' (*ibid.*, 415)
31. Galileo, *Dialogo, Opere di Galileo*, **7**, 53; *idem, Discorsi, ibid.*, **8**, 283
32. Koyré, *Newtonian Studies*, 219
33. Galileo, *Discorsi, Opere di Galileo*, **8**, 284
34. For the following discussion, see Koyré, *Newtonian Studies*, 215–220
35. Galileo, *Discorsi, Opere di Galileo*, **8**, 284

6. THE WORLD IN MOTION: THE SECOND AND THIRD DAYS OF THE *DIALOGUE*

The First Day of the *Dialogue* ruined the Aristotelian dichotomy between celestial and terrestrial bodies and established that heaven and earth belong to the same cosmic system. The next logical step is to ask whether the earth moves, and the remaining three days of the *Dialogue* are devoted to this problem. The daily rotation of the earth is discussed in the Second Day and its annual revolution around the sun in the Third. The Fourth Day attempts to show that it is only when these motions are acknowledged that the phenomenon of the tides can be adequately explained.

THE DIURNAL MOTION OF THE EARTH

The Classical Objections

The Second Day opens with the affirmation that the motion of the earth, if it exists, must be altogether imperceptible to its inhabitants. Consequently, opinion turns on what is more plausible, and Salviati, speaking for Galileo, argues that it is easier to believe that the earth rotates on its axis than that all the planets and the stars revolve around the earth.

> Who is going to believe that nature (which by general agreement does not perform by means of many things what it can do by a few) has chosen to make an immense number of very huge bodies move with incalculable speed, to achieve what could have been done by a moderate movement of one single body around its own centre?[1]

The diurnal motion of the earth would do away with a host of complexities in the geocentric system. First, it would remove the anomaly of a heavenly sphere of stars moving westward when all the planets move eastward. Secondly, it would explain the apparent variations in the orbits and periods of the stars, and, finally, it would dispense with the solid crystalline spheres that carry the stars around in the Ptolemaic system.

Salviati is eager that Simplicio should recognise that simplicity is the regulative principle that guides him in the interpretation of astronomical data. Simplicio complies : 'It seems to me that you base your case on the greater ease and simplicity in producing the same effects'.[2] But he does not query the general principle; rather he argues that it is more fitting that God, who is omnipotent, should display the infinite variety of his power in creating the world. There is no disagreement about the principle of simplicity itself; the difficulty arises entirely over its application.

In the ensuing debate, the 'classical' objections against the axial rotation of the earth are rehearsed : a stone dropped from a tower would not strike the ground at its base but some distance to the west; cannon-balls fired to the west would carry further than those fired to the east; a great wind would be felt constantly from the east; and the centrifugal force of the rotating earth would fling houses and trees into the air.

Salviati points out that these stock arguments rest on the same fallacy :

> The error of Aristotle, of Ptolemy, of Tycho and of all the others, is rooted in a fixed and inveterate impression that the earth stands still. You cannot or you do not know how to cast it off, even when you wish to speculate about what would follow if the earth moved.[3]

The motion of a stationary earth is so firmly imbedded in the imagination of the Aristotelians that when they hear that it moves they 'foolishly assume that it started moving when Pythagoras (or whoever it was) first said that it moved'.[4] The correct and indispensable procedure is to replace the Ptolemaic frame of reference by the Copernican. 'Anyone who does this', says Sagredo, 'will discern without any trouble the fallacy and the equivocation that make the arguments appear conclusive'.[5]

The difficulty of reasoning independently of a familiar picture is actually greater than Galileo realises. Cesare Marsili, one of his staunchest supporters, found himself trapped in the traditional graphic representation of the world when he concluded that the periods of the moon would be unequal if the earth moved around the sun. He reasoned (figure 15) that the moon completed one revolution when it reached *h* and not *l* from which it had started.[6] The error lies in supposing that the length of the period of the moon's revolution around the earth is affected by the earth's position relative to the sun.

Simplicio, however, will not have it that the immobility of the earth is not supported by empirical evidence. He appeals to the case of a stone dropped from the mast of a moving ship which, he contends, falls as far from the foot of the mast as the ship has progressed during the fall. Salviati first grants the alleged result, but he has second thoughts and asks Simplicio whether he has witnessed the experiment. When Simplicio admits that he has not, Salviati displays no eagerness to perform it himself; rather he proceeds by Socratic cross-examination to make Simplicio discover what the outcome of the experiment *must* be. The method is

circuitous and is characteristic of Galileo's technique throughout the
Dialogue. Simplicio is first interrogated on the motion of a perfectly
round ball on a perfectly smooth surface. 'Now tell me', asks Salviati,
'what do you consider to be the cause of a ball moving spontaneously on
a downward inclined plane but only by force on one tilted upward?'
Simplicio replies : 'Because heavy bodies have a tendency to move toward
the centre of the earth, and to move upward toward the circumference

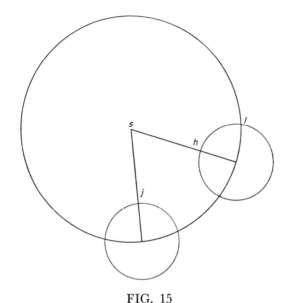

FIG. 15

only by force'.[7] It follows that a ball placed on a plane surface has neither
a tendency to move nor a reluctance to be moved, and that if it is set in
motion it will neither accelerate nor decelerate, but will continue to move
indefinitely at the same speed. Such, for instance, would be the state of
a ship given an impetus on a tranquil sea. It would move at a uniform
speed, and everything on board would share its motion. A stone dropped
from its mast would continue to move with the motion impressed upon
it and would strike the deck at the same place where it would have fallen
if the ship had been at rest.

Simplicio balks at the conclusion not because it clashes with experience
but because it is absurd in the context of his natural philosophy. It would
imply that motion is impressed in the projectile, something, he says, 'as
detestable in the Peripatetic philosophy as the transfer of an accidental
property from one subject to another'.[8] In order to avoid this objec-
tionable inference, conservative Aristotelians maintained that projectiles

were moved by the surrounding medium, usually the air. Salviati makes short shift of this theory by pointing out that a pendulum oscillates for a longer period of time with a heavy bob than with a light one. This would be impossible if it were impelled by air with does not move a heavy object with greater ease than a light one. The motion is impressed in the bob, as it impressed in the stone dropped from the mast of a moving ship.

Salviati attempts to determine in greater detail the path of a freely falling body with the aid of figure 16, where *BI* is the surface of the earth,

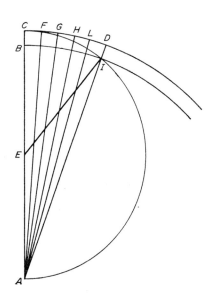

FIG. 16

and *BC* the height of a tower which is carried along by the earth and marks out with its top the arc *CD*. Assuming that the acceleration is constant and that the line of compound motion must terminate at the centre of the earth, Salviati uses *E*, the mid-point of *CA* as centre, and the length of *EC* as radius to draw the semicircle *CIA*, 'along which I think it most probable that a stone dropped from the top of the tower would move'.

The very slow speed of fall at the beginning, the constant acceleration and the tendency toward the centre of the earth are clear from the diagram. Further analysis reveals three more surprising features. First, the stone always follows a circular path whether it is at rest or in motion. This confirms the arguments of the First Day against the Aristotelian theory that rectilinear motion is a natural property of heavy bodies. Secondly, the distance travelled by the stone in falling is equal to the one it would have traversed if it had remained on top of the tower, because the arcs *CF*, *FG*, *GH*, *HL* and *LD* are equal. Thirdly, the true motion of the stone is not accelerated but uniform since all the arcs marked on the circumference are passed over in equal times. Sagredo is delighted and exclaims : 'If only the demonstrations of the philosophers had half the probability of this one !', but Salviati remains cautious : 'I do not wish to declare at present that the descent of heavy bodies takes place in exactly this way, but if the line described by a falling body is not exactly this one, it is very near to it'.[9]

As a matter of fact, Galileo overreached himself. The path of the projectile was discussed by Fermat whose criticism was forwarded to Galileo by Pierre Carcavy in 1637. Galileo, who by this time—perhaps with the help of Bonaventura Cavalieri—had deduced the correct parabolic path for projectiles, sought to dismiss his explanation as a jest.

> Although it was said in the *Dialogue* that the mixture of the straight motion of the falling body and the uniform motion of the diurnal motion would perhaps give rise to a semicircle that ended in the centre of the earth, this was said as a jest, as is clearly manifest, since it is called a caprice and a curiosity, that is *jocularis quaedam audacia*. I wish therefore to be excused especially since this poetic fiction carries with it three unexpected consequences.[10]

Galileo tried to convert his recantation into an apology, but it is almost certain that his speculation in the *Dialogue* is intended to be taken seriously. Otherwise, he would be poking fun at mathematicians, a privilege he reserves strictly for philosophers. In his eagerness to find further testimony against the Aristotelian antithesis between circular–celestial and rectilinear–terrestrial displacements, he welcomes circular motion wherever it can be found. But the theory has another advantage : it dispenses with the necessity of explaining acceleration since the absolute velocity of a body falling along the path Galileo describes is uniform. The acceleration relative to the earth's surface becomes merely apparent and can be visualised as the product of the uniform movement of observer and object along intersecting circular paths.

Another classical objection to the motion of the earth is that shots to the west would have a greater range than shots to the east. Salviati recognises the need for a testable model, and Sagredo suggests mounting a crossbow on an open carriage and shooting an arrow in the direction of the carriage's motion and then against it. If the arrow travels a distance of 300 yards while the carriage covers 100 yards, what happens when the arrow is shot from the carriage? Simplicio immediately replies that it will travel 200 yards in the direction of motion and 400 yards in the opposite direction. He grants Salviati that the distances could be equalised if the strength of the crossbow were increased in the first case and reduced in the second. Salviati points out that this is in fact what happens since the crossbow shares the motion of the carriage. In the direction of motion the arrow is given an impetus of 400 yards, and in the opposite direction it receives one of only 200 yards. Since the carriage moves 100 yards during the time of the arrow's flight, the distances are equalised. The same holds for shots fired from a moving earth : regardless of the direction in which they are aimed they will fall at the same distance from the mouth of the cannon.

Vertical shots can be interpreted in the same way. Assuming that the earth moves, it is true that a cannon-ball shot straight upward moves along a slanted line, but the cannon from which it is fired travels with it along the same horizontal distance. This can be illustrated (figure 17)

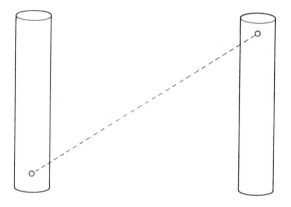

FIG. 17

even for the brief period the ball moves up the barrel. Galileo clearly recognises that the vertical and the horizontal motions are two independent components and he treats them as such. This represents a major conceptual advance; it was failure to grasp this principle that hampered Colombo and led him to believe that the impulse from the gunpowder would have to be added to that of the earth's rotation.

The problem of the flight of birds who would be unable to return to their nest because of a terrific east wind would seem to demand no additional explanation, and the modern reader is somewhat surprised to see the emphasis laid on it in the *Dialogue*. It must be remembered that it was a major difficulty for Galileo's contemporaries, and that it had once caused him some embarrassment. The solution, of course, is to affirm that air partakes of the earth's motion. The flight of birds is compared to the unimpaired motion of fishes in a bowl of water which is carried from one room to another. Salviati mentions that experiments performed in an enclosed cabin cannot establish whether the ship is stationary or moving at a uniform speed, and Sagredo says that he often wondered in his cabin whether the ship was moving, and that he sometimes thought they were going in the opposite direction. The surface of the rotating earth, however, is not like an enclosed cabin, but rather like an open deck when a strong gale is blowing. Salviati is not unaware of the problem, and he suggests that the air is carried between the mountains that cover the earth. He also produces an interesting analogy : 'For a similar reason, when riding horseback we sometimes see persistent flies and horseflies following the horse, flying now to one and now to another part of its body'.[11] The comparison is helpful, but it can hardly pass muster for a physical explanation. Simplicio can still argue that if the earth were spinning like a top at more than a thousand miles-per-hour, the trees and the houses, the cities and the seas would be flung into outer space like pieces of clay from a potter's wheel.

Salviati attemps to solve this difficulty by analysing the relationship between 'natural tendency' and 'natural resistance' in terms of the lever. If the sole internal resistance to motion was weight, we could not explain how a small body can move a heavier one on the steelyard. This is only possible if we acknowledge that the lighter body possesses, along with weight, the quality of speed. 'Fix it well in your mind as a true and well-known principle that the resistance coming from the speed of motion compensates that which depends upon the weight of another body'.[12] With this principle Salviati believes he can demonstrate that enlarging the circumference of a rotating body does not automatically lead to an increase in its power of extrusion.

Let two unequal wheels have A as centre, BG being on the circumference of the smaller, and CEH on that of the larger (figure 18). If the forces required to maintain the stone on the large circle and on the small one are measured by the secant ED (or by the perpendicular dropped from E), and the secant GF (or the perpendicular dropped from G on BF), then because GF is greater than DE a greater force will be required to hold the stone on the small wheel than on the large one. 'Thus it is obvious that as the wheel becomes larger, the cause for projection is diminished'.[13]

The conclusion is true, but the proof is mistaken for two reasons. First, centripetal acceleration is determined by the angles CAE and CAG, and not by the lines GF and ED. Secondly, the centrifugal force does not vary with the linear velocity, as Galileo's reasoning implies, but with its square. Galileo, however, does not invoke centrifugal and centripetal forces but only the stone's weight (i.e. its tendency to fall towards the centre of the earth), and it appears reasonable to him to assume that the force acting from within the stone is measured by *ED* and *GF*.

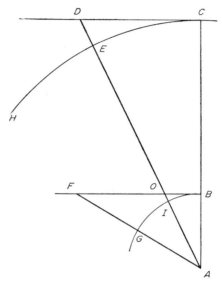

FIG. 18

The New Approach

Galileo recognises that to expect some extraordinary physical phenomenon to confirm the earth's diurnal motion is to prejudice the outcome in favour of Ptolemy. If the earth moved, its inhabitants would share its uniform motion and it will remain imperceptible to them. The correct strategy is to call upon the heavens, to seek a motion common to all celestial bodies, and then to ask—in the light of the principle of simplicity —whether this motion could not be explained more profitably by postulating that the earth itself moves.

This reference to simplicity as a criterion by which to judge cosmological systems is an indication of Galileo's intellectual stance. It reveals a larger and deeper commitment to an aesthetic view of nature in which perfect shapes enjoy a privileged status. 'The spherical shape', Salviati declares,

is the easiest and the simplest. It holds among solid figures the place occupied by the circle among surfaces. For the description of the circle, since it is the easiest of all, has alone been considered worthy by mathematicians to be placed among the postulates underlying the description of all other shapes.[14]

Galileo's artistic imagination as well as his scientific thought was dominated by a classical ideal of order and simplicity. This is evident from his praise of Ariosto and his objections to Tasso, and it probably explains why he gave no consideration to the elliptical paths of Kepler's planets.

The aesthetic approach conveniently by-passes the practical problems of dynamics. Because circular motion is natural (i.e. because it is an ultimate explanatory category), Galileo does not need a force acting on the planets to keep them orbiting. In the *Dialogue*, he can afford to remain agnostic about the principle of motion acting in or on bodies. When Simplicio declares : 'The cause of this effect is well known; everyone is aware that it is gravity [i.e. weight, not gravitational force]', Salviati declares :

> You are wrong, Simplicio; what you ought to say is that everyone knows that it is called gravity. What I am asking you for is not the name of the thing but its essence, of which you know not a bit more than you know about the essence of whatever moves the stars around, except the name which has been attached to it, and which has been made a familiar household word by the continual experience that we have of it daily. But we do not really understand what principle or what force moves stones downward, any more than we understand what moves them upward after they leave the thrower's hand, or what moves the moon around. We have merely, as I said, assigned to the first the more specific and definite name *gravity*, whereas to the second we assign the more general term *impressed* virtue, and to the last-named we give *intelligence,* either *assisting* or *inherent*, and as the cause of infinite other motions we give nature.[15]

The disagreement between Salviati and Simplicio is not merely about the nature of gravity, it is about the kind of question that is relevant in natural philosophy. When Simplicio goes on to say that even if gravity is imperfectly understood, it is still possible to determine whether it is intrinsic or extrinsic to falling bodies because rectilinear downward motion is natural to them, Salviati protests vigorously. The Aristotelian dichotomy between natural and violent motion is not only wrong but it creates a frame of reference that stultifies any meaningful discussion of the properties of motion. Salviati argues that upward and downward motion are equally natural because they are reversible, as is instanced by a pendulum which exchanges its downward motion for an upward motion every time it reaches its lowest point of descent. Simplicio does not query the evidence, but he equates the abandonment of the antithesis between natural and violent motion with conceptual chaos : 'If bodies did not have their special motions and operations which reveal their substances to us, we would have no way of understanding and distinguishing their natures'.[16]

The Aristotelians presupposed that the nature of a body was disclosed by its motion, which was apprehended by the senses. Hence a physical theory could never call in question the immediate data of perception. Galileo starts from diametrically opposed premises, namely that the nature of physical reality is not revealed by mere sensory perception but by reason, and that motion as such does not affect the body itself but only its spatial relations to other objects. The metaphysical barrier which precluded the presence of two 'natural' motions in one body turns out to be no more than a mental block.

Galileo is intent on illustrating that the Peripatetic cloud of unknowing is dispelled by mathematics. When Simplicio states that buildings would be flung into space if the earth rotated on its axis, Salviati asks him to state his case quantitatively. Simplicio complies and suggests that if the motion along the tangent to the terrestrial globe were a million times faster than the acceleration caused by gravity, bodies on the surface of the earth would be extruded. 'Saying this, you say what is false', replies Salviati, 'not from any deficiency in logic or physics or metaphysics, but in geometry'. If Simplicio grasped 'the first principles' of this science, he would realise that the weight of a body can never be sufficiently reduced, or its proximity to its point of departure sufficiently increased, for it to be projected from the surface of the earth.[17] Examining the line of contact, it appeared to Galileo that as the tangent along which the body would be projected approximates more and more closely to the circle in which it moves, the ratio between the length of the tangent and that of the secant grows greater and greater. For instance, in figure 19, however great the force acting along the tangent *AB*, it can never move the body since only a minute retaining force is required to pull it back along the much smaller distance of the secant *BC*. This interpretation, however ingenious, is defective, since the centrifugal force increases with the square of the velocity, and if the earth moved fast enough bodies would be projected into space. Galileo's analysis leads to a paradox which seems to have escaped him : if his theory were correct it would prevent a stone leaving a sling if the least force held it back.

Galileo may have been misled by a model mentioned by Sagredo : 'Thus it might be supposed that the whirling of the earth would no more suffice to throw off stones than would any small wheel which rotated so slowly as to make but one revolution every twenty-four hours'.[18] Failing to appreciate the true cause of acceleration, and the fact that centrifugal

forces increase with the radius when the *angular* velocity is constant,
Galileo does not perceive that the model of a small revolving wheel is
inadequate. Furthermore, his reasoning is dominated by the conviction
that bodies are endowed with a tendency to rotate around the centre of
the earth once every twenty-four hours. This explains why he compares not
forces but the lengths of lines as though a kinematical approach were fully

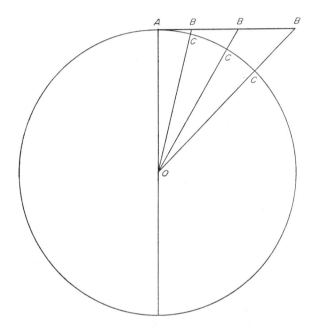

FIG. 19

adequate. The dynamics of the situation could only be handled by cal-
culating the centrifugal force arising from the earth's spin and comparing
it with the force of gravity. But this kind of explanation presupposes the
discoveries of Huygens and Newton which were only to come half a
century later. It should be noted, however, that the stone in the sling is
a convenient device for Galileo, rather than a means of experiment. As
Salviati explains, it is 'merely a rough example to arouse our minds to
investigate more accurately whether the cause of projection increases in
the same ratio as the speed'.[19] What is important is not so much the
outcome of Galileo's proof as the claims he makes for the explanatory
power of mathematics. Salviati's words : 'Take note, Simplicio, just how
far one may go without geometry and philosophise about nature', are

echoed by Sagredo : 'The argument is as convincing as it is subtle, and it must be admitted that trying to deal with physical problems without geometry is attempting the impossible'.[20]

A methodological clash occurs again in the Second Day, this time over the properties of falling bodies. The Aristotelians were content to speak of acceleration in purely qualitative terms. A body falls faster and faster, says Simplicio, 'for such is the nature of heavy bodies, which *vires acquirunt eundo*'.[21] Salviati spurns this vague knowledge as useless, and he urges a determination of the ratio according to which the increase in speed takes place. Simplicio finds this philosophically uninteresting :

> As far as the natural philosopher is concerned, I do not believe that it is necessary to get down to minute details. A general knowledge of the definition of motion and of the distinction between natural and constrained motions, uniform and accelerated motions, and the like, is sufficient.[22]

In another context, he had reminded Salviati that 'philosophers busy themselves principally about universals. They investigate the definitions and the more general properties, leaving certain details and subtleties— which are rather curiosities—to the mathematicians'. Aristotle himself 'left to mechanics and other low artisans the investigation of the ratios and other secondary features of acceleration'.[23]

Salviati sees in this disparagement of mathematics the cause of the conceptual blunder that led Aristotle to affirm that the speed of falling bodies is proportional to their weight, a notion that entails ridiculous consequences. For instance, if a hundred-pound ball and a one-pound ball of the same material were dropped at the same moment from a height of one hundred yards, the heavier one should reach the ground before the lighter one covered more than a single yard ! The proper method is to use a model, such as the pendulum, to determine the mathematical relationships that govern free fall. In an oscillating pendulum, the increasing velocity of the bob as it comes down the arc is followed by a decreasing velocity as it goes up the other side. As the increase and the decrease are in the same ratio, this suggests that a body moving uniformly at the velocity acquired when it reaches its maximum speed would pass over twice the distance it went through when it fell with constant acceleration from an initial state of rest in an equal amount of time.

Antonio Rocco reacted vigorously in his *Esercitazioni Filosofiche* to Galileo's criticism of Aristotle's theory of free fall. He alleged that the time bodies fell was too short for sensory discrimination, and he likened the phenomenon to the movement of the hands of a watch which is inferred but cannot be perceived. In his reply, Galileo mentions two experiments that disprove the anticipations of crude empiricism. First, a ball weighing one hundred pounds can be shown to fall from a height of one hundred yards in the time a man walks five or six paces. Hence, if Aristotle were right, one would expect a ball of one pound dropped from the same height to reach the ground only after five or six hundred paces had been covered. The outcome, of course, more than belies the theory. Secondly, hearing allows a fine discrimination between the times bodies fall. If two pebbles are released simultaneously, one from a height of one yard, and the other from a height of one and a half yards, the noise of the first one striking the floor can be distinctly heard before the second one.[24]

The confrontation reaches its climax when Salviati presses on to elucidate the nature of mathematics, and taunts Simplicio, 'although I do not believe that he is one of those Peripatetics who discourage their disciples from the study of mathematics as something that corrupts the understanding and renders it less fit for contemplation'. Simplicio's reply raises the discussion to a full-fledged debate between the Platonic and the Aristotelian conception of knowledge :

> I should be doing Plato an injustice. However, I would agree with Aristotle that he plunged too deeply into geometry and became too fascinated by it. After all, Salviati, mathematical subtleties may do very well in the abstract, but they do not work when applied to sensible and physical matters. For instance, mathematicians may prove well enough in theory that *sphaera tangit planum in punto*, a proposition similar to the one at hand, but when it comes to practical application, things happen otherwise.

Salviati's rejoinder is a vindication of mathematical realism :

> I should not like to leave you in that other error of thinking that a material sphere does not touch a plane in a single point alone, and I should hope that a conversation of only a few hours with persons who have some knowledge of geometry will make you appear a little more informed among those completely ignorant of it.[25]

Simplicio advocates an ontological 'looseness of fit' between abstract forms and concrete material realisations : 'I think that the proposition put forward by the philosophers is to be taken in that sense, for there can be no doubt that it is the imperfection of matter which prevents things taken concretely from corresponding to those considered in the abstract'. Salviati will have none of this. A perfect material sphere, he insists, would have the same properties as an ideal one, and it would touch a plane surface at one point only. Discrepancies are due entirely to errors of computation.

> Do you know what happens, Simplicio? Just as the accountant who wants to apply his calculations to sugar, silk and wool must discount

the boxes, bales and other packings, so the mathematical scientist [filosofo geometra] when he wants to recognise in the concrete the effects which he has proved in the abstract, must deduct the material hindrances, and, if he knows how to do so, I assure you that things are in no less agreement than arithmetical computations. The errors, then, lie not in the abstractness or concreteness, nor in geometry or physics, but in the man who counts and does not know how to make his sums properly.[26]

Antonio Rocco sought to defend the traditional Aristotelian position by accusing Galileo of contradiction. If it were true that a sphere touched a plane in one point, a line could be made up of points. But this is absurd because points are indivisible while lines can be divided. Galileo attached some importance to this question, and he wrote in his copy of Rocco's book a lengthy postil, which he later extended into a note for eventual publication. Galileo's solution is to swallow the apparent paradox, that is, he affirms that a line is divisible although it is composed of indivisible points. If division can go on indefinitely, he reasons, the number of parts must be infinite. But if the number of parts are infinite, they cannot be extended since an infinite number of extended parts would result in an infinitely extended body while the extensions considered are finite. Therefore, the ultimate parts of a continuum are necessarily indivisible. Or to put it in slightly different terms : if the continuum is composed of divisible parts, division can never extend to the first components. Hence, the first components must no longer be divisible and these are points.

Galileo is aware that the Aristotelians, who discuss the problem in terms of act and potency, assert that the number of divisible parts in the continuum are actually finite but potentially infinite. He considers this distinction meaningless, but he is willing to use it to defeat his opponents on their own ground. If they can 'actualise' a finite number of parts, he can 'actualise' an infinite number of points merely by folding a line repeatedly, first to give it the shape of a polygon with a large number of sides, and, finally, the shape of a circle, a polygon of infinite sides. When this circle is rotated on a plane surface it will trace out a line composed of the infinite number of its points. Galileo does not pursue this idea, but concludes with a promise of greater mathematical things to come, and a jeer at the conceptual tools of the Peripatetics :

You will hear other admirable consequences on some other occasion, when I hope to prove that the way commonly followed to understand the workings of nature, which banishes the concept of infinity, indivisibility and the void as superfluous, useless and dangerous, leads philosophers to the intended goal as surely as a painter or a carpenter would put his apprentice on the right path by teaching him to cast aside paint and brushes, or hammer, file and anvil as useless, indeed as dangerous materials and instruments for their trades.[27]

What was particularly offensive to the Aristotelians in this passage was the key-importance assigned to concepts that have no empirical counter-part. Simplicio's attitude throughout the Second Day is that of the indig-nant empiricist who is challenged for the first time on the solid ground of common sense. He is convinced that the senses of sight and touch would be invalidated if the earth moved since bodies are *seen* to fall in a straight line, and the earth is *felt* to be at rest. When Salviati asks him how the path of falling bodies should be investigated, he answers : 'By means of the senses which assure us that the tower is straight and per-pendicular, and that a falling stone grazes it.' Further on, he expostulates : 'But, good heavens, if it moves along a slant why do I see it falling straight down? This is a bald denial of manifest sense, and if the senses are not to be believed, by what other door shall we enter into philosophy?'[28] To meet these objections, Salviati calls upon 'experiment' to correct the misgivings of 'experience' : a man seated in a boat gazing at another boat cannot tell, without looking at the shore, whether his own vessel is moving or whether the other one is moving in the opposite direction. There is merely a prejudice in favour of the stability of one's own immediate frame of reference. Sagredo concludes the discussion with an amusing example. When we walk along a street on a moonlit night, we can see the moon gliding along the eaves of the roof and following us, 'an appearance which, if reason did not intervene, would only too obviously deceive us'.[29]

THE ANNUAL MOTION OF THE EARTH

The Third Day addresses itself to the central issue of the earth's annual motion. It begins with a vigorous denunciation of the crude errors of Chiaramonti, a Peripatetic philosopher who had attempted to show that recent astronomical data did not favour locating the *novae* beyond the moon. Galileo expends considerable time and energy in proving that Chiaramonti was hopelessly confused. He intends to demonstrate once and for all that the new stars were in the heavens; he also wishes to convey the impression that he can handle astronomical computations with great ease, thus preparing the reader for more startling claims. But his main objective is to persuade his contemporaries that the major objections against Copernicanism have been incontrovertibly removed by the telescope. It is now for all to see that Venus has phases like the moon, that the apparent diameters of Mars and Venus vary as much as forty and sixty times, and that a planet, Jupiter, orbits with not only one but

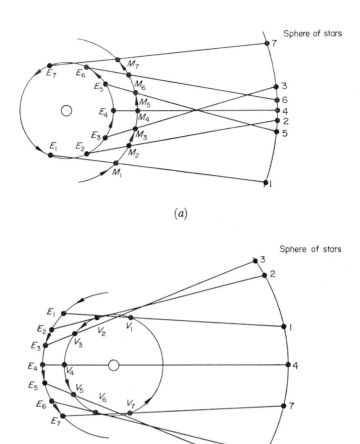

(a)

(b)

FIG. 20

four moons. Furthermore, since the telescope does not magnify the distant stars but reduces them to tiny dots, Tycho Brahe's fear that the stars would have to be gigantic in size is seen to be groundless.

With the removal of these difficulties, Salviati claims that there is no longer any bar to admitting the greater naturalness and simplicity of the Copernican hypothesis. Among other advantages, it accounts for apparent irregularities in the motions of the planets without cluttering the heavens with deferents and epicycles as in the Ptolemaic system. In figure 20(a), the sighting lines from the earth, E, show why a planet farther from the sun than the earth such as Mars, M, seems to reverse its direction against the background of distant stars. The retrograde motion is merely apparent and results from Mars travelling around the sun more slowly than the earth does. The motion of Venus, whose orbit lies between the earth and sun is explained on the same principle in figure 20(*b*). This time the planet travels faster than the earth. In the Ptolemaic model, these stations and retrogressions can only be explained by postulating an intricate series of interlocking wheels. Such a complicated celestial machinery is repugnant to Sagredo's well-tempered mind :

> If the universe were ordered according to such a multiplicity, one would have to remove from philosophy many axioms commonly adopted by all philosophers, such that nature does not multiply things unnecessarily, that she makes use of the easiest and simplest means for producing her effects, that she does nothing in vain and the like.[30]

But a major obstacle still stood in the way: the 'third motion' Copernicus had felt obliged to attribute to the earth to keep its axis tilted and pointed towards the pole-star. It is one of Galileo's great achievements that he was able to show that this motion was unnecessary. Salviati points out that the transport of the earth's axis parallel to itself is in reality not another motion but a kind of rest. This he exemplifies by the behaviour of a ball in a basin of water held by a person who turns completely around : with respect to the rim of the basin there is rotation, but with respect to the fixed objects in the room there is rest. He ignores, however, the precession of the equinoxes which Copernicus' third motion was also designed to explain.

The Decree of 1616 proscribing the heliocentric theory compelled Galileo to present it as tentative, but he would have considered restricting his aim to one of 'saving' the phenomena as a definite failure and renunciation. Salviati is willing to 'leave the others the determination of what position is true', but he is persuaded 'that the outcome will not be ambiguous for long, since one system must be true and the other false. It is not possible (speaking within the bounds of human knowledge) that the reasons adduced for the true hypothesis should not appear as conclusive as those against it will appear vain and ineffectual'.[31]

Once Galileo had convinced himself that the main objections against the motion of the earth had been solved, he became an apologist whose thought-processes were determined by the will to show that all evidence, properly interpreted, supported his case. In simple terms : 'the illnesses are in Ptolemy, and the cure for them in Copernicus'.[32] He presses the sunspots into service, and sees in the curvature of their paths across the surface of the sun 'the most solid and convincing confirmation of Copernicanism' ever offered.[33] Galileo's interpretation is somewhat complicated—not to say 'obscure' as he admits—but the main thrust is an appeal to simplicity. While in the heliocentric system, the varying slant of the sunspots over a yearly period can be sufficiently accounted for by a single solar rotation on a fixed axis, a compound of motions around two axes would be necessary in the geocentric system. There is no logical reason why two rotary motions cannot be compounded, but Galileo saw a mathematical gain in treating them separately. The argument is not decisive, but Galileo felt that the heliocentric theory should be preferred because it offered a simpler, and hence more natural explanation.

When Simplicio claims that all the celestial phenomena are equally well accounted for in the Ptolemaic system, Salviati replies that Ptolemy was excellent at computing the course of the planets piecemeal but that his system is incoherent. His calculations satisfy the 'pure astronomer', but they give no peace of mind to the 'philosophical astronomer'.[34] Galileo knows that a purely formal handling of observational data enables astronomers to make valid predictions, but he believes that this always involves contradictions. At no time will he entertain the idea of a divorce between mathematical theory and underlying physical reality. He expressed this view forcefully in his *Consideration on the Copernican Hypothesis* of 1616.

> If the stability of the earth and the motion of the sun are true in nature, and the contrary is absurd, how can anyone reasonably say that the erroneous position is in better agreement than the true one with the visible and manifest appearances in the movements and arrangements of the stars? Who does not know that all the truths in nature are in most exquisite harmony?[35]

This faith in a strict correspondence between simple mathematical reasoning and the working of nature is strongly allied to a view that allows for discrepancies between astronomical computations and actual observations. When Francesco Ingoli remarked that Tycho Brahe had established that some of Copernicus' calculations led to erroneous forecasts, Galileo merely shrugged his shoulders. Ingoli, he declared, reminded him of a man who wanted to pull his house down because the chimney smoked. Astronomers would never achieve any progress if they abandoned their system every time they encountered an apparently refractory phenomenon.

> I assure you that the movements, sizes, distances and arrangements of the orbs and stars will never be observed so accurately that they will not need endless corrections even if the world were filled with Tycho Brahes or men a hundred times as good as he was. We can be certain that there are many movements, alterations, anomalies and other things in the heavens as yet unknown or unobserved, and perhaps not even observable or explainable in themselves. Who can vouch that the movements of the planets are not incommensurable, and therefore susceptible

to, or rather in need of, eternal emendation, since we can only deal with them as though they were commensurable?[36]

This highly rhetorical justification of Copernicus carries with it a justification of Ptolemy, indeed of any system of astronomy that yields useful predictions. In the *Dialogue*, Galileo is careful not to repeat this error, and in the Second Day, after reasserting the value of mathematics, he avoids mentioning the possibility of incommensurable bodies. He acknowledges discrepancis between theory and practice but he attributes them entirely to bad reckoning, and compares them to the effect of the packing on the total weight of an object.

In the *Dialogue*, Galileo does not explain on what grounds he holds that Copernicus was not an instrumentalist as Osiander had made him out to be in the celebrated preface he had appended to the *De Revolutionibus Orbium Coelestium*. Galileo had already dealt with this problem in 1616 :

Until now astronomers have laid down two kinds of postulates : the first concern the absolute truth of nature; the others were imagined to account for the apparent motions of the celestial bodies which, in a way, disagree with the first and true postulates.[37]

Galileo is convinced that Copernicus considered the motion of the earth as an absolute truth of nature, and not as a mere device to facilitate calculations since he reverted to the Ptolemaic model whenever this made computations easier. The rival basic postulates of Ptolemy, according to Galileo, can be listed as follows : (*a*) celestial motion is uniform and circular; (*b*) the earth and the firmament are spheres; and (*c*) the earth is at rest at the centre of the universe. Galileo wishes to argue, however, that Ptolemy actually believed in the physical reality of deferents and epicycles which he introduced to explain the apparent motion of the planets. Galileo reasons that this is a necessary consequence of his first postulates : if the earth is stationary and the motions of heavenly bodies is necessarily circular, then their stations and retrogressions can only be accounted for by the action of real epicycles and deferents. It is only on the heliocentric system, he adds, that the principle of uniform motion in a circle can be retained without filling the heavens with an intricate series of gears and wheels. Ideal physical proofs should approximate geometrical demonstrations in rigour and simplicity. Salviati praises Gilbert for his experimental work on the loadstone, but he cannot help wishing

that he had been somewhat better at mathematics, and especially well grounded in geometry, the practice of which would have made him more cautious in accepting as rigorous proofs the reasons he puts forward as the real causes of the conclusions which he himself observed. These reasons, candidly speaking, do not compel with the strength which those adduced for natural, necessary and eternal conclusions should undoubtedly possess.[38]

For want of a mathematical training, intelligent people raise ridiculous objections against the motion of the earth, asking, for instance, why they do not feel themselves transported to Persia or to Japan. Mathematics would sharpen their intellect and enable them to penetrate beyond the veil of the senses. When Salviati lists the astronomical evidence in favour of the heliocentric theory, Sagredo is astonished that everyone has not embraced it yet. Salviati marvels rather that anyone should have upheld it prior to the invention of the telescope. Such a feat of intellectual daring is the hallmark of genius :

> I cannot sufficiently admire the intellectual eminence of those who received it and held it to be true. They have by sheer force of intellect done such violence to their own senses as to prefer what reason told them over that which sense experience plainly showed them to be the case . . . I repeat, I cannot find any bounds for my admiration when I consider that reason in Aristarchus and Copernicus was so able to conquer sense that, in spite of it, it became the mistress of their belief.[39]

They were unable to see the phases of Venus and the variations in the apparent diameters of Mars and Venus. Yet 'they trusted what reason told them and they confidently asserted that the structure of the universe could have no other form than the one they had outlined'.[40] 'What pleasure the telescope would have given Copernicus', says Sagredo. 'Yes', comments Salviati, 'but how much less the fame of his sublime intellect among the learned. For we see, as I have already mentioned, that he persistently continued to affirm, assisted by rational arguments, what sense experience showed to be just the opposite'.[41]

For Galileo, the scientific revolution, the passage from the old to the new world-view, is not primarily the result of more and better observations. It is the inspired mathematical reduction of a complex geometrical labyrinth into a beautifully simple and harmonious system. It is, in fact, a new vision worthy of Plato himself.

Galileo's Platonism

Platonism in the seventeenth century was a movement rather than a school, in the sense that those to whom the label was currently applied represented a broad range of interests and aims.[42] Their common bond was a rejection of some or all of Aristotle's doctrines, but they often disagreed over what constituted the alternatives and what was the proper method of choosing between them. Mathematicians who sought to determine the constitution of the universe by asking what was the simplest and most harmonious geometry that could be devised to fit the facts were considered Platonists. In the eyes of his contemporaries as well as in his own, Galileo had no doubt where he stood. When Salviati argues for the heliocentric theory on the grounds of mathematical elegance and economy, he meets with a rejoinder aimed at this 'Platonic' approach.

If I must tell you frankly how it looks to me, these appear to be some of those geometrical subtleties which Aristotle reprehended in Plato when he accused him of departing from sound philosophy by too much study of geometry. I have known some very great Peripatetic phil-osophers, and heard them advise their pupils against the study of mathematics as something which encourages haggling and makes the intellect inept to philosophise properly, a doctrine diametrically opposed to that of Plato, who would admit no one into philosophy who had not first mastered geometry.[43]

Plato believed that the ever-changing world of our experience had to be explained by ideal forms, and he considered uniform motion in a circle as one of these intellectually satisfying and self-explanatory forms. Galileo was not so heavily committed to the conception of ideal structures or, at least, he never vouchsafed a systematic account of his views on this subject. He was unquestionably convinced, however, that a rational universe of mathematical precision underpinned the empirically given world of the more-or-less. He showed a constant predilection for the perfect forms of the circle and the sphere, and he never wavered in his conviction that nature should be interrogated in the language of mathematics.

But there is another sense in which Galileo's idea of scientific knowledge was close to Plato.

Plato claimed that the soul, before it enters the body, is directly acquainted with the Forms upon which the world is modelled. When it enters the body, all this calm knowledge is drowned in the flood of new sensations. But although it is all forgotten, it is not destroyed. Later experience of things modelled after a certain Form may jog one into recollecting one's prior knowledge of the Form itself. Experience, on this view, is indispensible for arriving at knowledge which transcends ex-perience. Galileo does not say that the soul existed before the body. But he does say that the human mind is pre-attuned to nature : 'Nature first made things in her own way, and then made human reason skilful enough to be able to understand, but only by hard work, some part of her secrets'.[44] By 'hard work', Galileo meant the whole difficult business of framing hypotheses, mathematically deriving testable conclusions from them, devising well-chosen experiments to test them, and observing closely the results of experiments. 'It is entirely self-consistent with Plato's epistemology', writes J. W. N. Watkins, 'that an idea which at first seemed far from self-evident or even downright counter-intuitive should later be seen to be true. One's dormant knowledge of it may be slow to awaken'.[45] In the case of Copernicus, Galileo explicitly claimed that the counter-intuitiveness of truths at which one was first inclined to boggle melted away with the discovery of the telescope. New experiments may dispel the air of improbability initially surrounding a proposition arrived at by mathematical reasoning. Such 'hard work' removes the 'deep and thick mists' which veil our understanding, and allows us 'to know that wonderful arts lie hidden behind apparently trivial things'.

'Plato's theory implies that a teacher cannot lead a pupil to knowledge of a general truth by trying to instil it in him. His role should be that of an intellectual midwife who helps his pupils to bring their latent knowledge into consciousness. His role is to draw things out (as Socrates was supposed to have done), rather than to stuff things in'.[46] Galileo endorsed this. Salviati, like Socrates in the *Meno*, practised mental midwifery. The birth of some new ideas is worth attending to.

In the First Day, Salviati points out the shortcomings of Aristotle's proof that a body has three dimensions, and draw's Simplicio's attention to a better one 'already known to you, though perhaps without your realising it'.[47] Later in the same day, Salviati affirms that the speed of a body falling along the perpendicular of a triangle is equal to that of a body falling along the incline, and that yet, in a sense, it is faster.

> *Sagr.* To my ears these sound like contradictory propositions. What about you Simplicio?
> *Simp.* I feel the same way.
> *Salv.* I think you are poking fun at me, pretending not to grasp *what you understand better than I do.*

and turning to Sagredo,

> And what do you say, Sagredo? I do not want to teach you what you yourself know.[48]

When Simplicio says that the earth would be unable to reflect light because it is dark and opaque, Salviati steers him to a recognition of his mistake, and then adds :

> If you are satisfied now, Simplicio, you can see that you really knew that the earth shone no less than the moon, and that not my instruction but *merely the recollection* of certain things already known to you have made you sure of it. For I have not shown you that the moon shines more brilliantly by night than by day; you already knew it, as you also knew that a little cloud is brighter than the moon. Likewise you knew

that the illumination of the earth is not seen at night, and in short you knew everything in question without knowing that you knew it.

. . . . . .

Simp. I really thought that the secondary light of the moon was its own.

Salv. Again you know the answer by yourself and you are not aware of knowing it.[49]

Salviati knows what the outcome of dropping a stone from the mast of a moving ship will be even before the experiment is performed. And so does Simplicio!

Without experiment, I am sure that the effect will happen, as I tell you, because it must happen that way. Let me add, furthermore, that you yourself also know that it cannot happen otherwise; even though you pretend—or give the impression of pretending—that you do not know. But I am so handy at picking people's brains that I shall make you confess in spite of yourself . . . If only Simplicio is willing to reply to my questions, I cannot fail.[50]

Simplicio submits to the interrogation, and works out for himself that the stone must fall at the foot of the mast whether the ship moves or is at rest. One is reminded of Plato's *Meno*, where Socrates gets an unlettered slave-boy to replace his erroneous opinion about how to construct a square twice the area of a given square with a correct opinion, merely by asking questions, by eliciting what the slave-boy, without realising it, already knows.

The epistemological foundation of this technique is brought out by Sagredo:

If one does not know the truth by himself, it is impossible for anyone to make him know it. I can teach you things that are neither true nor false, but as for the true—that is the necessary; that which cannot be otherwise—every man of ordinary intelligence either knows this by himself or it is impossible for him ever to know it.[51]

This passage expresses very clearly the two-fold idea that the first principles of science are necessary rather than contingent, and that knowledge of them is inborn rather than acquired, so that it may be awakened but cannot be instilled. Salviati will help Simplicio find out whether the earth moves, 'by following our usual method and showing him that he has the solutions at his fingertips though he is not aware of it'.[52]

Rotating a pail of water with a hole on the side towards the bottom and noticing how the water comes out at right angles seems to confirm the Aristotelian position about the projection of objects on a whirling sphere, but as Salviati says to Simplicio:

The solution depends on information known and believed by you just as much as it is by me, but because you do not remember it, you fail to see the solution. Therefore, without teaching it to you, since you already know it, but merely by recalling it, I shall make you solve the objection by yourself.

This prompts Simplicio's famous query:

I have frequently considered your manner of arguing, which suggests to me that you lean toward Plato's opinion that *nostrum scire sit quoddam reminisci*. So please remove all doubt from my mind by telling me where you stand.

It would be nice to be able to report that Salviati replied, 'Four-square with Plato'. But at this point Galileo's epistemological caginess again reasserts itself. Salviati replies that he has already indicated what he felt about Plato's opinion by deeds rather than by words, and that he will continue to follow this method. What Galileo the philosopher does not wish to avow explicitly, Galileo the artist illustrates. By means of a series of questions in the Socratic manner, he gets Simplicio to 'remember' a fundamental physical truth about the motion of projectiles flung from a sling.

Salv. Well, then, what is the motion?
Simp. Let me think a moment here, for I have no longer a picture of it in my mind.
Salv. Listen to that, Sagredo, here is the *quoddam reminisci* in action.

Simplicio is made to see that the motion is impressed along a straight line, but he is word-bound.

Salv. I also see that you understand the thing itself, but lack the proper terms to express it. Now these I can indeed teach you; that is, I can teach you the words, but not the truths, which are things. And so that you may plainly feel that you know the thing and merely lack terms to express it, tell me: when you shoot a bullet with a gun, in what direction does it receive an impetus to go?

Simplicio is led to recall that a projectile moves along the tangent to its previous circle of motion, but his mind boggles at the speed of the earth's rotation. Given sufficient time, he would remember all that is necessary for the solution to this difficulty, but Salviati will hasten the process.

In the same way that you knew what went before, you will know—or rather, do know—the rest too. And by thinking over it you would also recall it by yourself. But, to save time, I shall help you remember it.[53]

Galileo takes an impish delight in pursuing this kind of eristic argument. His greatest triumph comes in the Third Day when he thrusts a pencil into Simplicio's hand and has him trace out the paths of the planets as he 'remembers' them.

> For your satisfaction and your enjoyment too, I want you to draw it yourself. Although you think you do not understand it, you will see that you understand it perfectly, and just by answering my questions you will describe it accurately.[54]

The result is a diagram of the Copernican universe!

Again, when Simplicio wrongly infers that because the movement of a ship by sixty miles makes a difference of 1° in the observed altitude of the polar star, a similar variation should be produced by the motion of the earth, Salviati replies :

> This, Simplicio, is another equivocation on your part, which you know but do not remember knowing, and I shall try to make you recall it.[55]

Salviati's friends attribute the emergence of new ideas in their minds to his intervention. 'I understand now that you have awakened my intellect', exclaims Sagredo,[56] and in another passage, Simplicio says : 'Your interrogation has awakened my mind'.[57] Socrates hardly expected more from his interlocutors.

Galileo was not a system builder, and he never gave theoretical constructs a completely free hand. He agreed with Plato that knowledge of at least some natural principles is self-evident, and, in a way, innate, but he stressed the importance of experience to awaken dormant knowledge. Ultimately, this is possible because the human mind shares in the divine mathematical knowledge that created and ordered the universe. In a sense, there exists between man's intellect and nature a pre-established harmony which experiments can recall rather than produce. For this reason there can be no substitute for mathematical vision.

The Role of Experiments

Galileo's Platonic conception of scientific procedure implies a predominance of reason over mere experience : while Colombo and Lagalla constantly appeal to untutored experience, he calls upon mathematics to interpret nature. The crucial distinction no longer lies between mental and factual but between mathematical and crudely empirical. Experiments —be they mental or real—are equally valid if they are set up in accordance with the requirements of mathematics. The spontaneous transformation of 'natural' motion into 'violent' motion is confirmed by dropping a cannon-ball through an imaginary tunnel passing through the centre of the earth, as well as by watching the oscillations of a pendulum. Galileo replaces the qualitative approach of the Scholastics by a more rigorous method where measurement, at least in principle, becomes fundamental. Thus Salviati insists that it is not enough to know that a falling body is constantly accelerated; the ratio must be ascertained. When objects are not open to direct inspection, real or imagined models are used to determine the spatial and temporal relationships that are basic to scientific understanding. In some cases the quest for geometrical simplicity and the conviction that mathematical elegance is an exclusive feature of Copernicanism exercises such a control on the thought-experiment that the conclusion is foregone.

Even the famous experiment of the stone dropped from the top of the mast of a ship can only be ascribed to mental ingenuity. In his *Letter to Ingoli*, Galileo says that he performed the experiment, but 'before making it', he adds, 'I had entirely convinced myself through reasoning that the result would be exactly what it turned out to be'.[58] In the *Dialogue*, Salviati does not repeat this claim, but merely states : 'Without experiment, I am sure that the effect will happen as I tell you, because it *must* happen that way'.[59] Simplicio is made to reason out the result of the experiment; there is no question of solving the problem by purely experimental methods. Salviati even introduces two alternative experiments that he cannot be credited with having performed or witnessed :

> If you want to produce a more suitable experiment, you should say that we ought to observe, if not with our physical eyes, at least with those of our mind, what would happen if an eagle, carried by the force of the wind, were to drop a rock from its talons.[60]

and,

> You will see the same thing happen by making the experiment on a ship with a ball thrown perpendicularly upward from a catapult. It returns to the same place whether the ship is moving or standing still.[61]

This is surely not an experiment that the captain of any ship would have welcomed ! But even if Galileo had performed the experiment and had dropped balls from the mast of a ship, this would hardly have settled the issue. Aristotelians knew of the alleged result and remained not only impenitent but unperturbed. The margin of experimental error was too great, they said, for how could the mast remain erect when the ship rolled and pitched, or when it was thrust forward by the uneven impulses of the wind or the oarsmen ?[62]

Merely to stumble on the correct answer through experiment is unworthy of the natural philosopher. When Rocco challenges Galileo to state his grounds for asserting that all bodies fall at the same speed regardless of their weights, Galileo replies that he was 'first convinced by reason rather than made certain by sense'.[63]

This attitude explains why Galileo can make preposterous claims for experiments plausible in theory but impossible in practice. For instance, after chiding Tycho and Clavius for their carelessness in determining the apparent diameter of the stars, Salviati suggests a better method which he affirms he has often carried out. He tells his two friends how he hung a light rope in the direction of Vega, and placed himself at a distance where the diameter of the cord just hid the star. From the ratio of the thickness of the cord to its distance from the eye, he determined the angle subtended by the star, taking care 'not to put the intersection of the visual rays at the centre of the eye, where they would not go if they were not refracted, but beyond the location of the eye where the actual width of the pupil would permit them to converge'. He concludes:

> By this very precise operation, I find that the apparent diameter of a star of the first magnitude, commonly believed to be two minutes, and even put at three by Tycho in his *Astronomical Letters*, p. 167, is no more than five seconds, which is one twenty-fourth or one thirty-sixth of what they thought. Now you see what a serious mistake their doctrine is based upon.[64]

Galileo was not above stretching a point to discredit an opponent. How he could have obtained these results with this method is quite beyond the art of experimentation. What probably happened is the following: the telescope revealed that the stars were not as large as commonly believed because they were not magnified but reduced to bright dots. This knowledge enabled Galileo to devise—in his mind—an experiment that could have been performed by his predecessors without the new instrument, and which would have allowed them to ascertain the relative size of the stars. The method he suggests is mathematically ingenious, but it is experimentally impractical. Since the pupil of the eye dilates and contracts with the amount of light available, the spot where the rays would actually converge is never the same. Salviati recognises this difficulty but he believes that the convergence of the rays can be determined by placing a white strip of paper on a wall and fastening a black strip half its width on a stick some fifteen yards away. If vision took place in a single point, the white strip of paper would just be concealed from that distance. Since this is not the case, the eye must be moved forward from the point of the true intersection of the visual rays. Salviati argues that the dilation of the pupil can be determined by this method since the diameter of the dilated pupil bears to the width of the paper the same ratio as the distance of the eye to the true intersection of the rays bears to the total distance of fifteen yards. But how could this experiment be performed in the middle of the night? And what of the refraction produced by the pupil? The fact that Galileo does not face up to these difficulties is sufficient evidence that he never made the experience.

In a subsequent passage, Galileo criticises the attempts made by his predecessors to determine the existence of parallax in distant stars. He complains that their measurements, including those of Tycho Brahe, were too crude, and he suggests a method which occurred to him as he was watching the sunset at the summer solstice from his villa near Florence. He noticed how the sun went down behind a cliff in the Pietropana mountains some sixty miles away 'leaving only a small shred of itself revealed to the north, the breadth of which was not the hundredth part of its diameter'.[65] The next evening the shred was noticeably thinner, although the sun's return between the first and the second observation amounted to less than one second of an arc. Thus, it seemed that nature itself provided an enormous instrument to determine the relative position of celestial bodies over a yearly period. This suggestive idea, which only occurred to Galileo in 1631, bears witness to the vitality of his mind and the alertness of his scientific imagination at the age of sixty-seven.[66] It leaves one doubtful, however, about the amount of thought he actually gave to the measurement of parallax prior to writing the *Dialogue*.

Galileo was conscious, however, that the results of mathematical reasoning must be open, at least in principle, to empirical verification. This condition was unimportant for his Aristotelian opponents, who viewed science in a different light. They accepted an instrumentalist interpretation of astronomy, and they considered explanations in terms of human purposes more real than explanations in terms of efficient causality which pointed the way to the regulative use experiments. The world, as they saw it, existed for man's enjoyment, instruction and use; it was subordinate to him and made sense in relation to him. The realm of nature was not only earth-centred but man-centred. It is largely a result of the Galilean revolution that we have come to view this attitude as a piece of intellectual arrogance. When Simplicio argues that nothing has been created in vain and that empty space between the orb of Saturn and the stellar sphere would serve no purpose, we instinctively side with Sagredo's criticism :

Say rather, and I believe more appropriately, 'which we do not know to serve us' . . . neither do I know how my arteries are of service to me, nor my cartilages, spleen or gall. I should not even know that I had a gall, or a spleen, or kidneys, if they had not been shown to me in many dissected corpses. Even then, I could understand what my spleen does for me only if it were removed. In order to understand what some celestial body produces in me (since you want all their actions to be directed toward us) it would be necessary to remove that body for a while, and say that whatever effect I might then feel to be missing in me depended upon that star.[67]

The correct procedure to be followed in science is illustrated by Salviati's discussion of the strengthening of a loadstone with an armature :

First, I ascertained that the virtue and strength of the stone did not increase at all by having an armature, for it does not attract through a greater distance . . . Hence there is no change in the virtue, and yet there is something new in the effect. And since for a new effect there must be a new cause, we seek what is newly introduced by the act of supporting the iron with the armature, and no other is to be found than a difference in contact, for where iron originally touched load-stone, now iron touches iron. Therefore, we must conclude that the difference in these contacts causes the difference in the results. Finally, I cannot see that the difference in the contacts can derive from any-thing else than the fact that the parts of the substance of iron are finer, purer and denser.[68]

Theory, nevertheless, loses none of its authoritative voice. Galileo rejects Gilbert's conjecture that a spherical loadstone might rotate on its axis if placed in a fluid medium, not because it contradicts well-defined experiments but because it conflicts with his theory that all parts of the terrestrial globe have a natural tendency to rotate around the centre of the earth once every twenty-four hours.[69] In a sense, there is no need to perform the experiment; given the conceptual framework in which Galileo would have carried it out, a single result was possible.

A particularly interesting case in point is the time of free fall given by Galileo in the *Dialogue*, which became a source of puzzlement for his more experimentally-minded contemporaries such as Mersenne and Baliani. The first edition of the *Dialogue* contains two pairs of distance–time values for a body in free fall. These two pairs, which correspond to a gravitational acceleration of about half the currently accepted value are : (i) a fall of 200 *braccia* in less than ten pulse-beats,[70] and (ii) a fall of 100 *braccia* in 5 seconds.[71] Since 1 *braccio* is approximately 22 inches, if we assume a normal pulse-rate of 72, Galileo's data correspond to accelerations respectively of (i) more than 10 feet/second^2, and (ii) 14 to 15 feet/second^2. If the expression 'more than' is liberally interpreted, the two values of acceleration can be considered consistent with each other. As David C. Lindberg points out, if we assume a rate slower than 72 for the pulse-beat, then the acceleration becomes smaller than 10 feet/second^2;

if we increase it even to 90 beats/minute, the acceleration is increased only by 10 feet/second^2, still leaving a discrepancy of 50 per cent, but bringing value (i) nearer to value (ii).[72]

In his copy of the *Dialogue*, Galileo added a third pair of distance–time values yielding (with the assumption of a pulse-rate of 72) a gravitational acceleration of 31.5 feet/second^2, almost exactly the modern value.[73] The problem is to account for the discrepancy between this new value and the other two. David C. Lindberg proposes an explanation based on the following facts : first, Mersenne had apparently no trouble in securing more accurate results,[74] and, secondly, Galileo's experiments with balls rolling down inclined planes can be shown to yield the data he claims for them.[75] Lindberg suggests that for expository purposes Galileo transposed into data for vertical fall the information he secured by rolling balls down an incline. The introduction of rotation (the dynamics of which Galileo did not understand) does not alter the proportionality between distance and time-squared, but it reduces the acceleration considerably. Assuming a single point of contact between the ball and the incline, and no frictional resistance, rotational inertia would reduce the gravitational acceleration transposed into data for free fall by 28 per cent. Frictional resistance or the existence of two points of contact between the ball and the grooved incline could easily account for the remaining discrepancy between Galileo's results and the currently accepted value of gravitational acceleration. But what about the third set of correct values? Lindberg surmises that they were obtained by measuring bodies in actual fall : 'there would have been no problem in finding a tower high enough —the campanile at Pisa is just over 100 braccia in height, though half that height would do—to allow for a time measurement accurate to 5 or 10 per cent'. But then why didn't Galileo correct the two other pairs of data? 'This might be explained', replies Lindberg, 'by his inability to choose one set of data over the other'.[76]

The main objection to this interpretation is that the third set of values is given by Simplicio who speaks of a ball weighing one hundred pounds. It is difficult to see how Galileo could have performed this experiment from any tower, let alone the tower of Pisa, 'since 100 *braccia* is more than 180 feet, 100 pounds is 100 pounds, and Galileo suffered from a double hernia for which he had to wear an iron truss'.[77]

G. B. Baliani was perplexed by Galileo's data. On 23 April 1632, he wrote to him, 'I should be grateful if you told me how you found that a heavy body falls through 100 braccia in five seconds'. Seven years later he was still waiting for a reply when he renewed his request.[78] Galileo finally answered, and explained how the speed of the vertical fall could be determined by experiments on inclined planes, the method Lindberg conjectures Galileo used. But there is no mention of the correct value;

rather the impression conveyed is that Galileo relied more on the validity of his method than on the accuracy of his measurements.

> This is the technique [artificio] which I believe you will find exquisite, even if upon making the experiment you were to find that what I wrote about the 100 braccia in 5 seconds is wrong. To show the exceeding silliness of the writer who assigned the time of fall for the cannon-ball dropped from the moon, it was not important that the 5 seconds of the 100 braccia should be accurate.[79]

Galileo's selection of round numbers—100 units of space for 5 units of time—can be regarded, therefore, as a convenience for illustration of his point rather than a serious assertion about nature. But what, precisely, is the point Galileo wishes to make? It is simply that a mathematically structured experiment will yield valid results when it is performed, and that mathematised physics can reveal the laws of nature in spite of what the Aristotelians, through their spokesman Simplicio, are fond of saying : 'In physical sciences there is no need to look for the precision of mathematical evidence'.[80]

Galileo vouchsafes, in his comments on Antonio Rocco's *Esercitazioni Filosofiche*, a personal account of how he detected and corrected the falsehood in Aristotle's law of free fall. When he read the passage in which Aristotle takes it for granted that the speeds of falling bodies are proportional to their weights, he instinctively felt that something was wrong. He remembered that he had seen hailstones ten times as large as the average size falling on the ground with the others without preceding them by any appreciable distance. 'I went on to think about this, and I laid down as an axiom not to be called in question by anyone that all heavy bodies fall with their own degree of speed limited and determined by nature'. He then considered the case of two bricks dropped from the same height. Since they both reached the ground in the same time when they fell side by side, he saw no reason why they should behave differently if they were tied together. 'From this first argument I passed on to a more rigorous demonstration, and I proved that if we supposed that the heavier body fell faster, we would have to conclude that the lighter body fell faster also'.[81] The proof, which he had elaborated at Pisa, consists in showing that it would be just as logical to claim that a light body detracts from the speed of a heavy body to which it is joined, than to suppose that the two bodies fall faster because their total weight is greater.

The law of equal acceleration is not fulfilled as such, explains Galileo, because of impediments arising from the retarding effect of the medium. These are, first, the resistance of the medium to be separated; second, the specific weight of the medium which in some cases, for instance with water with respect to wood, inverts the motion completely; third, the shape of the body which is more or less apt to cut through the medium; finally, 'a new resistance, as far as I know never observed until now . . . consisting in the contact between the fluid medium and the surface of the moving body'.[82] Examples of this resistance are a highly polished sphere sweeping air along with it as it rotates, and a ship whose progress is impeded because its hull is not greased. Furthermore, since division does not decrease the surface and the weight of a body in the same ratio, a very small body (such as a particle of sand) has a very large surface area respective to its weight, and is therefore much more subject to the retarding effect of the medium. Galileo also points out—and this is a major insight—that falling bodies are not indefinitely accelerated but reach a terminal velocity. Heavier bodies are accelerated for a longer period of time, and are therefore moving at a greater speed when their motion becomes uniform.

But the larger issue cannot be avoided : if Galileo admits that bodies never fall at the same rate because the medium always offers some resistance, however minimal, his law is either fictitious or obtains in the void, which seems equally fictitious since Aristotle demonstrated the impossibility of the void. Galileo replies by showing that Aristotle's argument, based on the postulate that speed is proportional to the viscosity of the medium, entails a paradox. If water is 10 times more viscous than air, and a ball of fir falls in the air with 20 degrees of speed, it should fall with 2 degrees of speed in water. But this is not the case since a ball of fir floats. Now it is theoretically possible to find a body heavier than fir which would sink in water with two degrees of speed. Hence, according to Aristotle, it should fall in the air with 20 degrees of speed. But this is the speed of fall of a ball of fir, which, by definition, is lighter than the body in question. Aristotle's argument thus leads to a contradiction and must, therefore, rest on a fallacy.

The logical possibility of the void does not automatically establish its relevance to physical problems. Galileo does not shirk this crucial difficulty. Is it sound philosophy—and good science—to go beyond the realm of normal occurrences? Is it not dangerous to seek an interpretation of nature by extrapolating beyond its apparent limits?

The scientific revolution has taught us that by compelling nature to do, so to speak, what it does not naturally do, new truths about the structure of the universe are often disclosed. For us, this assertion is supported by three hundred years of experimental science. For Galileo's contemporaries, and indeed for Galileo himself, who even doubted the experimental possibility of producing a vacuum, it was a leap of faith.

Finally, we must avoid the most dangerous shoal, and show by means of what kind of hypothesis (since it is perhaps impossible to make the experiment) I allowed myself to be persuaded that the innate speeds of all bodies falling in the void would be identical.[83]

He explains that because the difference in the speeds of falling bodies of varying weights decreases as the density of the medium grows less, he inferred that if the resistance were zero the difference would be nil. Galileo does not produce more evidence; he proposes to free the scientific method 'from the tendency to excessive empiricism which was the main defect of the Aristotelian tradition'.[84] The two erroneous assumptions in Antonio Rocco's reasoning are explained by his subservience to everyday experience. These are : first, the idea, apparently so plausible, that since bodies fall because they are heavy, they will fall more swiftly if they are heavier; and secondly, the notion, which seems equally obvious, that the medium is an essential feature of the law of falling bodies instead of merely a disturbing factor.

The unverifiable law of uniform acceleration can only be stated for the unattainable vacuum. For the Aristotelian, this is an insurmountable barrier. For Galileo, it merely proves that the frontiers of science are not coterminous with the frontiers of experience. Only 'by imagining an impossible situation can a clear and simple law of fall be formulated, and only by possessing that law is it possible to comprehend the complex things that actually happen'.[85] One can, indeed one must, go beyond sense experience but this presupposes a philosophical conviction that the real is described by the ideal, and the physical by the mathematical. It is no hazard that Galileo ends his discussion of the law of free fall by reminding Rocco of the noblest of the sciences and the greatest of the philosophers.

> Rocco, when you have carefully weighed, examined and compared your arguments and mine, remember the saying of the philosopher that *ignorato motu ignoratur natura*, and weigh on honest scales which of the two ways of philosophising reaches its goal, yours, quite simple and purely physical, or mine, seasoned with a dash of mathematics. At the same time, consider who reasoned more soundly, Plato, who said that we cannot learn philosophy without mathematics, or Aristotle, who accused Plato of studying too much geometry.[86]

THE TWO WORLDS

The Teleological World

The Middle Ages rediscovered and handed down to their successors a world vision inherited from the Greeks, whose main concern was not to seek out new facts but to provide an all-encompassing justification of world order. They were not interested in detailed explanation and prediction but in seeing how things formed part of a connected, rational and aesthetically satisfying whole. Under the influence of Judeo-Christian theology, this led to the belief that the entire realm of nature was tele- ologically subordinate to man and to his eternal destiny.

There is a neatness and tidiness about this conception which is not only gratifying to the mind but pleasing to the eye. The imagination is left with an orderly picture of the world where each thing has its proper place. In time, this world-view acquired a deceptive obviousness which went unchallenged for want of a better alternative. Man could, and did, marvel at the size of the universe, but he never doubted that it had been created for his use and benefit. Astrology was both popular and respectable because it was commonly assumed that human affairs would prosper when undertaken under the right conjunction of stars. Simplicio takes it for granted that the celestial bodies 'are ordained to no other use than that of service to the earth'.[87] He boggles at the empty space the Copernicans wish to introduce between Saturn and the stellar sphere :

> Now when we see the beautiful order of the planets, arranged around the earth at distances commensurate with their producing upon it their effects for our benefit, why go on to place between the highest orb, namely that of Saturn, and the stellar sphere an enormous, superfluous and vain space without any star whatsoever? To what end? For the use and convenience of whom?[88]

Under these rhetorical questions lies a method of philosophising, indeed a philosophy of life. On this view, before one gets down to the details of building and testing the Copernican hypothesis, one must know whether it 'stands to reason'. It is pointless to construct a new intellectual edifice, or even to examine its design until its possibility has been ascertained. In the Aristotelian context there are no working-hypotheses; there are only full-fledged theories.

Since the universe as a whole is interpreted on the broad analogy of a living organism, limited analogies drawn from human behaviour are assumed to be self-explanatory. Thus Simplicio accounts for magnetism in terms of 'sympathies' and antipathies' :

> We reduce the cause of this and other similar natural effects to sym- pathy, which is a certain correspondence and mutual desire that arises between things which are similar in quality among themselves, just as we call antipathy that hatred and enmity on account of which other things naturally fly apart and abhor each other.[89]

It would be unfair, however, to suppose that the conceptual tools of the Peripatetics were always so crude and primitive. Their intellectual instruments were highly sophisticated and enabled them to come to grips with the perennial puzzles of philosophy, and particularly the problem of identity and change. Aristotle accounts for the continuity and novelty in change by postulating that physical bodies have a species-individual structure. A body shares in the common properties of the members of its class by reason of its form, but it is its individual self because of its matter. Form individualised by matter, or, to put it the other way round, matter actualised by form constitutes the material substance. The substance is in turn affected by accidents which qualify it but do not alter its nature. Change is possible because the form is never so perfectly joined to the matter that it cannot be expelled and replaced by another one. In the case of the heavenly bodies, however, no change can occur because the form is completely welded to the matter and exhausts all its potentialities. The problem of how these perfect bodies can act without physical contact on sublunary bodies is solved on the analogy of human behaviour, where the will, a spiritual faculty, produces bodily movements without being itself affected in any physical way.

The very sophistication of this philosophy presented a danger. While more subtle minds would speak of matter and form as a structure, more naïvely realistic thinkers would assume that to know that an object had a form was to know what that form was. Aristotelian categories tended to become the only ones within which problems in natural philosophy could be legitimately discussed. Colombo's criticism, for instance, aims at proving that Copernicus' concept of force can neither be said to be a substance nor an accident, and therefore belongs to a metaphysical limbo. Simplicio rules out the concept of 'impressed virtue' for the same reason.

This teleological model of the universe with its panoply of metaphysical categories found an ally in unregenerate empiricism, or the belief that what is real is what is immediately perceived through the senses. It is this conception that led Galileo's opponents to suppose that a phenomenon must always be studied in the complicated form in which it appeared. Thus, the medium was considered an essential feature, instead of a merely disturbing factor. It is also for this reason that they made the assumption, equally plausible in appearance but just as mistaken in reality, that since a heavy body tends downward more strongly than a light body, it will fall faster when allowed to fall freely.

The teleological and metaphysical overtones of this empiricism kept the mind from any desire to pursue experiments. On the organic model, the constant acceleration of falling bodies is best described in qualitative terms as an increase in strength. The demand for precision and rigour— and thus the requirement of accurate measurements—could not arise within a framework that laid down that form and quality cannot be geometrised. As Simplicio reminded his friend, 'After all, Salviati, these mathematical subtleties do very well in the abstract, but they do not work out when applied to sensible and physical matters'.[90]

The Mathematical World

To the two basic tenets of Aristotelian empiricism, anthropocentric teleology and reliance on the immediate disclosures of sense experience, Galileo opposes the two main principles of mathematical Platonism, geometrical harmony of the universe and faith in the explanatory power of mathematics.

It would be wrong to say that Galileo shirks the problem of man's privileged status in the cosmos or that it fails to impinge on his intellectual consciousness. Galileo sees that man's unique position does not derive from the fact that he occupies the spatial centre of the universe but from his ability to encompass the entire world by grasping its mathematical structure. If we are to think in spatial images, it would be more appropriate to say that man's intellect girds the universe round than to describe him as sitting at the centre of things. God is in the firmament above, and man shares in the divine attribute of mathematical knowledge.

Since what qualifies as a scientific explanation for Galileo is no longer an analysis in terms of act and potency, matter and form, but a mathematical theory verifiable in nature, he rejects the very concept of substantial change. In the new perspective, only 'a simple transposition of parts' is amenable to mathematical treatment and, consequently, intelligible. The Aristotelians abuse themselves with words. When Salviati is asked whether the motive force of the planets is inherent or external, he professes ignorance, but it is the ignorance of a Socrates who exposes the sham knowledge of those who claim to know. If his adversaries can tell him what moves the planets and the stars, he will have found the force that moves the earth. Simplicio replies that everyone knows that the cause is gravity. 'You are wrong, Simplicio', says Salviati, 'you should have said that everyone knows that it is called gravity. But I am not asking you for the name, I am asking you for the essence of the thing, and you do not know a bit more about that essence than you do about the essence of whatever moves the stars around'. The same can be said of *virtus impressa*, and of *intelligenza assistente* or *informante*.[91] They are mere names for observed regularities.

In the *De Motu* Galileo had tried to establish that weight was the only natural property of bodies and that lightness was a mere name for the rising of bodies thrusted upward by a denser medium. 'Gravity' remains throughout Galileo's works the cause of bodies falling downward, but its epistemological status becomes obscure after the discussion on the nature of bodies in *The Assayer* (1623) where weight neither appears among the properties 'without which a body cannot be conceived' nor is listed among those which result from the interaction of those basic properties with the sensory apparatus. This puzzling feature arises from Galileo's geometrical approach. The properties of the bodies he studies are strictly Euclidean. There is no reason why they should fall, yet they do. They spontaneously start moving toward the earth when they are dropped. This is the empirical fact that differentiates them from purely geometrical constructs. 'En d'autres termes', writes Koyré, 'la gravité est la seule propriété physique qu'ils possèdent. Les corps "physiques" archimédiens sont donc graves, en quelque sorte, par définition. Et c'est pour cela qu'ils sont mobiles, ce que les corps géométriques ne sont aucunement'.[92] Galileo restricts himself to nominalism because he does not know the nature of weight. But as E. J. Dijksterhuis observed, 'This is a restriction he imposes upon himself, not upon science'.[93] Galileo was strongly persuaded that gravity was a force similar to that of magnetism, and that the terrestrial globe was a huge magnet. But in spite of repeated efforts he remained unable to establish a satisfactory theory, i.e. a pattern of relations deduced by mathematical reasoning from principles that appear more or less self-evident.

Galileo himself lapses, at least twice, into the loose qualitative terminology that he normally considered the bane of philosophy. On one occasion he attributes the fact that the moon always presents the same side to the earth to 'a correspondence and natural sympathy' between the two bodies, and in another context he accounts for the greater strength of an armed magnet by the transmission of the 'virtue' of the surrounding parts to the armature. This is a particularly serious inconsistency in view of the fact that he shortly afterward ridicules Simplicio for mentioning 'sympathies' and 'antipathies'.

What is much more important is that Galileo continues to think of natural motion as a tendency, an inclination, a natural instinct.[94] The main objection to the diurnal motion of the earth is solved by granting the earth a natural tendency to revolve around the centre of its mass once every twenty-four hours. In other words, the answer to the Aristotelians who suppose that the earth is naturally at rest is to postulate that it moves naturally in a circle. Galileo never formulated Newton's first law of motion, not because he was unwilling to postulate an infinite universe about which he remained uncommitted, but because had to to make circular inertia a cornerstone of his heliocentric system in order to answer the objections of his opponents.

Aristotle conceived uniform motion as a balance between force and resistance. Galileo justifies his circular inertia in the same way:

Acceleration occurs in a moving body when it is approaching the goal

toward which it has an inclination, and retardation occurs because of its
reluctance to leave and go away from that point; and since in circular
motion the moving body is always receding from its natural terminus
and at the same time moving toward it, therefore the reluctance and
the inclination are always of equal strength in it. The consequence of
this equality is a speed that is neither retarded nor accelerated, that is,
uniform motion.[95]

It is interesting to note that Galileo does not arrive at his concept of
inertia by studying the motion of a projectile, and, therefore, that it was
probably suggested to him by a different kind of question than that which
exercised the ingenuity of Buridan, his disciple Oresme, and the other
exponents of the medieval theory of impetus.[96] In the first version of his
De Motu, Galileo accepted the Aristotelian division of all motions into
'natural' and 'constrained' but as he pursued the Archimedean notion
that all bodies are heavy and differ only in density he came to question
whether all motions were either natural or constrained. A body might be
moving and yet be neither approaching nor receding from the centre of
the earth; the motion of such a body rotating around the centre of the
earth could be called neither natural nor constrained but 'neutral'. Galileo
was not original in pointing out that a rotating homogeneous sphere ill-
fitted Aristotelian categories of motion. Others before him had pursued
similar lines of reasoning. What is novel in Galileo's analysis is the idea
that this was a third kind of motion and not a mixture of the other two
kinds. There is another approach originating from a different example,
namely the problem of the force required to maintain a body on an
inclined plane. Analysing the situation, Galileo concluded that horizontal
motion of a body on the earth's surface would similarly be neither natural
nor violent, since an horizontal line on the surface of the earth is a small
part of the earth's circumference. The central picture from the De Motu
to the Dialogue is that of a perfect sphere rotating on its axis or revolving
in a circle. It may be discussed in the Aristotelian terminology of force
and resistance, but the image belongs to the Platonic world of ideal forms.

NOTES

1. Galileo, Dialogo, Opere di Galileo, 7, 143. (Drake trans., 117; Salusbury trans., 129–130)
2. Ibid., 148. (Drake trans., 122; Salusbury trans., 136)
3. Ibid., 196–197. (Drake trans., 171; Salusbury trans., 185)
4. Ibid., 215. (Drake trans., 188; Salusbury trans., 201)
5. Ibid., 209. (Drake trans., 183; Salusbury trans., 196)
6. Letter of Bonaventura Cavalieri to Galileo, 18 November 1631, ibid., 14, 308–309

7. Galileo, *Dialogo, ibid.*, **7**, 173–174. (Drake trans., 148; Salusbury trans., 162)
8. *Ibid.*, 175. (Drake trans., 149; Salusbury trans., 163–164)
9. *Ibid.*, 191–193. (Drake trans., 165–167; Salusbury trans., 179–181)
10. Letter to Pierre Carcavy, 5 June 1637, *ibid.*, **17**, 89
11. Galileo, *Dialogo, ibid.*, **7**, 214. (Drake trans., 186; Salusbury trans., 200)
12. *Ibid.*, 242. (Drake trans., 215; Salusbury trans., 230)
13. *Ibid.*, 243. (Drake trans., 217; Salusbury trans., 232)
14. *Ibid.*, 235. (Drake trans., 209; Salusbury trans., 223–224.) Erwin Panofsky spoke of Galileo's 'classicistic prejudice in favour of simplicity, order, and *séparation des genres*, and against complexity, imbalance, and all kinds of conflation' ('Galileo as a Critic of the Arts', *Isis*, **47** (1956), 9)
15. *Ibid.*, 260–261. (Drake trans., 234–235; Salusbury trans., 250–251)
16. *Ibid.*, 289. (Drake trans., 264; Salusbury trans., 279)
17. *Ibid.*, 224. (Drake trans., 197; Salusbury trans., 210.) For the simplified diagram in the text see A. Rupert Hall, *From Galileo to Newton 1630–1720* (London: Collins, 1964), 54
18. *Ibid.*, 244. (Drake trans., 217; Salusbury trans., 233)
19. *Ibid.*, 239. (Drake trans., 213; Salusbury trans., 227)
20. *Ibid.*, 227, 229. (Drake trans., 200, 203; Salusbury trans., 213, 216)
21. *Ibid.*, 172. (Drake trans., 146; Salusbury trans., 161)
22. *Ibid.*, 249. (Drake trans., 222; Salusbury trans., 238)
23. *Ibid.*, 189–190. (Drake trans., 163–164; Salusbury trans., 178)
24. Galileo's postil to Antonio Rocco's *Esercitazioni Filosofiche* (1633), *ibid.*, 728
25. Galileo, *Dialogo, ibid.*, 229–230. (Drake trans., 203–204; Salusbury trans., 216–217)
26. *Ibid.*, 233–234. (Drake trans., 207–208; Salusbury trans., 222.) As Alexandre Koyré observed: Galileo 'part de l'idée—préconçue sans doute, mais qui forme le fond de sa philosophie de la nature—que les lois de la nature sont des lois mathématiques. *Le réel incarne le mathématique.* Aussi n'y a-t-il pas, chez Galilée, d'écart entre l'expérience et la théorie; la théorie, la formule, ne s'applique pas aux phénomènes du dehors, elle ne "sauve" pas ces phénomènes, elle en exprime l'essence' (Alexandre Koyré, *Etudes Galiléennes* (1939), reprint Paris: Herman, 1966, 156)
27. Galileo's postil to Antonio Rocco's *Esercitazioni Filosofiche, Opere di Galileo*, **7**, 748. Later in the *Discorsi*, Galileo returned to the problem of the parts of a continuum and argued that objective mathematical reasoning requires that matter be constituted of an infinite number of indivisible atoms (see Wililam R. Shea, 'Galileo's Atomic Hypothesis', *Ambix*, **17** (1970), 24–27)
28. Galileo, *Dialogo, ibid.*, 165, 197. (Drake trans., 139, 171; Salusbury trans., 154, 185.) The problem of what Galileo considers crude empiricism is illustrated by several quotations from Scipione Chiaramonti's *De tribus novis stellis* (1628) where Copernicanism is decried as subverting the criterion of sensory evidence: '*Ex hac itaque opinione necesse est diffidere nostris sensibus, ut penitus fallacibus vel stupidis in sensibilibus, etiam conjunctissimis diudicandis*' (*ibid.*, 280); 'in dottrina del Copernico bisogna negare i sensi, e le sensazioni massime' (*ibid.*, 278); 'in via del Copernico bisogna negar le sensazioni proprie (*ibid.*, 279)
29. *Ibid.*, 281. (Drake trans., 256; Salusbury trans., 271)
30. *Ibid.*, 423. (Drake trans., 397; Salusbury trans., 406)
31. *Ibid.*, 383. (Drake trans., 356; Salusbury trans., 366)
32. *Ibid.*, 369. (Drake trans., 341; Salusbury trans., 350)
33. *Ibid.*, 374. (Drake trans., 347; Salusbury trans., 357.) See Stillman Drake, *Galileo Studies* (Ann Arbor: The University of Michigan Press, 1970), 191–196
34. *Ibid.*, 369. (Drake trans., 341; Salusbury trans., 349–350)
35. Galileo, *Consideration on the Copernican Hypothesis* (1616), *ibid.*, **5**, 356
36. Letter to Ingoli (1624), *ibid.*, **6**, 533
37. Galileo, *Consideration on the Copernican Hypothesis, ibid.*, **5**, 357

38. Galileo, *Dialogo*, **7**, 432. (Drake trans., 406; Salusbury trans., 415)
39. *Ibid.*, 355. (Drake trans., 328; Salusbury trans., 341)
40. *Ibid.*, 362–363. (Drake trans., 335; Salusbury trans., 343)
41. *Ibid.*, 367. (Drake trans., 339; Salusbury trans., 347)
42. To my knowledge there is no comprehensive study of Platonism in the second half of the sixteenth century and in the first decades of the seventeenth. For Koyré the line of demarcation between Platonism and Aristotelianism was clear: 'la ligne de partage entre aristotéliciens et platoniciens est très nette : si l'on proclame la *valeur supérieure* des mathématiques, si, au surplus, on leur attribue une valeur réelle et une position dominante dans et pour la physique, on est platonicien; si, au contraire, on voit dans les mathématiques une science "abstraite", et par conséquent de *valeur moindre* que les sciences —physique et métaphysique—qui s'occupent du réel, si, en particulier, on prétend fonder la physique *directement sur l'expérience*, en n'attribuant aux mathématiques qu'un rôle d'adjuvant, on est aristotélicien' (A. Koyré, *Etudes Galiléennes*, 279)
43. Galileo, *Dialogo, Opere di Galileo*, **7**, 423. (Drake trans., 397; Salusbury trans., 406)
44. *Ibid.*, 289. (Drake trans., 265; Salusbury trans., 279)
45. J. W. N. Watkins, *Hobbes's System of Ideas* (London: Hutchinson, 1965), 61
46. *Ibid.*, 62
47. Galileo, *Dialogo, Opere di Galileo*, **7**, 36. (Drake trans., 12; Salusbury trans., 15
48. *Ibid.*, 48, italics mine. (Drake trans., 24; Salusbury trans., 30)
49. *Ibid.*, 115, italics mine. (Drake trans., 89–90; Salusbury trans., 101)
50. *Ibid.*, 171. (Drake trans., 145; Salusbury trans., 159–160)
51. *Ibid.*, 183. (Drake trans., 157–158; Salusbury trans., 172)
52. *Ibid.*, 194. (Drake trans., 168; Salusbury trans., 183)
53. *Ibid.*, 217–220. (Drake trans., 190–193; Salusbury trans., 202–206)
54. *Ibid.*, 350. (Drake trans., 322; Salusbury trans., 336)
55. *Ibid.*, 403, italics mine. (Drake trans., 376; Salusbury trans., 387)
56. *Ibid.*, 409. (Drake trans., 382; Salusbury trans., 393)
57. *Ibid.*, 360. (Drake trans., 332.) This passage was added by Galileo in his copy of the *Dialogue* and is not in the Salusbury translation
58. Letter to Ingoli (1624), *ibid.*, **6**, 545
59. Galileo, *Dialogo, ibid.*, **7**, 171, italics mine. (Drake trans., 145; Salusbury trans., 159.) Galileo's contemporaries do not seem to have inferred that he had performed the experiment. G. B. Baliani, writing to Galileo seven years after the publication of the *Dialogo*, informs him that he had a sailor drop a musket ball several times from the mast of a ship in motion and that each time it fell at its foot (letter to Galileo, 16 November 1639, *ibid.*, **18**, 103). To my knowledge Giordano Bruno was the first to adduce this experiment as evidence for the motion of the earth in *La Cena de le ceneri* (1584), ed. Giovanni Aquilecchia (Turin: Einaudi, 1955), 178. Buonamico, Galileo's teacher at Pisa, mentions the experiment, but he gives the wrong explanation (Francesco Buonamico, *De motu* [Florence, 1591], 452 G)
60. Galileo, *Dialogo, Opere di Galileo*, **7**, 169. (Drake trans., 143; Salusbury trans., 157–158)
61. *Ibid.*, 200. (Drake trans., 174; Salusbury trans., 188)
62. Ludovico Colombo, *Contro il moto della terra, ibid.*, **3**, 259–260
63. Postil to Antonio Rocco's *Esercitazioni Filosofiche, ibid.*, **7**, 731
64. Galileo, *Dialogo*, 389, italics mine. (Drake trans., 362; Salusbury trans., 372)
65. *Ibid.*, 414. (Drake trans., 388; Salusbury trans., 398)
66. Letter to Cesare Marsili, 5 April 1631, *ibid.*, **14**, 240
67. Galileo, *Dialogo, ibid.*, **7**, 395. (Drake trans., 368; Salusbury trans., 379)
68. *Ibid.*, 433. (Drake trans., 407; Salusbury trans., 416)
69. *Ibid.*, 440. (Drake trans., 414; Salusbury trans., 422)
70. *Ibid.*, 46. (Drake trans., 22; Salusbury trans., 27)

71. *Ibid.*, 250. (Drake trans., 223; Salusbury trans., 239)
72. David C. Lindberg, 'Galileo's Experiments on Falling Bodies', *Isis*, **56** (1965), 352
73. Galileo, *Dialogo, Opere di Galileo*, **7**, 54. (Drake trans., 30.) This passage was added by Galileo in his copy of the *Dialogue* and is not in the Salusbury translation
74. He claimed that in many repetitions of the experiment the distance fallen was always farther (in an equivalent time) than that reported by Galileo (Marin Mersenne, *Harmonie Universelle*, t. I [Paris, 1637], quoted by A. Koyré, 'An Experiment in Measurement', *Proceedings of the Am. Phil. Soc.*, **97** (1953), 227, 235–236)
75. Thomas B. Settle, 'An experiment in the History of Science', *Science*, **133** (1961), 19–23
76. Lindberg, 'Galileo's Experiments', 354
77. Stillman Drake, 'Free Fall in Galileo's *Dialogue*', *Isis*, **57** (1966), 270
78. Letters to Galileo of 23 April 1632 and 1 July 1639, *Opere di Galileo*, **14**, 343; **18**, 69
79. Letter to G. B. Baliani, 1 August 1639, *ibid.*, **18**, 77. Hence the merely illustrative distance time pair given in the *Discorsi*: 4 seconds to fall through the height of a spear ('picca'). (Galileo, *Discorsi, ibid.*, **8**, 287)
80. Galileo, *Dialogo, ibid.*, **7**, 256. (Drake trans., 230; Salusbury trans., 246)
81. Postil to Antonio Rocco's *Esercitazioni Filosofiche, ibid.*, 731
82. *Ibid.*, 735–736
83. *Ibid.*, 742–743
84. A. C. Crombie, *Robert Grosseteste and the Origins of Experimental Science* (Oxford: Clarendon Press, 1953), 305
85. A. Rupert Hall, *From Galileo to Newton*, 63
86. Postil to Antonio Rocco's *Esercitazioni Filosofiche, Opere di Galileo*, **7**, 744
87. Galileo, *Dialogo, ibid.*, 84. (Drake trans., 59; Salusbury trans., 71)
88. *Ibid.*, 394. (Drake trans., 367; Salusbury trans., 377)
89. *Ibid.*, 436. (Drake trans., 410; Salusbury trans., 419)
90. *Ibid.*, 229. (Drake trans., 203; Salusbury trans., 216)
91. *Ibid.*, 261. (Drake trans., 234–235; Salusbury trans., 251)
92. Koyré, *Etudes Galiléennes*, 245–246
93. A. J. Dijksterhuis, *The Mechanization of the World Picture*, trans. C. Dikshoorn (Oxford: Clarendon Press, 1961), 338
94. Galileo terminology is revealing. In the First Day of the *Dialogue*, he uses the terms *inclinazione, instinto, repugnanza, affezione, natural simpatia* and *corrispondenza*. In the Second Day, he adds *talento* and *appetito*
95. Galileo, *Dialogo, Opere di Galileo*, **7**, 56. (Drake trans., 31–32.) This passage was added by Galileo in his copy of the *Dialogue* and is not in the Salusbury translation
96. See Marshall Clagett, *The Science of Mechanics in the Middle Ages* (Madison: University of Wisconsin Press, 1961), 505–540

7. THE PHYSICAL PROOF FROM THE TIDES: THE FOURTH DAY OF THE *DIALOGUE*

THE CONTEXT OF DISCOVERY

Francis Bacon and Galileo both wrote a treatise on the tides in the second decade of the seventeenth century. Bacon, who was not a professional scientist but a well-informed amateur, begins his essay by stating the observational evidence readily available to anyone interested in the problem. He recognises the *daily cycle* with high and low tides recurring at intervals of twelve hours; the *monthly cycle* whereby the tides lag behind fifty minutes each day until they have gone round the clock and are back to their original position; the *half-monthly cycle* with high tides at new and full moon and low tides at quadratures, and finally the *half-yearly cycle* with greater tides at the equinoxes than at the solstices.[1]

The phenomenon of the tides arrested the attention of Renaissance scholars, and several hypotheses were currently debated. They can be listed as follows:

(1) Apollonius' animistic interpretation of the tides on the analogy of respiration is set forth in Antonio Ferrari, called Galateo, *De Situ Elementorum*, published in 1558, but it does not appear to have been shared by many of Galileo's contemporaries.[2]

(2) The Aristotelians, drawing their inspiration from Aristotle's passing remark in the *Meteorology*, held that the natural slope of the Mediterranean and the winds were the main causes of the tides.[3]

(3) Scaliger seeks to explain the tides by appealing to some form of sympathy between the moon and the water of the ocean. On his interpretation, the waters move west under the influence of the moon, impinge upon the coast of America and are reflected backward, thus causing the ebbing and flowing of the tides. Scaliger is aware of the discrepancy between the motion of the flood current and that of the moon. Girolamo Cardano, whom he so bitterly criticises, might have been useful to him here, for Cardano meets the same difficulty by explaining that not all the water follows the moon since the motion is transmitted from one part to the next. Pandolfo Sfondrato, in a tract published in 1590, proposes a similar solution, but he emphasises the role of the heavenly sphere rather than that of the moon in causing the water to flow westward. Bacon's own conjecture is in substantial agreement with this view.[4]

(4)   Girolamo Borro, who lectured at Pisa when Galileo was a student there, invokes the 'temperate heat' of the moon, acting as an attractive force on the analogy of fire causing water to rise as it nears the boiling point. Bernardo Telesio suggests a rather more vague relationship between the sun, the moon and the tides. He assumes that the sea rises and tends to boil over when it is heated by the sun, and that it sets itself in motion to avoid evaporation, thus producing the flow and ebb of the tides.[5]

(5)   The physician Andrea Cesalpino, another lecturer at Pisa in Galileo's day, suggests that the tides are produced by the libration of the earth. This interesting, and, to my knowledge, novel idea, is closely connected with his astronomy. In order to avoid the necessity of postulating the existence of a ninth and tenth sphere—the former to explain the precession of the equinoxes, and the latter the imaginary phenomenon of their trepidation—he ascribes the motion by which the phenomena are produced to the earth itself. He explains trepidation by supposing that the earth has a libratory and irregular motion that gives rise to the tides.[6] R. L. Ellis, the editor of Francis Bacon's *Works*, has suggested that we pass naturally from the theory of Cesalpinus to that of Galileo,[7] since it is only natural for the latter to think of Copernicus in connection with any hypothesis about the motion of the earth. As a matter of fact, he is not the only one to do so. Otto Casmann in his *Marinarum questionum tractatio philosophica* of 1596 also discusses the motion of the earth after outlining Cesalpino's theory.[8]

(6)   Paolo Sarpi's contribution is more controversial. His notebook contains three paragraphs where he explains the tides by postulating that the earth moves. These notes were jotted down between 1595 and 1596, perhaps when Sarpi was thinking of writing a treatise on the tides which he subsequently completed but which is lost.[9] Stillman Drake has suggested that they reflect a conversation between Sarpi and Galileo.[10] This is a genuine possibility, but we have no evidence that Galileo believed in the heliocentric system prior to his letters to Mazzoni and Kepler in 1597. It is interesting to note that when Galileo informed Kepler that he had succeeded in explaining many natural effects with the aid of the Copernican theory, which on the contrary hypothesis were altogether inexplicable, Kepler immediately thought that Galileo was seeking to account for the tides by the motion of the earth, an idea that had occurred at the same time to his friend Hans Geörg Herwart von Hohenburg.[11]

THE DISCOURSE OF 1616

Galileo initially referred to the *Dialogue on the Two World Systems* as the *System of the World*. After 1616, he christened it the *Dialogue on the*

Tides, and it was only with considerable reluctance that he finally bowed to the censors and abandoned this title in 1632.[12] The change from the *System of the World* to the *Dialogue on the Tides* was motivated by the disclosure in 1615 of his new physical proof of the earth's motion. The reader will recall that Galileo journeyed to Rome in the winter of 1615 to save Copernicanism from the threat of censure. He failed in his attempt, but he impressed prelates and intellectuals alike with his amazing dialectical skill. At the request of the young Cardinal Alessandro Orsini he put down in writing what he considered his most cogent demonstration of the earth's motion : the argument from the tides. Although the *Discourse of 1616* was never published before it was revised and incorporated in the fuller discussion in the Fourth Day of the *Dialogue,* it was widely circulated, copies reaching Venice and Vienna by 1618. Francis Bacon was shown a copy by Richard White at the end of 1619, and in his *New Atlantis,* published the next year, he curtly rejects Galileo's theory as contrary to observational evidence.[13]

The *Discourse of 1616* is dated 6 January and purports to be a summary of the arguments Galileo produced a week earlier in a private debate among the friends and acquaintances of Cardinal Orsini.

In introducing the topic, Galileo appears to defer to experience :

> As we reason on the basis of sensory experience (reliable guide to true philosophising), we see that motion can be imparted to water in several ways. We shall examine them individually, to see whether one of them can reasonably be assigned as the primary cause of the flow and ebb of the sea.[14]

Galileo, however, does not mention any information he might have gathered in Pisa or Venice, two ports where he sojourned for more than thirty years. His first question is not, 'What do we know about the actual motion of the sea?' but, 'How can motion be imparted to water in a vessel?' He assumes that from the answer to this question the main cause of the tides will become apparent. Bacon begins his essay with a summary of observational reports; Galileo starts with a tribute to 'sensory experience', but in the absence of detailed evidence, this is hardly more than lip service.

Of the many ways that water can be made to flow, Galileo considers particularly suggestive the to-and-fro motion of water at the bottom of a boat that is alternatively speeded up and slowed down. He likens the piling of the water now at one end and now at the other to the action of the tide. The analogy is not entirely satisfactory, however, since the acceleration or retardation is shared uniformly by the whole boat whereas the flux and reflux of the tides is not uniform throughout the sea basins in which they occur. Galileo parries this criticism by introducing a more sophisticated model familiar to contemporary mathematicians and astronomers. He asks his readers to imagine that the ecliptic and the equator coincide. A point on the surface of the earth can be considered to move on an epicycle attached to a deferent representing the earth's orbit, as in figure 21.

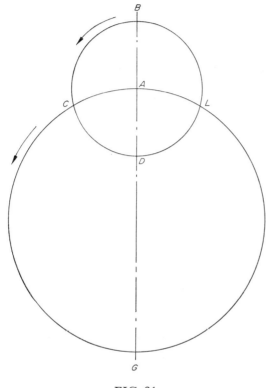

FIG 21

The epicycle revolves once daily. For half the day, the speed of the point is greater than that of the epicycle's centre (the centre of the earth); for the other half, the speed is less. Maximum and minimum velocities occur when a given point is collinear with the centres of both epicycle and deferent. As Ernst Mach pointed out in *The Science of Mechanics*, the theory of epicyclic motion is incorrect: Galileo makes the error of mixing two different frames of reference.[15] Whereas the motion of the earth is considered relative to the sun, the motion of the water is considered relative to the earth. But relative to the earth, the water can receive no acceleration due to the earth's annual motion, and the water must therefore be at rest relative to the earth. This non-technical criticism of Galileo's account was well within the compass of pre-inertial physics, and it was expressed as early as 1633 by a group of French physicists, of whom Jean-Jacques Bouchard wrote to Galileo :

> They draw attention to a difficulty raised by several members about the proposition you make that the tides are caused by the unevenness of the motion of different parts of the earth. They admit that these parts move with greater speed when they descend along the line of direction of the annual motion than when they move in the opposite direction. But this acceleration is only relative to the annual motion; relative to the body of the earth as well as to the water, the parts always move with the same speed. They say, therefore, that it is hard to understand how the parts of the earth, which always move in the same way relative to themselves and to the water, can impress varying motions to the water. They entreat me to try to obtain from you some solution to their difficulty.[16]

In other words, the centripetal acceleration arising from the earth's rotation is everywhere constant and can have no effect in generating the tides. Galileo's failure to distinguish centripetal acceleration from linear acceleration explains this oversight, but there is a direct observational consequence entailed by his model which he cannot be excused for over-looking. The axial and orbital speeds of the earth are so combined that a particle on the surface of the earth moves very fast once a day when both revolutions are in the same direction (point B in the diagram), and once very slowly when they are going in opposite directions (at point D). It follows immediately that high water should occur at noon, the time of greatest retardation, and low water at midnight, the time of greatest acceleration. Galileo never so much as mentions this obvious consequence of his theory. He expects his model to be challenged for a different reason : when the ocean is long enough, one end moves more rapidly than the other, whereas in a boat whose speed is varied, the acceleration or retardation is not greater at one end than at the other. His reply is that his mathematical model accounts for the difference. For instance, if the ocean is the length of BC in figure 21, the water near B will move faster than the water near C.[17]

Replacing physical models by mathematical ones raises the problem of empirical verification. Galileo recognises that it is 'very difficult, if not impossible, to duplicate its effect by any practical experiment',[18] but he promises to produce a mechanical model at some later date :

> And though to many people it may seem impossible to test the effects of such events in artificial devices and vessels, nevertheless this is not entirely impossible. I have a mechanical model that I will disclose at

the appropriate time in which the effects of this marvellous composi-
tions of movements may be observed in detail.[19]

These last two quotations reappear eighteen years later in the *Dialogue
on the Two World Systems* with minor but significant alterations. Galileo
rewrote the first passage to read no longer, 'it is very difficult, if not
impossible', but simply 'it is impossible', and he deleted the words 'that
I will disclose at the appropriate time' from the second passage.[20] He
maintained, however, that he had a mechanical model. But if he had
constructed such a model, or had plans for constructing one, why did he
fail to mention it to Cesare Marsili who wrote to inform him that an
engineer had produced a model of the tides? Galileo's only reply was
that the engineer's device merely indicated variations in temperature, and
had been discovered by himself twenty years before.[21] He was silent about
his own attempts to build a model. Knowing the priority claims Galileo
is wont to make for all his discoveries, his silence is more eloquent than
an explicit avowal that he had no more than a vague idea what a
mechanical model would really look like. He was persuaded that a
mathematical model was *in principle* translatable into physical reality,
and, in his eyes, this was enough to warrant the boast that he had
achieved what he intended. For Galileo, discovering a geometrical model
was an act of creative insight; building it was mere drudgery.

Having shown to his own satisfaction that the problem of the tides can
be solved because it is amenable to mathematical treatment, Galileo tries
to account for the discrepancies that appear to weaken his explanation.
The most serious one is the fact that high and low tides occur every six
hours, and not every twelve hours as his theory entails. Galileo, however,
does not consider this a dangerous indictment for, as such, it is merely an
observational report without any geometrical model to back it up.
Uninterpreted (non-geometrised) experience cannot be adduced as evidence against a consistent mathematical interpretation of the network of
laws that give rise to observational data. The most Galileo is prepared to
concede is that the six-hour period is common to the Mediterranean; he
maintains that in the Atlantic the period is a twelve-hour one as is 'daily
observed in Lisbon'. Galileo is so convinced of the truth of his theory that
he remarks: 'The belief that the periods of the tides were from six to
six hours was a fallacy which has led writers to imagine many useless
fantasies'.[22] In the *Dialogue on the Two World Systems*, Galileo re-
linquishes his erroneous claim that the tides have a twelve-hour period
in the Atlantic, and he simply states that the periods are conspicuously
less than six hours in the Hellespont and the Aegean. By 1630, therefore,
Galileo had realised that there was no proof whatever for a period greater
than the one normally observed in the Mediterranean. In spite of this

evidence, he did not revise his general theory, but maintained it in the purity of its geometrical structure.

THE FOURTH DAY OF THE *DIALOGUE*

The *Discourse of 1616* became the nucleus of the Fourth Day of the *Dialogue on the Two World Systems*. For the modern reader, this is a misguided appendix to a brilliant treatise, but for the author it was the climax of his work. The proof from the tides became increasingly important in Galileo's mind as the years went on, and it eventually became the only conclusive one. At the end of the Fourth Day, Galileo summarises the three main arguments for Copernicanism, and he voices the hope that a fourth and a fifth argument may soon be confirmed. The first rests on the stations and retrograde motions of the planets, the second on the revolution of the sun, and the third on the tides. The two others are the parallactic displacement of distant stars, and the change in the position of the meridian traced in the pavement of the church of Sant'Onofrio in Bologna, for which no evidence was available. Since the first and the second argument are equally compatible with Tycho Brahe's planetary system, this leaves only the argument from the tides as the decisive proof of the motion of the earth.

> If the terrestrial globe were immovable, the ebb and flow of the oceans could not occur naturally, . . . when we confer upon the globe the movements just assigned to it, the seas are necessarily subjected to an ebb and flow agreeing in all respects with what is to be observed in them.

Salviati admits at the beginning of the Fourth Day that he only observed what happens in the Adriatic and on the shores of the Tyrrhenian, and that for much of his information he has had to rely on reports made by others, 'which, being for the most part not in good agreement and accordingly rather unreliable, may contribute confusion rather than confirmation to our speculations'. From this avowal one would expect any theory that followed to be somewhat tentative. But this would be to misunderstand Galileo: his theory is not the result of observations but the outcome of a study of the mathematical implications of the motion of the earth. One ought not to be surprised therefore to read: 'From those accounts which we are sure of, and which happen to cover the principal events, it seems possible to arrive at the true and primary causes'.

What are these principal events? Are they the four periods mentioned by Bacon and acknowledged by the majority of contemporary writers on the subject? Not quite. Galileo enumerates three periods : the diurnal, whose 'intervals in the Mediterranean are for the most part about six hours each', the monthly, which 'seems to originate from the motion of the moon', and the annual, which 'appears to depend upon the sun'. But he fails to state the differences in the tides when the moon is new, full or at quadrature, and although he mentions that the tides at the solstices vary in size from those at the equinoxes, it is only twenty-eight pages later that he states, erroneously, that they are greater at the solstices. From this scanty information, Salviati, Galileo's spokesman, is willing to make the following bold generalisation :

> It seems to me that these true and certain effects alone, even if no others were to be seen, would probably persuade anyone who wished to stay within the bounds of nature that the earth moves.[23]

Simplicio reminds Salviati that several hypotheses have already been advanced to account for the tides, among which Marcantonio de Dominis' theory of an attractive force acting from the moon on the ocean.[24] The common objection to de Dominis' explanation was that high tide does not occur once a day when the moon is directly above the sea but twice, the second time when the moon is below the horizon. In other words, this theory, like Galileo's own hypothesis, entails a twenty-four-hour cycle and was rejected for failing to agree with experience. Galileo, of course, cannot level this criticism at de Dominis, and he attacks him for failing to realise that water rises and falls only at the extremities and not in the centre of the Mediterranean. De Dominis can hardly be blamed for failing to detect this phenomenon : it only exists as a consequence of Galileo's own theory.

Having cleared the seas of rival explanations, Galileo assumes that the rest is plain sailing. In the first part of the Fourth Day, he follows the itinerary of the *Discourse of 1616* until he reaches the argument from the Trade Winds which he introduces by raising an objection that stems from the 1616 discussion. If the motion of the earth caused the water to flow, it would produce an even greater effect on the air, and a strong east wind would be felt at all times. As Simplicio points out :

> Daily experience informs us that this should happen, for when we ride post at no more than eight or ten miles an hour in still air, we feel in our face what resembles a strong wind blowing against us. What would a rapid course of eight hundred or a thousand miles per hour produce?[25]

Salviati replies that water is more difficult to move than air but that it retains its impetus for a longer period of time; for instance, waves on a lake do not subside as soon as the wind dies down. He agrees that where the earth is smooth a constant breeze should be felt, and he adduces the case of the Trade Winds which blow from east to west at the equator. He also alleges that in the Mediterranean it takes less time to travel westward than eastward. Sagredo who has been consul in Aleppo is made to say :

> Keeping a special record and account of the days of departure and arrival of ships at the ports of Alexandria, Alexandretta and here at Venice, I found, when I compared many of them to satisfy my curiosity, that again and again the return here (that is the voyages from east to west over the Mediterranean) was made in less time than those in the opposite direction by 25 per cent. Thus, on the whole, the east winds are stronger than those from the west.[26]

Before discussing Galileo's argument, it may be useful to recall that the Trade Winds are set up by a somewhat different cause than the one he conjectured. The heat of the sun, stronger at the equator than at a point to the north, causes the air to be heated, thus creating a belt of low pressure at the equator. Colder air to the north results in a high pressure belt, and the wind blows from high to low pressure along the earth's surface. A particle having a motion in latitude tends to keep its angular momentum around the earth's axis unchanged, and so it alters its motion in longitude. In the mid-latitude high pressure belt a particle of air has less angular momentum than does a particle at the equator, and since angular momentum is conserved, the southward moving particle is deflected to the right, and the Trade Winds appear to an observer on the surface of the earth to be blowing from the north-east. Near the equator itself the deadly calms of the Doldrums and not the strong, steady breeze of the Trade Winds are experienced. Galileo knew that some of his contemporaries had found this to their sorrow, but he preferred to ignore the fact.[27] His claim to recorded evidence for the Mediterranean is equally puzzling for the prevailing wind east of Italy is a west wind in all seasons and not an east wind as Sagredo vouches for.

Simplicio raises another objection that had not been dealt with in the *Discourse of 1616* but was crucial since Sfondrato, Scaliger and Bacon had proposed it in some form or other. Standing Salviati's argument on its head, he argues that the constant motion of the air from east to west can be produced just as easily by the motion of the heavens revolving from east to west. This is a serious objection within the traditional system of astronomy which postulates a continuous linkage between the outer and the innermost spheres of the universe. For Galileo, who denies the very existence of such spheres, the argument appears ridiculous.

The section that follows in the Fourth Day is an original attempt to cope with the monthly and annual variations that the *Discourse of 1616* ignored. The widely held hypothesis that the moon exercises a causal

influence on the seas is firmly rejected at the outset. This is a possibility
Galileo *will not entertain.*

> I cannot bring myself to give credence to such causes as lights,
> temperate heats, predominances of occult qualities and similar idle
> imaginings. These are so far from being actual or possible causes of the
> tides that the very contrary is true. The tides are the cause of them;
> that is, make them occur in minds better equipped for loquacity and
> ostentation than for reflection upon, and investigation into, the most
> hidden works of nature.[28]

The basic presuppositions of a philosopher or a scientist are not only
disclosed in the conscious efforts he makes to justify his theories; they are
also revealed in the way he treats rival hypotheses. Galileo attacks few
theories with such bitterness. He is galled by the moon hypothesis, a key-
concept in a rival system of thought, but one that has no place in his own
conceptual framework. The idea of gravitation or attraction was em-
bedded in a philosophy which made much of sympathies and antipathies,
of occult forces and mysterious affinities. Galileo had worked himself out
of this universe of discourse and was in open revolt against it. He will
have nothing to do with the world of magic, and it is to the world of pure
geometrical forms that he turns for enlightenment. He is convinced that
his mathematical model will stand him in good stead, and he seeks to
account for the monthly variations of the tides by altering the speed of
the deferent (the orbital revolution), and the annual ones by modifying
the speed of the epicycle (the axial revolution). In no case does he wish
to appeal to external causes :

> It is fitting that we should resolve the whole problem according to the
> basic principles and hypotheses already established, without introducing
> any novelty either in astronomy or in the universe in favour of the
> tides, but demonstrating that the causes of all the various phenomena
> perceived in the tides reside in things already known and accepted as
> unquestionably true.[29]

Respecting the principle of economy implies finding the geometrical
structure underlying the welter of facts. In this case, it means realising
that when the motive force remains identical, a body will move more
slowly along a greater circle than along a smaller one, Galileo illustrates
this mathematical principle with the aid of two models. Firstly, he shows
how a movable weight can increase or decrease the vibrations of an
horizontally swinging stick, and thus regulate the period of a wheel clock.
Secondly, he points out that the frequency of a pendulum varies with its
length, and that an analogous law obtains in the heavens where the period

of revolution of the outer planets is greater than that of those close to the sun. If the moon, he concludes,

> continuing to be moved by the same motive force were drawn little by little into smaller circles, it would acquire a disposition to shorten the times of its periods in agreement with a pendulum which in the course of its vibrations has its cord shortened by us.[30]

But it is mainly on the analogy of a straight stick with the earth not quite at the end, and the moon acting as a weight sliding now to the right and now to the left of the spot marked earth that Galileo relies to explain the monthly variations in the earth's orbital velocity.[31]

Two objections to Galileo's account spring to mind. Firstly, the moon revolves around the earth; it does not move backward and forward the way a weight does on a rigid bar. Secondly, if the movement of the earth were so irregular it would surely have been observed by astronomers. Only the second of these objections is raised by Sagredo to whom Salviati replies that the irregularity cannot fail to be detected upon a closer inspection of the sun's progress through the signs of the zodiac. Galileo deftly shifts the debate from the earth to the heavens, but in the process he admits an astronomical fact that clearly challenges his own theory:

> It [the earth] passes the two semicircles of the ecliptic (divided by the equinoctial points) in very different times, consuming about nine days more in passing over one half than the air; a difference which is, as you see, very conspicuous.[32]

An irregularity of nine days is completely unexpected on Galileo's hypothesis of monthly variations, and it contradicts the explanation of the annual variation he proceeds to give with the aid of his geometrical model. This time the epicycle is inclined to the plane of the deferent to account for the irregularity of the additions and subtractions which the diurnal rotation makes upon the annual motion (figure 22).

Galileo's argument was involved and caused embarrassment to his more competent readers such as Baliani.[33] Fortunately, it can be expressed in simple terms: the inclination of the earth's axis with respect to its orbit entails a modification of the original model. The annual and the diurnal motions are in the same line only at the solstices when their combination produces the greatest acceleration and the greatest retardation. At the equinoxes, the two motions are inclined at their maximum angle and the effect of their combination is consequently least. Unfortunately for Galileo's theory, it is the reverse which holds true: the equinoctial tides are most extreme because they receive the maximum effects of the sun's gravitational pull. This was known to Francis Bacon, and it is one of

G. B. Riccioli's strictures against Galileo's theory.[34] But Galileo was thinking of the perfect fit and not of the wrinkles in the garment :

> This is all I can tell you about the matter, and perhaps it is as much
> as can be comprehended within our knowledge—which, as is well
> known, can be only of such conclusions as are fixed and constant, such
> as the three general periods of the tides, since they depend upon
> invariable, unified and eternal causes.[35]

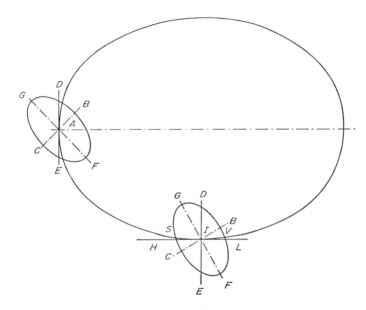

FIG. 22

He proceeds to lament the lack of insight of those who either thought
that one motion of the earth would suffice[36] or appealed to a conflict
between the motion of the earth and that of the lunar sphere.[37] Finally,
in the name of the clean, clear light of rationality, he criticises Kepler for
failing to free himself from occult qualities and accepting the dominion
of the moon. The discussion ends with Sagredo admitting that he has not
grasped the argument, and expressing the hope that he will do so, not
by testing its consequences against experience, but by thinking about it
and surmounting the initial difficulty of a new mathematical proposition.

   It is understandable that the Aristotelian professor Antonio Rocco
should have concluded his discussion of Galileo's theory of the tides by
querying his outspoken reliance on experience :

At the beginning of your work, you often proclaim that you wish to

follow the way of the senses so closely that Aristotle (who promised to
follow this method and taught it to others) would have changed opinion,
having seen what you have observed. Nonetheless, in the progress of
the book you have always been so much a stranger to this way of
proceeding that . . . all your controversial conclusions go against our
sense knowledge, as anyone can see by himself, and as you expressly
say yourself on page 325 [*Opere di Galileo*, vol. 7, p. 355] speaking of
the theory of Copernicus, which was rendered plausible and admirable
to many by abstract reasoning although it was against all sensory
experience.[38]

Conclusion

History of science is not restricted to the enumeration of successful
investigations but has to tell of unsuccessful enquiries and explain why
some of the ablest men failed to find the key to knowledge. There can
be no doubt that Galileo's theory of the tides opened no new scientific
vista to his successors. He neglected to take cognizance of the four well
known periods of the tides, he rode roughshod over the discrepancies
between his theory and experience, he did not investigate striking observational consequences entailed by his explanation, and he brushed aside
contemptuously any appeal to the influence of the moon. This last refusal
is easier to understand if we recall that theories making use of the attraction of the moon were formulated with the aid of occult qualities that
Galileo considered the bane of philosophy. But why his blatant disregard
for facts? In the *Discourse of 1616*, he only mentioned the diurnal period,
and he distorted this fact by claiming that there was only one high and
one low tide every twenty-four hours in the Atlantic. In the *Dialogue on
the Two World Systems*, he acknowledged the correct daily cycle, but he
denied the dependence of the half-monthly period on the moon, failed to
relate the tides at the solstices with the position of the sun, and omitted
the monthly period whereby the tides occur later each day by the same
time as the moon's transit. He did not attend to three obvious and easily
testable consequences of his theory. First, his explanation of diurnal
motion required high water to occur at noon, the time of greatest
retardation, and low tide at midnight, the time of greatest acceleration.
Secondly, his description of monthly motion on the analogy of a movable
weight on the regulating rod of a wheel-clock implied that orbital speed
should be greater at new moon than at full moon, and consequently that
the tides should be greater at new moon.[39] Finally, his account of the
annual period called for greater tides at the solstices than at the equinoxes.
All these implications were abundantly contradicted by experience.

The fact that Galileo stuck to his idea in the teeth of all these difficulties, not only undaunted but apparently unperturbed, may be taken as a testimonial to his faith in Copernicanism. There is no doubt that he overstrained himself in his attempt to create a unified cosmos with which to replace Aristotle's. In his anxiety to establish a mathematical science uniting heaven and earth in a single physics, he pressed eagerly forward over obstacles. The new cosmology had to have terrestrially observable consequences, and since Galileo had shown in the first three days of the *Dialogue* that these could not be found in the motion of projectiles or anywhere on earth, he was determined to find them in the sea. He displayed a scornful impatience with the complexity of the data, a kind of self-righteousness, which is characteristic of minds whose goals, when they address themselves to nature, is order and simplicity. His instinct for theoretical elegance told him that Copernicus was right, and although the actual observations were only partially in his favour, he was convinced that the burden of proof rested with his opponents. If they were to refute him they had to produce not more and better experiments, but a simpler and geometrically more satisfying alternative. Galileo's discussion of the tides fails to make sense if we forget that he was more than a physicist. He was a natural philosopher who saw beyond the problem of determining the periods of the tides, about which he did not feel strongly, to the great vision of a science in which the real is described by the ideal, the physical by the mathematical, matter by mind. He was convinced that his analogy of epicycle and deferent and his models of the pendulum and the regulating weight of a wheel-clock enabled him to understand and express the unifying structure of reality. The isochronism of the pendulum was the key to the comprehension of the motion of bodies on earth and in the heavens. It was only natural to expect that it would help to explain the main properties of motion in the ocean. The basic, albeit implicit, assumption is that there is a perfect correspondence between the human mind and reality by virtue of mathematics. This is the hidden root of a large part of natural science in the Renaissance. Galileo loathed people who reiterated 'trumpet-like' everything that was old, but he adhered dogmatically to the notion that the world was written in mathematical symbols. He would sacrifice his theory only if a mathematically more elegant or more comprehensive one was forthcoming. It is the irony of history that this should have happened in 1637 when he abandoned his theory of the tides for another equally ill-fated explanation. In November of that year, he informed Fra Fulgenzio Micanzio that he had discovered that the moon moved its face in three ways,

namely it moves it slightly now to the right and now to the left, it raises and lowers it, and finally it inclines it now toward the right and now toward the left shoulder. All these variations can be seen on the face of the moon, and what I say is manifest and obvious to the senses from the great and ancient spots that are on the surface of the moon. Furthermore add a second marvel : these three different variations have three different periods, for the first changes from day to day and so has its diurnal period, the second changes from month to month and has a monthly period, and the third has an annual period whereby it completes its cycle. Now what will your Reverence say when you compare these three lunar periods with the three diurnal, monthly and annual periods of the motions of the sea, of which, by unanimous consent, the moon is arbiter and superintendent.[40]

Did the man who pitied Kepler for lending his ear to 'such puerilities' as the moon's dominion over the waters capitulate before the overwhelming observational evidence? Not in the least, for the moon's diurnal parallax and its librations in longitude and latitude have nothing to do with the periods of the tides. From the standpoint of mathematics, however, the hypothetical correlation of these rocking motions with the periods of the tides had all the advantages of simplicity and elegance. It is for this reason only that Galileo was willing to discard his original model of epicycle and deferent.

The ill-fated theory of the tides is a skeleton in the cupboard of the scientific revolution. When allowed into the light, it serves as a reminder that Galilean science was not so much an experimental game as a Platonic gamble. In this sense, it is deservedly famous.

NOTES

1. Francis Bacon, *De fluxu et refluxu maris* in *The Works of Francis Bacon*, eds. Spedding *et al.*, 14 vols. (London, 1857), vol. 3, p. 47. Information about the first three periods was readily available in two works to which Galileo was referred by G. B. Baliani (letter of 23 April 1632, *Opere di Galileo*, **14**, 343). These are Pietro da Medina, *L'arte del navegar* (Venice, 1554), 123r, 123v, 126r, and Lucas Waghenaer (known as Aurigarius), *Speculum nauticum* (Leiden, 1586), 29. For Bacon's account of the tides, see Paolo Rossi, *Aspetti della rivoluzione scientifica* (Naples: Morano, 1971), 151–222
2. Antonio Ferrari [Galateo], *Liber de situ elementorum* (Basel, 1558), 91. This opinion is attributed to Apollonius by Bacon, *Works*, **3**, 50
3. Aristotle, *Meteorologica*, bk. 2, ch. 1, 354a
4. Scaliger's opinion is discussed by Francesco Patrizzi, *Nova de universis philosophia* (Venice, 1593), 139r; Girolamo Cardano, *De subtilitate libri XXI* (Basel, 1560), 96; Pandolfo Sfondrato, *Causa aestus maris* (Ferrara, 1590), 7v–8v; Bacon, *Works*, **3**, 55
5. Girolamo Borro, *Del flusso e reflusso del mare e dell' inondatione del Nilo* (Florence, 1577); Bernardo Telesio, *De rerum natura* (Geneva, 1588), bk. 1, ch. 12, col. 572–573

6. Andrea Cesalpino, *Questionum peripateticorum libri V* (Venice, 1593), 70r–71v. Various theories on the tides are summarised by Otto Casmann, *Marinarum questionum tractatio philosophica* (Frankfurt, 1596), 173 ff., who draws heavily from another summary in Patrizzi, *Nova de universis philosophia*, 137v ff. Patrizzi does not mention Cesalpino however.

7. Robert Leslie Ellis, 'Preface to the *De fluxu et refluxu maris*', in Bacon, *Works*, **3**, 44

8. Otto Casmann, *Marinarum questionum tractatio*, 200–216. Casmann follows Giovanni Costeo, *Disquisitionum physiologicarum* (Bologna, 1598), 90–100, in answering the objections raised against Copernicus

9. Paolo Sarpi, *Scritti filosofici e teologici*, ed. Romano Amerio (Bari: Laterza, 1951), 115. Fra Fulgenzio Micanzio in his life of Sarpi deplored 'the loss of what the Father wrote on the motion of the water, for I am convinced that it would have given food to many intellects that go hungry without any hope of finding something that would at least appear to satisfy them'. Fulgenzio Micanzio, *Vita del Padre Paolo dell' Ordine de' Servi* (Leiden, 1646), 105–106

10. Stillman Drake, 'Galileo Gleanings X. Origin and Fate of Galileo's Theory of the Tides', *Physis*, **3** (1961), 188–189

11. Letter of Galileo to Kepler, 4 August 1597, *Opere di Galileo*, **10**, 68; letter of Kepler to Hans Geörg Herwart von Hohenburg, 26 March 1598, *ibid.*, 72. Herwart von Hohenburg expressed surprise that no-one had used the tides as an argument for the motion of the earth (letter to Kepler, 12 March 1598, in Johann Kepler, *Gesammelte Werke*, ed. F. Hammer *et al.*, 18 vols. to date (Munich: C. H. Beck, 1938–), **13**, 178. It is noteworthy that Galileo and Herwart were both looking for a *physical* proof of the motion of the earth

12. 'I have not been able to obtain permission to mention the tides in the title of the book although it is the principal argument that I consider in it' (letter to Elia Diodati, 16 August 1631), *Opere di Galileo*, **14**, 289. The idea of a Dialogue on the tides was not novel. Galileo may have got it from Ambrosio Florido's *Dialogismus de natura universa Maris, ac eius genesi, et de causa fluxus, et refluxus eiusdem, atque de alijs accidentibus, quae eius naturam comitantur. Interlocutores Philonauticus et Philosophus* (Pavia, 1613). Galileo does not mention this work, but it would be surprising if he had not heard of it since his friend Luca Valerio was closely associated with the Aldobrandini family, and Galileo himself corresponded with Card. Ippolito Aldobrandini to whom the book is dedicated

13. Bacon, *Works*, **1**, 327

14. Galileo, *Discorso del flusso e reflusso del mare*, *Opere di Galileo*, **5**, 378. Hereafter cited as *Discourse of 1616*

15. Ernst Mach, *The Science of Mechanics*, trans. Thomas J. McCormac, 6th ed. (La Salle: Open Court Classics, 1960), 262–264

16. Letter to Galileo, 5 September 1633, *Opere di Galileo*, **14**, 251–252. Unfortunately, we do not know whether Galileo answered this query. Arthur Koestler remarks that Galileo unconsciously smuggles in the absent parallax through the back door by referring the motion of the water to the earth's axis but the motion of the land to the fixed stars. 'The tides became an Ersatz for parallax' (Arthur Koestler, *The Sleepwalkers* [London: Hutchinson, 1959], 466)

17. Galileo, *Discourse of 1616*, *Opere di Galileo*, **5**, 386. This does not deter Galileo from having Salviati say in the Fourth Day of the *Dialogue*: 'Now gentlemen, what the boat does with regard to the water it contains, and what the water does with respect to the boat containing it, is *precisely the same* as what the Mediterranean basin does with respect to the water contained in it' (*ibid.*, **7**, 451, italics mine)

18. *Ibid.*, 385

19. *Ibid.*, 386–387

20. Galileo, *Dialogo, ibid.*, **7**, 456. (Drake trans., 430–431; Salusbury trans., 439)

21. Letter of Cesare Marsili to Galileo, 3 April 1626, *ibid.*, **13**, 316–317; letter

of Galileo to Cesare Marsili, 25 April 1626, *ibid.*, 320

22. Galileo, *Discourse of 1616*, *ibid.*, **5**, 388–389
23. Galileo, *Dialogo*, *ibid.*, **7**, 443–445. (Drake trans., 417–419; Salusbury trans., 425–427)
24. Marcantonio de Dominis, *Euripus, seu de fluxu et refluxu maris sententia* (Rome, 1624)
25. Galileo, *Dialogo*, *Opere di Galileo*, **7**, 462–463. (Drake trans., 437; Salusbury trans., 444)
26. *Ibid.*, 466. (Drake trans., 440; Salusbury trans., 447)
27. Giovanfrancesco Buonamici, writing from Madrid on 1 February 1630, explicitly informed Galileo of the existence of the doldrums (*ibid.*, **14**, 75)
28. Galileo, *Dialogo*, *ibid.*, **7**, 470. (Drake trans., 445; Salusbury trans., 452.) Cardano had remarked, more than half a century earlier, that no-one could deny the influence of the moon and the sun on the tides and still account for daily experience (Girolamo Cardano, *De rerum varietate* [Basel, 1557], 697)
29. *Ibid.*, 474. (Drake trans., 449; Salusbury trans., 456)
30. *Ibid.*, 477. (Drake trans., 452; Salusbury trans., 459)
31. This argument has been adduced by Harold L. Burstyn as evidence that Galileo was the first to point out that the earth's orbit around the sun is not described by the centre of the earth but by the centre of mass of the earth–moon system. According to Burstyn, Galileo 'shows clearly, by an argument similar to that for the falling body, that the earth and the moon—if in some dynamic relation—must revolve about a point which we call their common center of mass' (Harold L. Burstyn, 'Galileo's Attempt to Prove that the Earth Moves', *Isis*, **53** [1962], 179). Burstyn's interpretation is open to criticism on the grounds that the analogy directly invoked by Galileo is not the pendulum but the movable lead-weight in the wheel-clock. See A. J. Aiton, 'On Galileo and the Earth–Moon System', *Isis*, **54** (1963), 265–266
32. Galileo, *Dialogo*, *Opere di Galileo*, **7**, 481. (Drake trans., 455–456; Salusbury trans., 463)
33. G. B. Baliani found that Galileo explained everything very clearly 'except the last discussion on the irregularities in the additions and subtractions of the diurnal and annual revolutions' (letter to Galileo, 23 April 1632, *ibid.*, **14**, 343). Francesco Rinuccini also failed to see how the diurnal motion could produce greater tides at the equinoxes (letter to Galileo, 23 November 1637, *ibid.*, **17**, 227)
34. Bacon, *Works*, **3**, 47; G. B. Riccioli, *Almagestum novum* (Bologna, 1651), 380
35. Galileo, *Dialogo*, *Opere di Galileo*, **7**, 483. (Drake trans., 460; Salusbury trans., 467)
36. *Ibid.*, 486. (Drake trans., 461–462; Salusbury trans., 469.) In the Fourth Day, Galileo gives no references, but in a letter to Cesare Marsili, 20 March 1632, he mentions Cesalpino and Origano (*ibid.*, **14**, 334–335). Origano affirms that the earth rotates on its axis but he denies its orbital revolution around the sun (D. Origano, *Ephemerides* [Frankfurt, 1609], 2v of the Introduction)
37. In the margin, Galileo refers to the Greek mathematician Seleucus, and in a letter written shortly after the publication of the *Dialogue*, he comments: 'I received the *Discourses* of Roffeni [this work has been lost] several days ago . . . See the place where the Signor Roffeni honours me by putting me on the same footing as the ancient mathematician Seleucus in the study of the cause of the tides. I am glad that I chanced to agree with the opinion of such a great philosopher. This will add weight to the theory. However, I should have thought that I was the first to entertain the idea, I do not say of locating the cause of such an effect in the motion of the earth, but of doing so in such a way that the effect might follow, and not in such a way that it bears no relation to it whatsoever, as Origano and Cesalpino have done, and perhaps Seleucus himself if we could know how he arrived at it. For attributing to the earth a simple and uniform motion cannot cause such a change in the sea' (letter to Cesare Marsili, 20 March 1632, *ibid.*, **14**, 334–335)

38. Antonio Rocco, *Esercitazioni filosofiche* (Venice, 1633), *ibid.*, **7**, 712
39. I have found only one author who held that the tides were unequal at new and full moon. This is Cesalpino who believed that the tides were greater at full moon, the reverse of what Galileo's theory entailed (Andrea Cesalpino, *Questionum peripateticorum,* 70r
40. Letter to F. Micanzio, 7 November 1637, *Opere di Galileo,* **17**, 214–215

SELECTED BIBLIOGRAPHY

The secondary literature on Galileo is vast and this bibliography makes no claim to completeness. Its purpose is merely to indicate the works that have been found most useful in writing this book.

I—GALILEO'S WORKS

The standard edition is :

Galileo Galilei. *Le opere.* Edited by Antonio Favaro, 20 vols. Florence : G. Barbèra, 1899–1909. Reprinted 1929–1939, 1964–1966, and 1968

There is an excellent annotated edition of the *Discorsi e dimostrazioni matematiche intorno a due nuove scienze* by A. Carugo and L. Geymonat. Turin : Paolo Boringhieri, 1958

Translations

The Assayer. Translated by Stillman Drake in Galileo Galilei *et al. The Controversy on the Comets of 1618.* Philadelphia : University of Pennsylvania Press, 1960

Dialogue Concerning the Two Chief World Systems – Ptolemaic and Copernican. Translated by Stillman Drake, Berkeley and Los Angeles : University of California Press, 1962

Dialogue on the Great World Systems. Translated by Thomas Salusbury, revised and annotated by Giorgio de Santillana. Chicago : University of Chicago Press, 1953

Dialogues Concerning two New Sciences. Translated by Henry Crew and Alfonso de Salvio. New York : Dover Publications, 1953

Discourse on the Comets. Translated by Stillman Drake in Galileo Galilei *et al. The Controversy on the Comets of 1618.* Philadelphia : University of Pennsylvania Press, 1960

Letter to the Grand Duchess Christina. Translated by Stillman Drake in *Discoveries and Opinions of Galileo.* Garden City, N.Y. : Doubleday Anchor Books, 1957

Letters on the Sunspots. Partly translated by Stillman Drake. *Ibid.*

The Little Balance. Translated by Laura Fermi and Gilberto Bernardini. *Galileo and the Scientific Revolution.* Greenwich, Connecticut : Fawcet Publications, 1965

On Motion and *On Mechanics.* Translated by I. E. Drabkin and Stillman Drake. Madison : The University of Wisconsin Press, 1960

II—BIBLIOGRAPHIES

Favaro, Antonio, and Carli, Alarico. *Bibliografia Galileiana* (1568–1895). Rome : Fratelli Bencini, 1896

Boffito Giuseppe. *Bibliografia Galileiana* (1896–1940). Rome : La Libreria dello Stato, 1943

McMullin, Ernan. *Addenda to the Carli–Favaro (1564–1895) and Boffito (1896–1940) Bibliografia Galileiana* in *Galileo: Man of Science.* Edited by Ernan McMullin. New York : Basic Books, 1967, Appendix B, pp. LXX–LXXXII

McMullin, Ernan. *Bibliografia Galileiana (1940–1964)* in *Galileo: Man of Science.* Edited by Ernan McMullin. New York : Basic Books, 1967, Appendix A, pp. I–LXIX

Cinti, Dino. *Biblioteca Galileiana raccolta dal Principe Giampolo Rocco di Torrepadula.* Florence : Sansoni, 1957

Procissi, Angelo. *La Collezione Galileiana della Biblioteca Nazionale di Firenze.* Roma : Ministero della Publica Istruzione, 1959

Cosenza, Mario Emilio. *Biographical and Bibliographical Dictionary of the Italian Humanists and the World of Classical Scholarship in Italy.* 5 vols. Boston : G. K. Hall, 1962

III—PRIMARY SOURCES

Archimedes. *The Works of Archimedes.* Edited and paraphrased by T. H. Heath, 1897. Reprint. New York : Dover Publications, 1953

Aristotle. *Meteorologica.* Edited and translated by H. D. P. Lee. Loeb Classical Library. London : Heinemann, 1962

Aristotle. *Minor Works.* Edited and translated by W. S. Hett. Loeb Classical Library. London : Heinemann, 1955

Aristotle. *On the Heavens.* Edited and translated by W. K. C. Guthrie. Loeb Classical Library. London : Heinemann, 1960

Aristotle. *Physics.* Edited and translated by P. H. Wicksteed and F. M. Cornford. Loeb Classical Library. London : Heinemann, 1960

Benedetti, G. B. *Diversarum speculationum mathematicarum et physicorum liber.* Turin, 1585

Borro, Girolamo. *De motu gravium et levium.* Florence, 1575

Borro, Girolamo. *Del flusso e reflusso del mare, e dell' inondatione del Nilo.* Florence, 1577

Brahe, Tycho. *Opera Omnia.* Edited by I. L. E. Dreyer, 14 vols. and index. Copenhagen, 1913–1929

Bruno, Giordano. *Le cena de le Ceneri* (1584). Edited by Giovanni Aquilecchia. Turin : Einaudi, 1955

Buonamico, Francesco. *De motu libri X.* Florence, 1591

Calcagnini, Celio. *Opera aliquot.* Basel, 1544

Campanella, Tommaso. *Apologia pro Galileo.* Frankfurt, 1622

Cardano, Girolamo. *De rerum varietate libri XVII.* Basel, 1557

Cardano, Girolamo. *De Subtilitate libri XXI.* Basel, 1560

Cassman, Otto. *Marinarum questionum tractatio philosophica.* Frankfurt, 1596

Cesalpino, Andrea. *Questionum peripateticorum libri V.* Venice, 1593

Chiaramonti, Scipione. *Antitycho.* Venice, 1621

Chiaramonti, Scipione. *Apologia Scipionis Claramontii pro Antitychone suo adversum Hyperaspistem Joannis Kepleri.* Venice, 1626

Chiaramonti, Scipione. *De tribus stellis, quae annis 1572, 1600, 1604 comparuere, libri tres.* Cesena, 1628

Clavius, Christoph. *Opera mathematica.* 5 vols. Mainz, 1611–1612

Copernicus, Nicolaus. *De revolutionibus orbium caelestium.* Nuremberg, 1543

Costeo, Giovanni. *Disquisitionum physiologicarum . . . libri sex.* Bologna, 1589

de Dominis, Marcantonio. *Euripus, sive de fluxu et refluxu maris sententia.* Rome, 1624

Descartes, René. *Oeuvres.* Edited by Charles Adam and Paul Tannery, 12 vols. and index, 1897–1913. Reprint. Paris : Vrin, 1956–1957

Doni, Anton Francesco. *Mondi celesti, terrestri, et infernali de gli academici pellegrini.* Venice, 1567

Florido, Ambrosio. *Dialogismus de natura universa maris, ac eius genesi et de causa fluxus et refluxus eiusdem atque de alijs accidentibus, quae eius naturam comitantur.* Pavia, 1613

Ferrari, Antoni [Galateo]. *Liber de situ elementorum.* Basel, 1558

Foscarini, Paolo Antonio. *Lettera sopra l'opinione de' Pittagorici e del Copernico della mobilità della terra e stabilità del sole e del nuovo Pittagorico sistema del mondo.* Naples, 1615

Fracastoro, Girolamo. *Opera omnia.* Venice, 1555

Gilbert, William. *De magnete.* London, 1600

Hero of Alexandria. *Spiritualium liber.* Edited and trans. into Latin by Federico Commandino. Urbino, 1575

Kepler, Johann, *Gesammelte Werke.* Edited by Max Caspar and Franz Hammer. 18 vols. to date. Munich : C. H. Beck, 1938–

Magini, Giovanni Antonio. *Ephemerides coelestium motuum ab anno Domini 1581 usque ad annum 1620.* Venice, 1582

Malapert, Charles. *Austriaca sidera heliocyclica astronomicis hypothesibus illigata.* Douay, 1633

Mazzoni, Jacopo. *In universam Platonis et Aristotelis praeludia, sive de comparatione Platonis et Aristotelis.* Venice, 1597

Medina, Pietro da. *L'arte del navegar.* Venice, 1554

Mersenne, Marin. *Harmonicarum libri XII.* Paris, 1636

Mersenne, Marin. *Harmonie universelle.* Paris, 1636 (There are at least two Parisian editions in the same year. One is by Sébastien Cramoisy, and the other by Pierre Ballard)

Mersenne, Marin. *Correspondence.* Edited by Cornelis de Waard, 10 vols. Paris : Vrin, 1945–1967

Micanzio, Fulgenzio. *Vita del Padre Paolo dell'Ordine de' Servi.* Leiden, 1646

Monte, Guidobaldo del. *Mechanicorum liber.* Pesaro, 1577

Origano, Davide. *Ephemerides.* Frankfurt, 1609

Pascal, Blaise. *Oeuvres complètes.* Edited by Jacques Chevalier. Paris : Bibliothèque de la Pléiade, 1962

Patrizzi, Francesco. *Discussiones peripateticae.* Basel, 1581

Patrizzi, Francesco. *Nova de universis philosophia.* Venice, 1593

Ptolemy. *Almagest.* Translated by R. Catesby Taliafero in *Great Books of the Western World,* no. 16. Chicago : The University of Chicago Press, 1952

Riccioli, Giovanni Battista. *Almagestum novum.* Bologna, 1651

Sarpi, Paolo. *Scritti teologici.* Edited by Romano Amerio. Bari : Laterza, 1951

Sfondrato, Pandolfo. *Causa aestus maris.* Ferrara, 1590

Stevin, Simon. *Principal Works.* Edited by E. Crone, E. J. Dijksterhuis, R. J. Forbes, M. G. J. Minnaert, A. Pannekoek, 2 vols. in 3. Amsterdam: C. V. Swets and Zeitliner, 1955–1958

Tarde, Jean. *Borbonia Sidera, id est planetae qui solis limine circumvolitant motu proprio ab regulari, falso hactenus et helioscopis maculae solis nuncupati.* Paris, 1620

Telesio, Bernardo. *De rerum natura.* Geneva, 1588

Torricelli, Evangelista. *Opera geometrica.* Florence, 1644

Vitruvius. *De architectura.* Edited and translated by F. Granger. Loeb Classical Library. London : Heinemann, 1962

Waghenaer, Lucas Janz [Aurigarius]. *Speculum nauticum.* Leiden, 1586

IV—SECONDARY SOURCES

Aiton, E. J. 'Galileo's Theory of the Tides'. *Annals of Science,* **10** (1954), 44–57

Aiton, E. J. 'On Galileo and the Earth–Moon System'. *Isis*, **54** (1963), 265–266

Aiton, E. J. 'Galileo and the Theory of the Tides'. *Isis*, **55** (1965), 56–61

Ashley Montagu, F. M. *Studies and Essays . . . Offered . . . to George Sarton*. 1946. Reprint. New York : Kraus Reprint, 1969

Bernardini, Gilbert and Fermi, Laura. *Galileo and the Scientific Revolution*. Greenwich, Connecticut : Fawcet Publications, 1965

Biagi, Maria Luisa Altieri. *Galileo e la terminologia tecnico-scientifica*. Florence : Leo S. Olschki Editore, 1965

Boas, Marie. *The Scientific Renaissance 1450–1630*. London : Collins, 1962

Bonelli, Maria Luisa. 'Un'esperienza di Vincenzo Viviani fatta dalla Torre di Pisa'. *Physics*, **1** (1959), 41–44

Bulferetti, Luigi. *Galileo Galilei nella società del suo tempo*. Manduria : Lacaita Editore, 1964

Burstyn, Harold. 'Galileo's Attempt to Prove that the Earth Moves'. *Isis*, **53** (1962), 161–165

Burstyn, Harold. 'Galileo and the Earth–Moon System : Reply to Dr. Aiton'. *Isis*, **54** (1963), 400–401

Burstyn, Harold. 'The Deflecting Force of the Earth's Rotation from Galileo to Newton'. *Annals of Science*, **21** (1965), 47–80

Burtt, E. A. *The Metaphysical Foundations of Modern Physical Science*. 2nd. ed. rev. London : Routledge and Kegan Paul, 1932

Clagett, Marshall, and Moody, Ernest. *The Medieval Science of Weights*. Madison : The University of Wisconsin Press, 1952

Clagett, Marshall. *The Science of Mechanics in the Middle Ages*. Madison : The University of Wisconsin Press, 1961

Clagett, Marshall. *Archimedes in the Middle Ages*, **1** The Arabo-Latin Tradition. Madison : The University of Wisconsin Press, 1964

Crombie, A. C. 'Galileo's *Dialogues Concerning the Two Principal Systems of the World*'. *Dominican Studies*, **3** (1950), 105–138

Crombie, A. C. *Robert Grosseteste and the Origins of Experimental Science 1100–1700*. Oxford : Clarendon Press, 1953

Crombie, A. C. *Medieval and Early Modern Science*, 2nd ed. rev., 2 vols. Garden City, New York : Doubleday Anchor Books, 1959

Curtius, E. R. *Europäische Literatur und lateinisches Mittelalter*, 2nd ed. rev. Bern : A. Francke Verlag, 1953

Dijksterhuis, E. J. *Archimedes*. Copenhagen : Ejnar Munksgaard, 1956

Dijksterhuis, E. J. *The Mechanization of the World Picture*. Translated by C. Dikshoorn. Oxford : The University Press, 1961

Drake, Stillman. 'Free Fall in Galileo's *Dialogue*'. *Isis*, **57** (1966), 269–271

Drake, Stillman. *Galileo Studies*. Ann Arbor : The University of Michigan Press, 1970

Dreyer, J. L. E. *A History of Astronomy from Thales to Kepler.* Revised edition with a Foreword by W. H. Stahl. New York : Dover Publications, 1953

Duhem, Pierre. *Les origines de la statique,* 2 vols. Paris : Hermann, 1905–1906

Duhem, Pierre. *Le système du monde,* 10 vols. Paris : Herman, 1913–1959

Favaro, Antonio. *Galileo Galilei e lo Studio di Padova,* 2 vols. 1883. Reprinted Padua : Antenore, 1966

Favaro, Antonio. *Galileo Galilei a Padova.* Padua : Antenore, 1968

Favaro, Antonio. *Oppositore di Galileo. III. Cristoforo Scheiner.* Venice : Carlo Ferrari, 1919

Figurowski, N. A. *et al. Sowjetische Beiträge zur Geschichte der Naturwissenschaft.* Berlin : VEB Deutscher Verlag der Wissenschaft, 1960

Garin, Eugenio. *La cultura filosofica del Rinascimento.* Florence: Sansoni, 1961

Garin, Eugenio. *Scienza e vita civile nel Rinascimento italiano.* Bari : Universale Laterza, 1965

Geymonat, Ludovico. *Galileo Galilei: a Biography and Inquiry into his Philosophy of Science.* Translated with additional notes and appendix by Stillman Drake. New York : McGraw-Hill, 1965

Gilbert, Neal. 'Galileo and the School of Padua'. *Journal of the History of Philosophy,* **1** (1963), 223–231

Gilbert, Neal. *Renaissance Concepts of Method.* New York : Columbia University Press, 1960

Goldbeck, Ernst. 'Galileis Atomistik und ihre Quellen'. *Biblioteca Mathematica,* **3** (1902), 84–112

Golino, Carlo L., ed. *Galileo Reappraised.* Berkeley and Los Angeles : The University of California Press, 1966

Hall, A. Rupert. *From Galileo to Newton 1630–1720.* London : Collins, 1964

Hall, A. Rupert. 'Galileo and the Science of Motion'. *British Journal for the History of Science,* **2** (1965), 185–200

Jammer, Max. *Concepts of Force.* Cambridge Mass. : Harvard University Press, 1957

Kaplon, Morton F. *Homage to Galileo.* Cambridge, Mass. : M. I. T. Press, 1965

Koestler, Arthur. *The Sleepwalkers.* London : Hutchison, 1959

Koyré, Alexandre. 'Galileo and Plato'. *Journal of the History of Ideas,* **4** (1943), 400–428

Koyré, Alexandre. *Etudes Galiléennes.* 1939. Reprint. Paris : Hermann, 1966

Koyré, Alexandre. *Etudes d'histoire de la pensée scientifique.* Paris : Hermann, 1966

Kuhn, Thomas. *The Copernican Revolution.* Cambridge, Mass.: Harvard University Press, 1957

Lindberg, Davis. 'Galileo's Experiments on Falling Bodies'. *Isis,* **56** (1965), 352–354

Löwenheim. 'Der Einfluss Demokrit's auf Galilei'. *Archiv für Geschichte der Philosophie,* 7 (1894), 230–268

Maier, Annaliese. *Die Vorläufer Galileis im 14. Jahrhundert.* Rome: Edizioni di storia e litteratura, 1949

McMullin, Ernan, ed. *Galileo: Man of Science.* New York: Basic Books, 1967

Moody, E. A. 'Galileo and Avempace: the Dynamics of the Leaning Tower Experiment'. *Journal of the History of Ideas,* **12** (1951), 163–193, 375–422

Nicolson, Marjorie Hope. *The Breaking of the Circle.* Rev. ed. New York: Columbia University Press, 1960

Olschki, Leonardo. *Galilei und seine Zeit.* Halle (Saale): Max Niemeger Verlag, 1927

Olschki, Leonardo. 'Galileo's Philosophy of Science'. *Philosophical Review,* **52** (1943), 349–365

Panofsky, Erwin. 'Galileo as a Critic of the Arts'. *Isis,* **47** (1956), 3–15

Planck, Max. *Scientific Autobiography and Other Papers.* Edited and translated by F. Gaymor. London: Williams and Norgate, 1950

Randall, John Herman Jr. *The School of Padua and the Emergence of Modern Science.* Padua: Antenore, 1961

Ronchi, Vasco. *Il cannochiale di Galilei e la scienza del Seicento.* 2nd ed. rev. Turin: Einaudi, 1958

Rossi, Paolo. *Aspetti della rivoluzione scientifica.* Naples: Morano Editore, 1971

Schmitt, Charles B. *Gianfrancesco Pico della Mirandola (1469–1533) and His Critique of Aristotle.* The Hague: Martinus Nijhoff, 1967

Schmitt, Charles B. 'Experimental evidence for and against a Void: the Sixteenth-Century Arguments'. *Isis,* **58** (1967), 352–366

Schmitt, Charles B. 'Experience and Experiment: A Comparison of Zabarella's Views with Galileo's in *De Motu*'. *Studies in the Renaissance,* **16** (1969), 80–138

Schreiber, Johann. 'P. Christoph Scheiner S. J. und seine Sonnenbeobachtungen'. *Natur und Offenbarung,* **48** (1898), 1–20, 78–93, 145–158, 209–228

Settle, Thomas B. 'An Experiment in the History of Science'. *Science,* **133** (1961), 19–23

Settle, Thomas B. *Galilean Science. Essays in the Mechanics and Dynamics of the Discorsi.* MSS. A thesis presented to the Faculty of

the Graduate School of Cornell University for the Degree of Doctor of Philosophy, June, 1966
Strong, Edward. *Procedure and Metaphysics*. 1936. Reprint. Hildesheim: Georg Olms, 1966

INDEX

The letter 'n' following a page number indicates that the reference is to be found in the notes following each chapter